D1083681

I Was Hitler's Doctor

From the German of KURT KRUEGER, M.D.

Foreword by
UPTON SINCLAIR

Introduction by OTTO STRASSER

Preface by
K. ARVID ENLIND, M.D.
Lt. Col. Medical Reserve, U.S.A.

NEW YORK
BILTMORE PUBLISHING CO. INC.

FOREWORD

By Upton Sinclair

For the writing of an introduction to this book I possess two important qualifications. First, I have read the book; and second, I have read many other books on the same and allied subjects. One other qualification I lack: I do not know the author of the book. I assume that he exists, because I have a letter from him; a pleasant letter, telling me that *The Jungle* was his "earliest literary enthusiasm." That is, of course, the way to the heart of any author.

Dr. Krueger is a stranger in a strange land. His book appears in a language not his own, and in the last pages he tells us that it is not entirely satisfactory to him. That makes it easier for me to say that I could have improved it in many ways, and so could any trained writer. You will not read it for its graces of style, but for the information it gives you on an important subject. You will be content if it conveys facts in an ordered sequence, and offers you interpretations of those facts which you can consider, and accept if they convince your reason.

There is a sense in which this book is of necessity fiction. The author tells us that he did not succeed in getting his notes out of Germany. No man living can recollect long conversations such as we have in this book. He has to recreate them with the help of his imagination; but the fact that any one sentence is thus fiction does not keep the whole from being truth. Behind the mass of detail we become aware of a living, breathing, suffering human figure, which is Adolf Hitler, one-time Shicklgruber, and now Fuehrer of the Nazis.

Just the other day I had a visit from another refugee, one of the German writers best known in my own country. He said: "I do not consider Hitler a man of any importance or interest. Soon he will be overthrown, and after that no one will consider him worth thinking about." I replied: "I cannot agree with you.

v

To me he is one of the most interesting men who have ever lived, and I feel certain that history will devote more time and thought to him than to Napoleon. He is the world's greatest conqueror; he has brought death or ruin to more human beings than any other man who has trod this earth—and he is not yet done. If you say that he is a puppet, you are deceiving yourself; he is one of mankind's most dynamic personalities. I have called him a genius-lunatic, and no matter which of these two words you place in advance, the question of how his mind works is a problem of supreme importance, not merely to political and military strategists of the present, but to psychologists and sociologists of all future time."

And now comes Dr. Krueger to justify my claim. He makes Hitler interesting; he takes us behind the curtains which shield his mind, not merely from the world, but from Hitler himself. I take the liberty of telling the book-critics and readers of my country that this volume, in spite of its literary crudities, is one of great importance to our time; it deserves to be read and studied carefully by all who have to fight Hitler, whether with guns, tanks, and airplanes, or with words, ideas, and ideals. And that includes just about every adult man and woman in the Western hemisphere.

More than that: it is a book about the Nazi party and the Nazi movement; and these are still more important for us to understand. Before these words see the light we may turn the dials of our radio and hear that there has been another Blood Purge, and that Hitler has been murdered by Goering, or by a group of the deposed Reichswehr generals. And will that mean the end of the war? Will that cleanse Germany of Hitlerism, will it neutralize the poisons which for the past twenty-three years have been spreading from the soul of one genius-lunatic and his associates to the soul of one of the world's most highly cultured nations? If we let ourselves be persuaded that this is so, it will go hard with us indeed; ten million young Nazi fanatics may revise and make use of an old-time American battle-song, and shout at their "Party Days":

Adolf Hitler's body lies a-mouldering in the grave
But his soul goes marching on!

PREFACE

By K. Arvid Enlind, M.D.

THIS is a book of unusual personal revelations and unconditional psychological surprises. As a doctor, I recognize the phenomena described as human and, as such, understandable.

Very likely the story will prove of irresistible general interest. Always excited by any artistic display of itself in miniature, the general public should get a vicarious kick out of seeing the most devastating of its functioning members taken apart like a watch on the stone of a jeweler. But in times as troubled and potent as ours, it is my opinion that seizing the public interest is something of a responsibility. It seems to me important that tension as dynamic as the reaction to such a book should be accompanied by a proper and balanced understanding of the momentous issues involved.

That we can make ourselves believe what we like to believe is one of the basic discoveries of modern psychology. The mind creates angels and fairies to counteract the fear of witches and demons, and it posits a God who is eternally at war with Satan as in the Persian and Judeo-Christian theologies. In the West, the battle between Christ and Anti-Christ has been going on for two thousand years, chiefly in the mind of European man who is still in doubt as to whether he should follow the path of Caesar or the man of Galilee.

To this historic indecision and searching of the heart on the part of Western man may be traced some of the psychological confusion which prevails with regard to the central character of this book, Adolf Hitler, the Fuehrer of the Third Reich. Hitler, the man, has been lost sight of, and Hitler, the myth, has taken possession of the Western mind which is torn between the spirits of affirmation and denial, the desire to embrace Jesus, and the counter-wish to trample down all his works beneath the bloody hoofs of Caesar.

The little man in Germany, eager to create a God in his own image, wraps all his wish-dreams around the ex-house-painter who, like the divine carpenter of Galilee, embodies his aspirations for spiritual and mental integrity and his passion for a place in the dying sun of the West. To the fanatical Nazi, Hitler is both God and the Holy Ghost, while the enraged Anti-Nazi is equally convinced that the Fuehrer is the Devil himself, whose forked tail has been twisted into a swastika by the deft fingers of the demon-folk.

Freud tells us that religion is a compulsion-neurosis. It is this religious attitude toward Hitler on the part of Western man that has driven us to the conclusion that the ex-house-painter, ex-cement-mixer, ex-corporal and ex-street-brawler has become an ex-human embodiment of the spirit of Good or Evil, depending upon our cultural point of view, our outlook upon the historic conflict between Rome and Jerusalem, Caesar and Christ, the spirit of profit and the spirit of the prophets, of whom Christ was perhaps the greatest. We refuse to accept Hitler as a man, and demand that he be treated as a myth, because all our gods and devils have fled and we must have an absolute upon which to hang our prejudices, our hungers, our need for a constructive faith, or our passion for destruction in a world that is being bombed to smithereens by fierce raiders of the air.

Because the author of this volume treats Hitler as a human being with all the failings of the mind and the frailties of the flesh, he will probably be attacked as an imposter and fraud by certain critics and readers who cling to Hitler, the myth, the cloudy creature floating in the sky of the neurotic West. Like the Greeks, they would rather erect a shrine to their unknown god or anti-god, praise or curse him, than subject the ex-human Fuehrer to the merciless probing of the psychoanalyst. In their estimate of Hitler, they would prefer to place him in heaven or hell, rob him of all contact with earth, with our time-spirit which has created him in its own neurotic image. Rather than give up Hitler, the myth, they will probably carry on bitter factual disputes with the author of this book, who has had the rare opportunity of getting inside Hitler's brain and discovering the important psychological streams which fertilize it. Like the psychotic, they must conjure

up a demonic concept of Hitler, because, like poor Jim Jay in
Walter de la Mare's jingle, they are mired in the thinking of
our medieval past.

"Da diddle di do
Poor Jim Jay
Got stuck fast
In yesterday."

Few fair-minded readers, however, will be fooled by them.
As a practicing psychiatrist, I recognize the facts in this volume
as belonging to a peculiar species of neurosis: not only did their
discovery depend on a close analyst-patient association, but even
their understanding is only possible to those who feel in themselves the pressure of the general world-neurosis of our time, to
which every one of us is more or less subject. Those who come
to this book with the proper humility will find in it not merely
the analysis of a man, but the revelation of an age, our own,
which is struggling blindly against the mental and spiritual health
of the individual, and clings to its delusions with the desperate
firmness of the neurotic who lives and breathes, and has his
being in the private world of his phantasies. I congratulate Dr.
Krueger on having produced a psychiatric portrait of such
startling accuracy that it has the impact of unchallenged truth.
He has served science and mankind equally well.

Western man will never rid himself of the Hitlerian-Caesar
complex until he breaks away from the spell of the past, from the
wish-magic and prayer-magic of his frustrated life that seeks in
the Leader-principle the great Father who will take his lost children to his paternal bosom and guard them against life's terrors.

Hitler calls Democracy "an institution which is filthy and
untrue," because democracy preaches self-reliance, mental auton-
omy, and fosters the belief that "the kingdom of God is within
you." Hitler-Caesar insists that the kingdom is within his own
neurotic mind thronging with the numerous obsessions of a dying
era, and as long as the millions seek redemption in Hitlerism, in a
Messiah outside of themselves, humanity is destined to slip back
into the jungle, as Bertrand Russell prophesied.

Inside Hitler gives us the clue to *outside* Hitler, to that treach-

erous labyrinth of neurosis which snares the minds and hearts of
the suffering millions today. To the madman who controls Europe, madness is the "manifest destiny" of a continent, the "new
order" to which sane people must conform or be flung into concentration camps where they will go mad in any event.

Intelligent people easily concede these premises, but without a
willingness to assume the responsibilities implied by them. They
shift the moral burden by refusing to believe that what has
happened in Europe can possibly come to pass in our own hemisphere. "But do you really believe that there is as much as the
faintest possibility that such danger will ever confront us in
America?" they ask.

I unhesitatingly answer this question in the complete affirmative. *The danger is not only possible. It is here with us already.*

Europe once before accepted madness as a norm, and it is
possible for Hitler (I am referring to the movement rather than
to the man), to impose a new Dark Age of witches, dancing
maniacs, inquisitions and intolerable tortures upon an entire world
which is lost in the fog of neurosis. The human mind is capable
of accepting torment as a permanent state. It is like the fox who
lost his tail: he went around telling everybody how stylish it
was to be without a tail. There are numerous people in Europe
and America who model their minds after the Hitler pattern,
and look upon cruelty, lust, homosexuality, rape, rapine, algolag-
nia, sadism and pathological hatred as healthy and normal states
of mind that make for human happiness and joy.

The terrible fact is that Hitlerism has proceeded to nationalize
the brutal instincts of man at an alarming *blitzkrieg* pace. Nazi
Germany got its idea of planned cruelty and murder from Italy,
the breeding place of the Borgias, the Macchiavellis and the pious
inventors of Inquisitional torments. The neuroses of one nation
have spread to another, and the fires of hysterical sadism have
finally enveloped a continent, threatening the basic sanity of the
West and the entire world itself.

"Sometimes," said Mussolini, "I play with the idea of a laboratory for making generations, that is, of creating a class of
warriors ever ready to die, etc., etc." Hitler, who is a devoted
student of Macchiavelli and Mussolini, has outdone them in his

psychological ruthlessness; he is not interested in a class society of professional killers; he plans a classless world of assassins where all human instincts have given way to the single desire for bestial expression in murder and rapine.

In war and the horrors of war Hitler has found the paradise of his psychotic dreams. In war, bestialism becomes a patriotic duty, a call from the neurotic god of destruction to wreak vengeance on humanity and the higher aspirations of manhood. "War," says Hitler's mentor Mussolini, "is to man what motherhood is to woman." From the womb of war are torn all those acts of hysterical madness that reduce man to a level below that of the beast, and, therefore, war has a horrible fascination for a neurotic like Hitler whose mind is at war with itself and with the world, and seeks to lash the universe with its own torment.

Hitler first unleashed the dogs of war upon a section of the people of Germany, the defenseless Jews who were made the scapegoats for his own psychosexual frustrations as well as for the little Aryans of the Reich who identified themselves with the Fuehrer and his wild power-complex. Napoleon bragged: "A man like me cares little for the lives of a million men." The lives of a half million Jews meant nothing to Hitler and his Nazis if they could satisy their Napoleonic lust for power, their will to nationalize brutality and make it the dominant instinct not only of Germany but of the world. Judaism, Christianity, democracy and socialism threatened to usher in the reign of the mass-man; Hitler countered this threat by imposing the reign of mass-murder, first upon the Jews, and then upon all those who were infected with the Jew-cancer of humanitarian effort. Since all Europe was plagued with this disease of the soul, Hitler declared war upon all Europe, identifying his own mental disorder with the "new order" of his neurotic imagination.

Hans Johst, the prince of Nazi poets, has sung:

"Man is meat and blood."

As the Nazi mind conceives him, man is a beast without a mind, without a soul; only instinct and a dark animal cunning are necessary for his salvation. It must not be forgotten that

Hitler and Hitlerism are the brutal expression of the mental and spiritual bankruptcy of our day; that the glorification of instinct, irrationalism, racism and bestialism was implicit in the world of Spengler, as well as in the books of our own social scientists such as Lothrop Stoddard and Madison Grant. Hitler, therefore, as we have sought to point out, must not be mistaken as a personal devil, wicked as his acts make him out to be; he must be considered as simply giving concrete expression to an age that was hell-bent for war as a means of defeating the human mind and soul which sought peace in a world of justice and truth.

That man can be treated as a domestic animal, exactly as a cat and dog, was not discovered by the Fuehrer, but by social scientists like Pavlov, who proved by laboratory experiments that men respond to conditional reflexes in the same manner as a hound whose mouth fills with saliva every time he hears the dinner bell ring. Because Hitler knew that men would rather commit suicide than think for themselves, he glorified stupidity, instinct, blind faith and action. The Nazi hounds foamed at the mouth every time they heard the bell of Jew-hatred ring out across the Reich, and they barked *Heil Hitler* and *Sieg Heil* at the signal of a Nazi functionary who was under orders from Goebbels, the crooked little Minister of Propaganda and Enlightenment. Hitler preached the warrior creed of brute instinct and energy to fit Germany and the world into his own fear of rational thought.

"One energetic man is worth more than a thousand intellectual babblers who are the useless waste-products of the nation," is a fundamental Nazi article of faith. It has appealed to all the morons and half-wits of the world, and it is not strange that the Hitler movement in the West has been recruited from the ranks of the mentally and sexually maladjusted who seek to resolve their inner conflicts by giving vent to their hatred of mankind in the instinctive violence of war and bloodshed.

The breakdown of the European mind resulted in a paralysis of action, for when thought cannot be resolved in deeds, it becomes a hindrance to progress, even the progress of a crab which goes forward by going backward. Hence we have the strange phenomenon of college professors and savants who have joined

the nit-wits and imbeciles in a stampede towards a new Dark
Age which Hitler calls the "new order." Believing with Epictetus
that "the end of man is an action, not a thought," they have
joined Hitler's "revolution of nihilism," regardless of the consequences to themselves or the world.

People want to go places even if they know they are going
to Hell. The Moslem world has been held together by the eternal
pilgrimage to Mecca, which has become the focus of Moham-
medan thought and spiritual striving. In the same manner Hitler
has succeeded in making Munich the shrine of the European
neurosis, and all men of ill will who suffer from Hitlerian frustrations, hatreds, ambitions, jealousies and greeds are going to
Munich in great streams, propelled by the desire to go places,
lured on by the Pied Piper of mental conflict who is leading
them to destruction.

So Hitler flows into the madness of our age, and the madness of our age flows into Hitler. A loveless world is given
meaning and devilish significance in the words and actions of a
loveless man, a man suffering from psychic impotence who has
flogged his sexual sterility into a nightmare of world-sadism, a
Walpurgis Night of terror for all mankind. "In my youthful
years when I have been out walking," Goethe tells us, "the sensation of longing for some desired girl has overtaken me, and I
thought long enough about it until I really met her." The creative mind of Goethe was able to dream a woman into being,
but Hitler's diseased brain can only attract the bloody ghosts of
nihilism and world chaos, and he has rallied about him the victims of neuroses who are lured to destruction by this terrible
Messiah unwombed from the madness of our age.

Hitler suffers from an Oedipus complex, which is analyzed
minutely in this volume. His jealousy of his father in his early
adolescence, and his desire to take his place in his mother's
affections, has been projected on a world scale, so that he now
aspires to become the great Father of all humanity, keeping a
loveless world in terror with the lash of his whip and the wild
fury of his tongue. To him, the future society, the fatherless
society of brethren which he calls "Jewish Bolshevism," represents a dangerous threat to his power-complex; to keep partially

sane he must drive the world totally mad. To him, as to the medieval monk, the arch-fiend has his abode in sex, and he has turned the phallic symbol of life into a scourge with which to flog all mankind.

But Attila the Hun and all the other scourges of humanity have been overcome by man's will toward reason, sanity, justice and order, and Hitler will be conquered by the West as the West has triumphed over other tyrannical Caesars who declared war against it. Europe, when it becomes sober, will repeat the epic tale of Bayazid I, whom Tamerlane carted around like a beast in an iron cage. The homosexual gorillas who now rule Germany will be clapped into asylums for the mentally ill, and the creative currents of love will again seep into the veins of humanity, dispelling the nightmare of the present.

HITLER AS I KNEW HIM
SOME INTRODUCTORY REVELATIONS

By Otto Strasser

THERE are three characteristics which emphasize Hitler in his *milieu:* (1) Asceticism in food; (2) indifference to suffering; and (3) opportunism in love.

These are negative qualities, you are reflecting. How, then, have they been built into the most positive personality in the international activity of our time?

The simple answer is, that every negative in Hitler's composition has a lining of positiveness—a positiveness so powerful that it takes on the imminence of a direct and immediate influence.

I have seen and observed Hitler in every one of the three levels of his psyche, and it seems to me that only a reproduction of all these facets can give some idea of the mercurial nature of his character.

Hitler is known as a vegetarian, a word intended to describe a human being who (either through preference or necessity) subsists on a diet of vegetables and their derivatives; it is therefore only partially applicable to Hitler's eating habits. Hitler is not satisfied with preferring vegetables for breakfast, dinner and supper, he eschews meat, and positively hates it in all forms and substances.

This amply describes the positive of Hitler's first negative, from which a psychoanalyst should be able to derive much that is both pointed and poignant.

Most of the suffering imposed on the world by Hitler took shape in the fleeing forms of dozens of his comrades-at-arms, and the hundreds of thousands of the humbler German citizenry scattered to the far ends of the earth because of political, racial and religious persecutions. I am among those who fled the land of my birth, because my political opinions had streaked so dangerously away from Hitler's that since 1930 we were deadly enemies. Naturally, when he came into power my life was endangered. It mattered nothing to him that most of the solid structure of national socialism in North Germany rests on the labors of my brother, Gregor, and me, who pooled our resources to spread the work which he had already begun in Munich. He reaped the benefit of our work, as well as the labors of others like us, yet saw the ground cut from under the feet of those of us who were not murdered outright, like my brother Gregor, without a twinge of pain or remorse.

No one in the world can be as indifferent as is the Fuehrer to the sufferings and adverse fortune of others. But no one lived whose own misfortunes ever moved him so easily to tears. Hitler always threatens to commit suicide if anything goes wrong with his program. As to that, I have no doubt of what will really happen. There are only two ways of meeting a major personal disaster. The way of Brutus was to run into his sword. The way of Hitler will be to burst into tears. This is the fearful positive of the second of Hitler's outstanding negatives; his indifference to human suffering.

I have said that he is an opportunist in love. That is the negative aspect of the creative third of his life. The positive lining of this negative is a species of murder, best known to the biologist. Science has discovered that in most of the observable species of life on this planet the act of love on the part of the male is envisioned as an act of virtual suicide. Spiritually this may be said to define the whole gamut of the movement of man in our society. But Hitler has broken away from this natural tendency, as he has managed to break away from every other law of human conduct. He makes love to women casually, in the spirit of opportunism. But he either uses a woman toward furthering his political (and deadly) ends, or his "love" is so unnatural and perverse that it means almost always deadly danger for the woman's soul or her body.

Hitler had given up a good deal of his life to the romantic passion. Even the official Nazi press has had occasionally to pay its respects to the affairs of the handsome Adolf. And what the press does not print, the human tongue spreads consciencelessly and endlessly. But I speak only of things within the limits of my own experience. I have known three women, every one of whom played a distinct part in the life of this ascetic with the perverse imagination. Every affair was trivial, negative, but the effect it had on the life of the world about us was as positive as acid.

The first of these was a faded, middle-aged woman, the wife of the famous Berlin piano-maker Bechstein. Frau Bechstein was twenty years older than Adolf, but she had an infinite reserve of tenderness which she lavished on Hitler—perhaps because he alone was receptive to it. When he went to Berlin, he generally put up at her house, where he met the politicians whose acquaintance he desired to make.

When they were alone, or occasionally in front of his friends, he would sit at his hostess's feet, lay his head on her opulent bosom and close his eyes, while her beautiful white hand caressed her big baby's hair, disturbing the historic forelock on the future dictator's brow. *"Wolfchen,"* she murmured tenderly, *"mein wolfchen."*

But the tenderness remained on one side. Once his political and social objectives were realized, Hitler forgot Frau Bechstein and turned his attention to a younger and unquestionably more attractive female, the daughter of Hofmann, the photographer. Fraulein Hofmann was an exceedingly attractive young blonde, with frank and boyish ways. Like most adolescent girls, she was not very discreet, chattered so freely and to such effect that her family was both flabbergasted and scandalized. Pressure having been brought on him, her father one day went to demand an explanation from the Fuehrer, who was beginning to be known as "the seducer of Munich."

Hitler was not yet Chancellor of the Reich, but his fame was growing, and Europe was beginning to talk about him. The matter was soon settled; Hofmann left, holding the exclusive world right's for Adolf Hitler's photographs. The complaisant father has become one of the richest and most respected men in Germany. But when, after Hitler's release from Landsberg Prison, interest in Hitler and his movement was at the lowest level of apathy, it was the marvelous photography of Hofmann which revived both the man and the movement. Again the leit-motif of love was converted into the heavy measure of political achievement. Once more a negative aspect of Hitler's registered in its positive effect on the living world!

The third of these affairs brought no aggrandizement to the party. But to the object of his affections it brought death.

About 1926 Hitler sent for his half-sister Angela Raubal, the child of his father's first wife, to take charge of his home. With her came a daughter, his little niece, an Austrian, amusing, pretty and gay. Grete, or Geli, as he fondly called her, was only fifteen when she arrived, but Uncle Adolf's *menage* bored her. She wanted to go about, meet people, dance. I used to pay her attentions. She was no prude.

One day I arranged to take her to one of the famous Munich masked balls. While I was dressing, my brother Gregor burst into my room.

"Adolf doesn't want you to go out with Geli," he said.

Before I had time to recover from my astonishment, the telephone rang. It was Hitler.

"I learned," he roared, "that you are going out with young Geli this evening. I won't allow her to go out with a married man. I'm not going to have any of your filthy Berlin tricks in Munich."

I had no choice but to submit.

Next day Geli came to see me. She was red-eyed, her round little face was wan, and she had the terrified look of a hunted beast.

"He locked me up," she sobbed. "He locks me up every time I say no."

She did not need much questioning. With anger, horror and disgust she told me of the strange proposition with which her uncle pestered her.

I knew all about Hitler's abnormality. Like all others in the know, I had heard all about the eccentric practices to which Fraulein Hofmann was alleged to have lent herself, but I had genuinely believed that the photographer's daughter was a little hysteric who told lies for the sheer fun of it. But Geli, who was completely ignorant of this other affair of her uncle's, confirmed point by point a story scarcely credible to a healthy-minded man.

What could I say? What advice could I give Geli?

Her confidences, once set flowing, were inexhaustible. Her uncle kept her literally isolated. She was not allowed to see a man. One evening, driven crazy by this treatment, she had yielded to the importunities of Emile Maurice, Hitler's chauffeur. Hitler had surprised them.

Her ear to the door, she had heard the words that passed between these two men, both of whom she dreaded equally.

"You'll never set foot in this house again!"

"Sack me and I'll take the whole story to the *Frankfurter Zeitung!*"

The blackmail succeeded. Emile Maurice, richer by twenty thousand marks, set himself up in a watchmaker's shop in Munich.

All this was incredibly disgusting and I could find no words of comfort for this girl who, had she not been prematurely corrupted, might one day have made a good wife and mother. But it was tame to what I learned later, as tragedy descended on my family on all fours.

My brother Gregor's murder was a terrible blow to me. Afterwards my most earnest desire was to see my brother Paul, who had been with Gregor and so had received his last confidences. I wanted to learn and to understand to put myself in a better position to judge Adolf's guilt.

Paul, like Gregor and myself, was an officer during the great war. In August, 1918, he was in command of a battery which had succeeded in recrossing the Marne at Dormans and maintained itself there for forty-eight hours. He was badly wounded in the course of this engagement, and after the war he took orders and became a Benedictine.

After the June 30 massacre, Paul went to Rome. I kept up a lively correspondence with him and was impatient to see him. Two years passed, however, before we met in Austria in the spring of 1936, and spent a few days together.

"And to think," Paul murmured one evening, "that Gregor once stopped Hitler from committing suicide."

"When was that?" I asked not very attentively.

Paul hesitated, then continued in a low voice.

"After the murder of his niece Geli."

At this I started.

"Did Gregor tell you that too?"

Paul nodded.

"I swore to keep it a secret. Gregor spent three days and three nights with Adolf, who was like a madman. Gregor told me he shot her during a quarrel, that perhaps he did not realize what he was doing. As soon as he had done it, he wanted to commit suicide, but Gregor prevented him."

I wanted further details.

"Do you know who was there at the time of the murder, and how it happened?"

"I know nothing more. Gregor did not tell me any more. He told me this during a fit of profound depression, and I kept the secret as long as he lived."

"But Paul, in 1931 Hitler was a nobody. How did he escape justice? Didn't Gregor tell you that?"

"An inquest was opened at Munich. The public prosecutor, who had lived abroad since Hitler's accession to power, wished to charge him with the murder, but Gurtner, the Bavarian Minister of Justice, stopped the case. It was announced that Geli had committed suicide."

Meanwhile Gurtner had become Reich Minister of Justice.

"Gurtner again!" I exclaimed. "Always Gurtner. Did anyone else know about it?"

"Yes, there was someone else," Paul replied. "He was murdered on the same day as Gregor. You remember Gehrlich, the editor of the *Right Way?* He made a private investigation at the same time as the police, and collected overwhelming evidence against Hitler. Voss, Gregor's lawyer, no doubt knew all about it too. He had all our brother's secret papers at his house, but he was killed like Gehrlich."

Nine years have passed since Geli's death; six years have passed since a madman and a brute gave the signal for Germany's Saint Bartholomew.

In November, 1939, I was in Paris, where I wrote several articles for the *Journal,* mentioning Geli's death and Hitler's guilt.

Three days later the editor of the *Courrier D'Autriche* called on me.

"Do you know Father Pant?"

"No, not personally, but I know he lived in Munich, and that he was the brother of the prelate and Senator Pant, the former leader of the anti-Nazi Germans in Poland."

"Yes," he said. "Father Pant is now in exile, but he asks me to send you the following message, which I repeat verbatim:

" 'It was I who buried Grete Raubal, the little Geli of whom Otto Strasser wrote. They pretended that she committed suicide; I should never have allowed a suicide to be buried in consecrated ground. From the fact that I gave her Christian burial you can draw conclusions which I cannot communicate to you.' "

This is the very tip of the black pyramid of murder which Adolf Hitler and his Nazis have molded with the most precious of the energies of the Third Reich. It flies a swastika flag, each side of which has a different emblem inscribed on it. You see the design according to the slant of the breeze blowing against the banner. Sometimes it is the pale, grim, determined face of the Fuehrer that we glimpse on it. This is the flying symbol of Hitler's positive achievement. On other occasions, and more frequently, we discern the comparatively softer outline of the skull and bones of timeless piracy.

CONTENTS

CHAPTER ONE

The Man and the Disease

*Ernst Schmidt—How Hitler Was Introduced to Me—
"Put me down as Adolf Schicklgruber"—A Visit to
Dr. Freud—Hitler's Complications Introduced—A Dif-
ficult Beginning—Escape and Revenge—When the
Violation of a Physician's Oath Is Not a Violation.*

It was in the twilight of a day late in August, 1919, about a
year after the debacle of German hope, that the door of my
humble residence office was pulled open, and I saw for the first
time in some five years the form of my old friend Ernst Schmidt.
We were approximately the same age, had done our early schooling together, and I had not seen him since the war consigned us
to different duties in different regiments. I recognized him by
instinct rather than by the familiarity of his features. Familiarity
was there, of course. But time and the bitterness of the conflict
had wrought profound changes in him.

"Well, Herr Doktor!" he cried as he gripped my hand. "You
look tough enough to crack nuts with."

"And you don't look as if you were in professional need of
me, either," I laughed, and held out a chair for him. As he slipped
into it and faced my desk I asked him why he had not looked me
up before.

"For that matter I might ask you the same thing," he droned.
"I guess it's pretty much the same story all around. I've had you
in mind a hundred times. But what would I say to you when I
saw you? I guess I just couldn't actually make the journey till I
needed you."

"Then you *do* need me!" I exclaimed. "What's wrong?"

"I need you—but not for myself," he replied with a grin.

"It's for a friend, a man of my regiment. In fact, he's waiting outside your door for me now."

"Outside!" I cried. "Is that a way to treat a prospective patient of mine? You must go to him immediately and bring him in."

Ernst smiled.

"Very nice," he murmured, "and just the spirit I expected of you, old comrade. But before I do that little thing, there are two important matters that must first be disposed of. Number one: I have no idea what ails my friend. But whatever it is, he's damned sensitive about it, and requires from his doctor assurance of absolute secrecy."

I thought that was an odd request to make of a physician.

"Doesn't he know anything about the Hippocratic oath?" I laughed. "But never mind. Give him every assurance possible. Tell him I haven't even a wife's ear into which to babble such matters. But say, this has all the atmosphere of high-class intrigue. There should be a fat fee somewhere in the offing. Don't tell me I'll have to split with you."

Ernst grinned.

"And this brings me to the second condition I mentioned, my dear doctor," he wheezed. "There will be no fee in this case whatever. My friend, your patient to be, is a trifle on the wayward side financially. To put it as gently as possible, he's flat broke."

At this we both burst into spontaneous laughter.

"As who among us is not?" I cried. "But let us waste no more time. Bring in your prodigy of secrecy, and I will shake his hand and call him brother."

Schmidt rose swiftly, barged out of my office, and a moment later returned with a medium-sized, slender, somewhat dishevelled man with a sparse, curious little goatee decorating his weak chin. He wore an old trench coat, probably to hide the shabbiness of the rest of his attire, I guessed.

"I am sorry Ernst thought it was necessary to keep you waiting at my door," I said to him apologetically.

He gave me a wry smile.

"It's better to wait at the doors of the wise than to languish on the doorsteps of the rich," he replied, and it became obvious that he was putting forth a great effort to please me.

"Your friend is something of a philosopher," I said to Ernst. "I think you should have warned me of that."

Ernst laughed.

"I warn you now," he said, "that it's dangerous to call a man a philosopher when he really considers himself a soldier. But you will both have to excuse me now. I have a very important engagement—with a prospective employer. You will both get along without me, I'm sure. And to show you how much confidence I have in your ability to help my friend here, I promise to come back in a few days so that we may have a really good chat for old times' sake."

Left alone with the man in the trench coat, I confess that I felt not a little ill at ease. Aside from his bizarre presence, he seemed, despite a show of verbal self-confidence, profoundly unhappy with me, as well as with himself, and kept straining within his clothes as if it would have greatly relieved him to scratch himself.

It would have been better all around, I thought, if the poor fellow could forget his good manners and give himself a good healthy scratching. But there was no way in which I could communicate this assurance to him, so he sat in misery, pulling away at that curious goatee of his in the manner of old Polish Jews I had met while on the Eastern front.

"Please make yourself comfortable," I began, sitting down opposite him. "And I hope you don't need any further assurance of the privacy of your visit," I added. "You're as safe with me as you would be at the Confessional. You're Catholic, aren't you?"

"Born," he replied, "but not practicing."

"We shall find out soon enough what you really practice," was my rejoinder. "And now let me know what's on your mind."

He placed both his elbows on his side of my desk, and let his head sink into his two open hands, in a gesture of utter weariness and despair. Then, looking up at me suddenly, quizzically, he said:

"I guess I've nothing more or less than the old French sickness."

I smiled.

"You mean syphilis?"

He nodded.

I made a mental note of his curious preference for giving the destructive disease a foreign, non-Germanic label. It might have been his peculiar way of thinking. It could have been no more than a whim of the moment. I would find out.

"Aren't you something of a defeatist?" I asked him. "If you insist on continuing to think of syphilis as 'the French sickness' there will never be a German-French war in which, as far as you are concerned, France will not have triumphed over us even before we managed to get started."

He must have guessed at what I was after, and he was apparently not pleased. He blinked by way of dismissing the whole business as something out of his sphere of interest, and said:

"Forgive my having taken you so far afield, Doctor. The truth is, I just don't like the word syphilis."

"And a dreadful word it is to be sure," I agreed quickly. "It tells whole volumes which one would hardly find easy to fit into words. But will you tell me why you're so abysmally secretive about it?"

He looked troubled.

"You don't think it is anything ordinary to happen to a man?" he asked.

"Dreadful, yes," I said to him. "But really ordinary, quite ordinary."

He shook his head dolefully.

"I didn't expect a time to come when people would go around confessing syphilis as if it were a common cold," he mused.

"They might as well," I assured him solemnly, "when almost every fifth German suffers from it. But tell me something about your particular case. How long have you been running around with it?"

Once more he concentrated on me those large stray-dog eyes of his.

"Running around with it is a good way of putting it," he replied. "And quite apt in my case. I've been entertaining it since 1913, Doctor."

I whistled.

"You've certainly been a long-suffering host. Did you begin taking treatments immediately?"

He nodded.

"Well, maybe not so immediately. I was a few months in finding out about it. But I wasn't far gone, according to the doctor, and he was rather cheerful about it."

"Doctors can better afford being cheerful than patients," I warned him. "Have you ever been pronounced cured?"

He shook his head.

"But you couldn't say that that was the doctor's fault," he added hurriedly. "You see, when I got into the army I let myself go entirely."

I stared at him incredulously.

"You let yourself go?"

"I mean that I stopped taking treatments."

"But why?"

He shrugged, and his eyes transfixed mine with a ferocious intensity.

"It just became impossible."

"I don't understand," I protested, "I was an army doctor myself. There was absolutely no reason for anyone in my regiment neglecting himself—while he remained alive."

He pulled his goatee in a nervous gesture.

"I know what you're thinking, Doctor. The medical facilities of my regiment were not inferior to those of any other regiment. As I told you to begin with, the fault was entirely mine. I felt when I got into the army that a man either served himself or his country. He couldn't do both at the same time. At least I couldn't."

I made a mental note of the fact that my patient appeared to be a man of character, despite his hang-dog look and his more than normal share of foolishness.

"Can you remember the name of the doctor who treated you?" I asked.

He nodded and mentioned the name.

"Did you go to him with this new trouble of yours?"

He hunched his shoulders despairingly.

"I went to him. He made a blood-test, told me there was nothing wrong with me that he could help, and practically dismissed me."

I reflected on this for a few minutes.

"He might have been right, you know," I suggested.

At this my new patient made a snapping noise with his mouth, a sort of half-snarl.

"He's just a Jew," he mumbled, "so how can he be right?"

"Medically," I corrected him, "Jews have been in the right all too often."

I could see his eyes flashing challenge.

"I don't believe it," he vowed passionately. "And I am here to tell you that this damned Jew wouldn't treat me because he knew I couldn't pay him."

"Did you pay for the treatments he gave you before?" I asked.

"As well as I could," he replied sullenly. "There are some obligations," he reminded me, "which precede those of capital."

"That's very interesting," I murmured. "But I'm afraid every doctor insists on deciding this matter for himself in every individual case."

"Suppose we go into my laboratory?" I suggested.

He followed me a little sheepishly into the next room and fumblingly removed his ragged clothing. I had examined literally hundreds of syphilitics, but never before had I been so amazed by a first cursory examination of an old neglected case. I expected to find my patient in at least the second stage of the dreadful disease, for it was already more than six years old. But no, he still enjoyed a powerful growth of hair, his skin was almost without blemish, and the bleariness of his eyes, which might have been a symptom, turned out to be due to a gas attack which had hospitalized and almost blinded him. His complexion also was that of a normally healthy man. I looked critically at my patient. I wondered whether he might not be hoaxing me.

"Outwardly you show so little of the usual signs of syphilis,"

I said to him, "that I would say, off hand, that there might have been a mistake made in the original diagnosis of your case."

He looked at me with astonishment.

"Then you agree with the Jew that I have no syphilis?"

"There is still your blood-test to be disposed of," I replied, "but by all outward signs I would say that I agree with him."

"But if I haven't syphilis," my patient insisted, "how is it that I have become totally impotent?"

I saw instantly that it was that—his impotence—which weighed most heavily on him.

"Impotence could be due to a great many other things," I told him. "But I think we'll do very well not to discuss this any further until I have had an opportunity to read your Wassermann."

He began to dress, and I remember distinctly that he had his back to me when he asked whether an impotent man stood much of a chance of a restoration of his powers.

"That would depend largely on the nature of his impotence," I explained. "Sometimes the cause of impotence is entirely psychological. In such a case the removal of it is purely a problem in suggestion or hypnosis. But if you happen to have syphilis, I don't supposed you care much whether the power to recreate is restored to you or not."

He turned about suddenly, with a certain fierceness.

"Why not?" he asked savagely. "Why shouldn't a man, though he suffer the most dreadful diseases, want to feel running through him again the sweet waters of the river of life?"

"Because if the waters of the river are badly infected they might bring the blight on everything along the shores it touches."

"It's an unfair comparison," he cried. "I know that I want to live, and I know that I love life well enough to make sure that I do not contaminate others while I work out my own happiness. What do you say, Doctor?"

I smiled at him reassuringly.

"I promise you that I will try to restore you to normal health if it is at all possible. But let us talk no more about it till we know a little more of what's wrong with you."

We returned to the office and I drew out a card.

"Forgive me if I've forgotten your name," I said to him. "But I must have it for my files."

He hesitated a moment, then said:

"Put me down as 'Adolf Schicklgruber'."

That was how Hitler was brought to me, and how he became my patient.

You may, if you like, compare this book to the case history a general practitioner might draw up on the state of health of a difficult patient for the scrutiny of a specialist whom he is calling for help in prescribing treatment. It contains a diagnosis and prognosis, but it does not pretend to be the final word on Hitler, or the social universe of which he is a part. Only the Fuehrer himself in his Eagle's Nest, where God is his only neighbor, can pronounce the ultimate word on his life and destiny. I can only give the psychic facts as I ferreted them out of my patient, and from their contents draw certain conclusions.

I realized from the beginning that I could place but little reliance on my new patient's knowledge of himself. Few laymen have any practical understanding, while they are in a state of illness, of what is happening to their physical members. When a patient has a stone in the bladder he feels the pain in his right shoulder, and points to it when the doctor asks what is wrong with him. If patients are so deluded with regard to their somatic troubles, they enjoy even less information with regard to the ailments of that more elusive organism, the psyche.

Hitler's ignorance was just sufficiently mixed with far-flung splinters of information to keep him in a state of desperate confusion. He remembered that he had had syphilis. But he had no means of knowing whether or not he had been cured. He also knew that he was impotent and, having no inkling of its nature or origin, he quite naturally attributed it to the older and more devouring ailment.

Hitler's sexual helplessness did not extend beyond the failure of his physical organs to function. Like most soldiers returned from the privations and ignominies of warfare, he was hungry for the society of women. Memories of fundamental (if somewhat hurried) relationships must have burned through him whenever he saw or remembered a woman. Mentally and spiritually, he was, if possible, in more desperate need than ever of completing that cycle of creation before which a man and a woman are each never more than the negligible part of a unit.

Despair was the keynote of his personality that first afternoon in my office. There is no greater tragedy for the would-be Don Juan (a role Hitler has played ever since people can remember him) than to discover his biological exile from the body of the fair sex, that enchanted island of bliss that lies between heaven and earth, and keeps him suspended in a state of permanent indescribable rapture. Life without women becomes a nightmare, a meaningless horror perpetrated by the gods of frustration to prod the mind into madness.

As we can see from our study of Hitler's dreams, analyzed in this volume, the conviction of sexual helplessness can consign the erotic-minded man to a hell of despair, a nightmarish whirligig of emotions that spins his thoughts into feelings of lust, sadism and revenge. Ever since a certain fatal assignation with a Munich harlot (which led him into the syphilitic heaven) Hitler has had a rendezvous with madness.

He has felt himself trapped inside his body and mind, and the fate of the modern world coincides with the passionate efforts on his part to escape the trap of the subconscious. Deluded into a sense of impotence, he has made the world a victim of his syphilitic fears. Disappointment and despair have found in him a bloody and violent outlet.

A careful physical examination and a series of bloodtests proved beyond any reasonable doubt that in some miraculous way the dreaded syphilis had been ousted from Hitler's blood-system. There still remained his impotence, and concerning that, my early questioning of him led me to believe that it was psychic. Psychic impotence may descend on one who has suffered severely of a venereal disease—as if the man's nature had decided that the only way to forestall any similar catastrophe was to refuse to function sexually.

All womankind had been recast in his brain in the image of the Munich street-walker, that tainted daughter of Eve whose kiss spelled death and shame, like the kisses of Lilith, the primal passion of man who, in the Dark Ages, assumed the form of a witch and the voluptuous body of a Jewess in the new Dark Ages that had descended upon Germany.*

If my patient's psyche was to be readjusted, cured, recharged, he would have to subject himself to a thorough analysis, the kind a patient can only undertake when he has a sincere faith in the ability of his physician. Our doctor-patient relationship began rather badly, I must confess, with Hitler confiding to me during his very first visit that he had no faith whatever in what he called "the talking cure."

Psychoanalysis, as Hitler saw it, was a Jewish science invented by Israel as a means of bedevilling the rest of the world. Satan, who was a Jew in disguise, was swishing his Freudian tail into the faces of naive Aryans and making them blush with knowledge of themselves. Since self-knowledge leads to self-distrust and even self-contempt, the proud Aryan was being dragged into the dust by that devil with the hooked nose who never failed to appear on the pages of Streicher's *Stuermer* as a warning to German men and women, honest burghers who knew not sin.

It being only too obvious that in my new patient anti-Semitism was a violent social mania, which it would be wiser to humor than to oppose, I admitted that Dr. Freud, one of the founders of psychoanalysis, was a Jew. But he was only one of the founders, I insisted, the only one of them who could be called a Jew. As for psychoanalysis being a Jewish science, it was neither a science nor Jewish. On the contrary, I argued, if psychoanalysis could be said to have any tinge of race, the taint would have to be Aryan, because, whereas there were Jews in every country in the world, the development of psychoanalysis has taken place, during its formative stages, almost exclusively in Germany and Austria.

---

*In this connection it is interesting to note that Nazi Germany has reduced woman to the status of a harlot or a breeding-machine, because Hitler and his lieutenants fear the fatal lure of the female whose veil of mystery must be torn from her treacherous flesh that she might stand naked before the contempt of Hitler, Goebbels and Himmler. To these psychopaths, German womanhood is the Whore of Babylon whose harlotries are so public and obvious that they are no longer traps for innocents like the Fuehrer.

But to cover up their lewd opinion of the German female, they create the myth of the Lilith-Jewess, the Palestinian witch, who is forever luring the Aryan male into an act of racial shame. So German womanhood feels itself vindicated by the daughter of Israel cast in the role of a sexual scapegoat.

I may say that I won him over quite completely. My treatment, which began immediately, stretched over a period of fifteen years. But though I did everything to overcome the deficiencies in the nature of my patient, I am obliged to admit in advance that this book is a record of failure, a failure moral as well as medical. The business of an analyst, says Alfred Adler, is to win his patient's good will and then transfer it to his environment. If there is any good will in Adolf Hitler I failed to find it, and now society is in the agonizing grip of a monster who, in the hands of a more competent doctor, might have become a man.

In the early days of my practice, I got a friend of the family to intercede in my behalf for an interview with the late Sigmund Freud.

He received me in the narrow book-ridden study of his house in Vienna where, after joking a little about my expectations of him, he gave utterance to some very luminous bits of advice, the most significant of which he seems never to have put into print.

"You know, of course, that psychoanalysis is not really a science," he confided to me. "Never mind the imbeciles who write about it as a science in the making. Psychoanalysis can no more become a science than any other form of conversation. It is at best guided, probing conversation.

"But you mustn't misunderstand me to underestimate it as a species of healing," he added quickly. "It's a very helpful branch of medicine, and is bound to increase in importance in a world in which multiplying social restrictions are gradually isolating the individual out of all healing association with his kind. A Robinson Crusoe cast upon the island of his private neurosis with no man Friday to keep him company, no sympathetic soul to listen to his complaints.

"There you have it, my boy!" he cried out with a sudden determination, as if the idea had just hit him amidships. "There was a time when a crowd of troubled men could track the feet of Socrates and pick up pearls of wisdom as they dropped from his mouth. The Athenian philosopher, the counterpart of the modern analyst, treated his patients on the run, as it were. They chased

him and his thoughts through crooked alleys and by-ways till they reached the broad road of understanding and mental health.

"But chasing philosophers became, after a time, a hazardous occupation, what with the danger of being kicked by a horse, or bumping into a harlot whose line of talk might be more persuasive than that of a Socrates or a Plato." Freud's eyes twinkled as his imagination went on a holiday. "When the hit-and-run philosopher became extinct, the troubled soul discovered his neighbor or his neighbor's wife, and sought to cure himself through intimate conversation.

"As often happens in Vienna, and elsewhere, the conversation, when the state of mind demanded it, took on a sexual, confessional tone, and the neighbor, or the neighbor's wife, became more than a sympathetic listener. This would occasionally result in a breach of the seventh commandment in the wife, or a psychic trauma in the aggrieved husband; but it never failed to do a great deal to clear a compressed and depressed atmosphere.

"People must, in every generation, find some means of confiding in each other, as a part of the general process of psychic disengagement and disillusionment. Yielding to this necessity, the backyard fence became an unconscious substitute for the parlor and the bedroom. It was a good fence, a good institution, and for a long time it did noble duty in the healing of the race of man.

"But with the dreadful march of civilization, the fences have all been turned into stone walls. No one can look through them or over them. As a result of this, men who would go to their backyard fence to clear out the cobwebs in their subconscious now either rot away in the privacy of their miserable lives, or find a good doctor in whom to confide their mental troubles.

"This is the whole business of psychoanalysis. If, when one of those dumb, desolate oxen comes to you for psychotherapeutic treatment, you remember that you are just his neighbor behind the old fence (now represented by your desk), you will be a good doctor, and earn your fee," he concluded.

Everything I had learned in previous lectures faded away in my mind under those simple, direct words of the great wizard of Vienna. Hitler was only one of a few patients on whom I

experimented those days, and in no case did I deviate from the method laid out for me in this conversation. As in my treatment of other patients, I did not make any effort to arrange my interviews in line with any of the several accepted methods of treatment; and I am recording them in this book (as well as I can remember and arrange them without my notes), in the same unscientific spirit.

It did not take me all of fifteen years to realize that I was losing out with my patient. It came to me quite clearly and decisively on a particular occasion during the first few months of my treatments, in the course of a compromise with my patient such as no doctor has a right to make. We had been discussing his party associations, and remembering some of the stories being told around town of the prevalence of homosexualism among his followers, I warned him that it was not good for a man in his condition to develop too great a sympathy for such people.

Instantly Hitler became indignant and demanded to know why he could not maintain political contact with a homosexual Nazi on a purely impersonal basis.

"According to your peculiar logic, Herr Doktor," he grinned, "a virgin dare not share the company of married women for fear that her chastity might be compromised by the sated ways of females who have already tasted the bliss of the nuptial couch."

I reasoned the matter out with him as carefully as I knew how. A man in a state of sexual impotence lives on such a susceptible plane of consciousness that he is constantly exposed to suggestions emanating from the behavior of those about him. "If you are not careful," I warned him, "your nature may, without consulting you, turn to their ways of living, as the easiest means for its gratification."

"You talk as if my nature could do things without even consulting me," he protested.

"You forget," I reminded him, "that *you* are your nature."

"I don't care whether you think my nature is myself or God," he stormed. "I don't see things that way at all, and I absolutely refuse to follow that kind of reasoning."

"Or any kind of reasoning of a purely civilized nature," I

suggested. "You see only that it is important that you make as many converts as possible to your movement, and keep all those already in your ranks. You refuse to see that the strength of any movement lies as much in the quality of its integers as in their numbers, and that adherents of a certain character can never be a source of credit or strength to a nationalist movement. But you've long ago formed the habit of debating with yourself emotionally. Yet the only helpful sort of reasoning is that which is done with the full co-operation of the intellect."

A spirited argument ensued between us. At the end he said to me with frigid finality:

"I suppose the truth is that I don't ever really reason with my intellect. My method has always been to let my emotions lead me on."

And then, in a moment of self-recrimination, he revealed to me his basic primitive nature, which was a prey to the most fantastic of superstitions. I had noticed throughout the interview that his face was twitching with pain while his hands kept drumming beneath his diaphragm in that erogenous zone that had become to him a region as painful as Dante's Circle of Hell.

"What is the trouble?" I interrupted him at this point.

"I went to a Buddhist cultist yesterday," he confessed shamefacedly, "and he advised me to do a certain thing that would cure my impotence."

"What was it?" I pried him, expecting the worst.

"He told me to have it bitten by a wasp. 'An old Buddhist custom,' he said."

I could not help emitting a laugh, but noticing his pained expression, I instantly proceeded to ease him by a few simple applications.

"That is the penalty you must pay, my friend," I cautioned him, "for surrendering reason to instinct. You prefer a Buddhist quack to a medical doctor to do your thinking for you."

"I prefer to do my own thinking," he barked, as if he thought to reassert his dignity with a display of wrath. The effort was highly pathetic.

There were other contributing causes for my inability to cure my patient into which there is no time to enter now. Many factors helped to aggravate my failure and extend the lines of the disaster. It is one of the sad phases of our profession that where a layman may commit an ordinary piece of folly, a doctor can be the cause of a blunder serious enough to warrant police interference. A doctor in this respect is like a dictator whose pomp and power may be cast in the dust by a trifling error of judgment.

In those days Hitler's leading characteristic was a peculiarly credulous, automatic exuberance which he habitually lavished on the first conceit that entered his mind. In happier times the result of such a characteristic could not be anti-social enough to be a cause for worry. But what dangerous notions could not penetrate the mind of a soldier in a defeated army which, till the last day of the war, had looked upon itself as a victorious one?

Take, for instance, my simple agreement to cure him of his impotence. I had merely suggested to him that if he would subject himself to a complete analysis, I might be able to affect a readjustment of his nervous energies that would restore his procreative powers. I had no sooner uttered the words than in his mind the thing was already accomplished. He could plan on it as if he had already subdued to his will the restored energies that lay dormant. Like a man spending an uncertain inheritance, he began to go about with women, wooed them as if he could really love them, and, subconsciously, made promises to himself that were even more dangerous than those he made to the objects of his affections.

And never did an ambitious Don Juan have a wider field to traverse and draw from. The center of increasingly large numbers of people who paused to listen to his haranguing in beer halls and on street corners, Hitler had no difficulty whatever attracting women to himself. After every public appearance there would be at least one new woman overcome by the spellbinder's magnetism who would remain to let herself be won over.

And so, day by day, he built for himself the cause of a new double-tragedy, for it was as easy for him to fascinate a woman as it was difficult to sustain her interest once she learned the nature of the bliss which he had in store for her. Frustration was piled upon frustration, creating a tower of Babel that was bound to go crashing about my patient's head with dire results to his delicate psyche.

When this travesty of unfulfilled love reached its high mark in the reported suicide of his young niece Grete Raubal (or Geli, as he affectionately called her), I began to suspect that, in persisting in an apparently hopeless case, I had undertaken a greater moral responsibility than I had a right to as a physician. But by that time the die had been cast. It was too late to make an honest retreat.

I confess that the "Geli" scandal influenced me profoundly against my patient, and in a sense even frightened me. Materially I had profited greatly from this venture that had begun so unprofitably, because once it was known that Hitler consulted me regularly, the wives of his chieftains would have no one but me for whatever ailed anyone in their remarkable households. My relationship with Hitler was a broad highway, but there were too many danger signs on it, and too many of the signs appeared to be pointed mortally at me.

There was an indirect way of breaking such a bond, without the dishonor of an ignominious retreat, and that was to introduce other doctors for consultation. There was always a chance that one of them might be so pleased with the association that he would plot to make it exclusive. But from the beginning Hitler would not hear of it. His patent objection when I mentioned the name of another physician was that he was a Jew. If he was not a Jew, then he had a Jewish clientele, which was worse.

The thoughts of any people associated in any sort of enterprise run in related cycles. Panic in the mother communicates itself to the child, and the lack of self-confidence on the part of the physician demoralizes the patient, stampeding him into acts of rashness. I suppose that at about the time when I realized that my efforts to cure my patient were doomed to failure, he, without taking the matter consciously into his own consideration, began to yield himself more and more fully to practices of amorous enslavement by which he was able, in his own way, to consummate the many love-affairs in which he kept involving himself continually. He had abandoned himself to the world of fantasy and delirium where the neurotic male can compensate for his lack of normalcy in a lesbian-like relationship to a woman, or in acts of sexual violence against a female that might result in a homicidal mania with fatal consequences to the victim. I began to suspect a murder-complex in my patient when he confessed to me that he had used an S.S. Guard bayonet-knife in an orgiastic ritual of a *"Blut und Ehre"* (Blood and Honor) cult born in the imagination of a Nazi sadist who combined Oriental eroticism with Aryan mythology in a concoction of terror, lust and unspeakable cruelty with credulous Hitler youth as the willing victims. He had made use of the bayonet-knife to cut a bleeding swastika between the breasts of a female cultist, and then, in a moment of erotic madness, he had made a homicidal attack upon the young blonde girl, whom he had rushed to me for treatment.

Fearing my knowledge of his homicidal taint, my celebrated patient doubtless harbored a semi-conscious desire to erase me from his mind by blotting me out of mortal existence as an undesirable non-Aryan who became a Jew by virtue of the fact that some of his best friends were Jewish. He kept pumping me about the Jew-doctors I knew, betraying an unhealthy light in his eyes, a weird flame that made me wince with a sense of impending doom.

The crisis came for me on June 30, 1934, the day of the famous Purge. The world learned that, pistol in hand, Hitler had led a death-raid against certain political opponents, and personally liquidated his first political mentor and friend, Captain Roehm. My patient's murder-complex had broken loose in homicidal violence on a wholesale patriotic scale. But while the rest of the world read in Roehm's death no more than a political maneuver, if a rather bloody one, to me it was much more than that. As Hitler's doctor I had, during the course of an analysis, wrung from him a confession of intimacy with that man. From that moment on, it was inevitable that if Hitler ever became a power in Germany both of us would have to be eliminated, so that the deed and the man would be liquidated with a single blow. Those being the days when people were already finding refuge in other countries from the storm-clouds crawling over Germany, I trumped up a visit to Switzerland, and from there made my way to London, where I finally took passage for America.

That was in 1934. Once it became certain that I had voluntarily made myself a refugee, my guilt was assumed, and full vengeance was visited on my poor family. It must have hurt Hitler to the quick that an aged mother and one uncle were all he could lay his hands on, in reprisal against me. In the case of my mother the Gestapo contented themselves with taking away her home and her slender savings. But my uncle staggered through three concentration camps before a personal quarrel with a guard released the bullet which put an end to his suffering.

In this connection it seems to me highly possible that Hitlerism may yet revive in our time the idea of tribal guilt which existed before the days when the Jews demanded *"an eye for an eye, a tooth for a tooth."* By dragging Germany so far beneath the civilizational level of individual guilt (because Hitler himself can only erase his personal conscience through tribal blood-lust masquerading as patrotic necessity), Hitlerism may force an avenging world to pass a sentence on Germany whose execution will involve a complete disregard for guiltless individuals who were actively or silently opposed to the Nazi regime of violence and terror.

I am moved to this thought by the bloody details of my uncle's death which I heard from a refugee who followed me to America a year and a half later. But of what use can it be to go into the details of this gruesome business, which in other instances has been so hideously multiplied? The story I have to tell is of greater importance than one of mere carnage.

The tale would have made better telling if I had been able to bring along with me from Berlin my numerous notes on the subject. I made some feeble attempts to repossess them, first from Switzerland, then from London, but my efforts were of no avail. They seem to have been doomed from the start. But once I was launched on my task, the lack of notes ceased being such a handicap. I had only to write down the first words describing a scene, and the rest followed irresistibly.

But a physician does not submit such a report to the public; is in fact forbidden to do so by his sacred oath as a physician.

This is the argument that will be interposed by those not stupid enough to try to dispose of me by calling me a Jew.

Ordinarily this would be a valid objection. In the case of a man like Hitler, however, circumstances alter cases in the deepest psychological sense. As long as syphilis was Hitler's major disease, he was entitled to the consideration the medical profession accords to all members of society. Hitler graduated himself from this class when he crossed the Polish frontier and blazed into a world-conqueror. His syphilitic taint became henceforth a part of the social disease that is ravaging contemporary civilization. The delirium inside the mind of Hitler has become a saturnalia of slaughter that is leaping across seas and continents. The Fuehrer's private feelings no longer matter in the least.

Every patient is entitled to have a specialist brought into his case, when his recovery is beset by difficulties requiring consultation with a variety of medical opinions. This solace is not being denied the subject of this inquiry, for the only specialist who has it in his power to bring healing into the life of Adolf Hitler is General Public.

CHAPTER TWO

Laughter in a Void

*The Outer Shell—The Reports on His Blood-tests—
I Propose a Cure—Psychoanalysis as a Talking Cure
—Sense of His Personal Importance to Germany—
I Promise Him My Assistance.*

"In those days," writes Adolf Hitler in one of the few passages of *Mein Kampf* in which he surrenders to the temptation to see himself in his own German style, as in a pocket-mirror, "I lived in the barracks of the Second Infantry Regiment, in a tiny room which still showed very clearly the traces of the Revolution. During the day I was out, mostly, with Rifle Regiment 4, or at meetings or lectures with some other army unit, etc. Only at night I slept in my quarters. As I used to wake up in the morning before five o'clock, I had gotten into the habit of throwing pieces of bread or hard crusts to the little mice which spent their time in the small room, and then to watch these droll little animals romp and scuffle for these few delicacies. I had already known so much misery during my lifetime that I was able to imagine only too well the hunger, and therefore also the pleasure, of the little things."

As he sat making these notes in Landsburg Prison (where he spent the sentence for the unsuccessful *Putsch* of 1923), he must have remembered the many humiliating confessions he had made to me, his analyst. It is not, therefore, at all surprising to me that almost every personal remark of his to be found in that world-famous literary botch appears to be directed as a curative, as if he already anticipated that some day I might make those confidences public. His episodic kindness to mice, for instance, was obviously intended to overcome the bad impression created

44

by the incident in which his father found him playfully biting the back of the neck of a field mouse.

For the curiosity of mankind, therefore,a nd the consolation of history (which will probably credit him with a greater mass of misery than any other man since Genghis Khan), I will try to recapture some more of his image as it impressed itself on my imagination that fatal day he first walked into my office. It was an image tragically human : human in the softness of its helplessness no less than in the crust of hardness it had acquired during the four years of intermittent slaughter. His face looked both fear-driven and disease-hounded; it resembled the broken face of the world.

Yes, I remember him, and his memory is luminous with the dread of unrealized possibilities which I overlooked. I remember him by virtue of that facility in us which clings more tenaciously to the things we hate than to those we love, as if we lived more by the sands slipping away from under our feet, than by those which roll in from the seven seas to reinforce our existence. The man who imposed his life on mine that afternoon late in August is still alive for me under the war-paint in which he is marching and swimming through the tidal blood of the world.

Physically he was not at all impressive. Yet you looked at him again quickly, as if your senses warned you that your first glance had missed something important. When you probed his face a second time, you grew aware of a pair of wild suffering eyes, and the impression became overwhelming that the man before you was, above all, lonely and in secret pain. He had black shaggy hair, a carelessness of attire which was by no means assumed, a little unkempt goatee (which was to be the first of his many sacrifices to success), and a habit of nervously clenching and unclenching his fists, as if he were constantly preoccupied either with attacking or being attacked. Psychologically he was still on the battlefield, spying a foe behind every blasted tree, an enemy behind every denial of an economic privilege; but, most of all, fearful of being ambushed by Life, that eternal antagonist who is more terrible even than Death. He was a soldier of misfortune who could not be demobilized, his shattered nerves driving him on to an eternal combat with himself, which he mistook for the hostility of the world.

He had come to me in the unhappy knowledge that he was deeply, fundamentally maimed, to plead with me to help restore him to normalcy. His sole call on me being that a friend of his was also a friend of mine, the very least of the emotions I must have read in his lost eyes was faith in the fruitfulness of human relationships, and such a desperate craving for the ordinary, everyday pleasures of life that, for their restoration, he was prepared to undergo the bitterest of all the humiliations—accepting a doctor's office as the box of a father confessor. Beyond all this he also gave the impression of laboring under the delusion of final pontifical authority, though all of his opinions—sociological, political and personal—were molded along one simple grotesque pattern. A thing was good because he liked it. Conversely it was bad if he didn't like it. It could also be bad for any number of other reasons which had nothing to do with logic or good sense. If he had heard an antagonistic opinion during his impressionable years, even though he had never given that opinion a moment's consideration, the thing stood condemned in his heart forever.

He returned to my office a few days later at the appointed time. To my great surprise, there was no longer in his bearing any of the anxiety that had hung over him like a black cloud, during his previous appearance. He moved more freely through my office, shook hands with me vigorously, and took his place opposite me at my desk, like a man awaiting orders. As far as he was concerned, his worst troubles seemed to be over. A doctor having taken charge of the trouble, the responsibility for his care was no longer his.

He listened very solemnly as I explained that though the result of the blood-test was negative, the matter could not be regarded as concluded. I would not be satisfied till we had made several tests and had him under observation for a while. My opinion was that he might very well have been cured of syphilis —unless this treacherous disease, known as the great imitator, was working under an especially clever disguise. In that case, there was danger, if the disease was still latent within him, that it might yet overpower him, unless he was continually careful. As to his impotence, that was quite a different matter. Nothing in my cursory examination of him had as yet given me any clue as to its nature. I would have to continue to examine and question him. And the cure, if a cure was possible, would have to come as the result of my findings in the course of my study of his case.

"What do you mean by study?" he asked me.

"It is imperative that I acquire a fairly comprehensive idea of your psychological past," I informed him, "if you are ever to enjoy any kind of future."

My words made a peculiar impression on him, and he slowly shook his head as I reached the end of my sentence. Hitler had an almost peasant-like way of pretending dull-wittedness when it suited him to do so.

"I don't understand what psychology or my past can have to do with what's ailing me," he complained.

I tried to clarify the matter for him.

"Your failure to function sexually is not due to an accident to your body, but to a disorder in your brain, is that not true?"

He nodded silently.

"The difference between the ailments of the body and those of the brain," I went on, "is that damage done directly to the body is measured by the eye, and accounted for in the present. Injury done to the brain, however, usually comes at the end of a long cycle of past events. It's quite simple: If you came to me with a stomach ailment, the very first thing I would think of would be to obtain and place under a microscope specimens of the contents of your stomach. But, you complain of a central deficiency of locomotion, in that part of your body which initiates the beginnings and motives of all locomotions. Doctors have learned that the seat of all such deficiencies is in the brain. That's why I am going to get specimens of the contents of your brain and place them under as strong a glass as I can possibly find in the old archives."

He nodded slowly, reflectively.

"And how do you intend getting specimens of the contents of my brain?"

"The simplest way possible. By asking you important questions relating to your life."

He leaned forward anxiously.

"Isn't that psychoanalysis, Doctor?"

I nodded, and then I noticed that suddenly my patient's face had been drained almost completely of its self-assurance. It was as if he had discovered that he had been nourishing a false hope. I remembered that there were still many people who looked upon mental healing as a species of quackery.

"Do you know anything about psychoanalysis?" I asked him.

He bent forward gravely and I saw him fondling his shabby hat as if he were contemplating running out of my office.

"Enough to mistrust it," he mumbled.

I controlled myself as well as I could. I realized that it would not do to get myself unduly excited.

"Why?" I demanded.

He hesitated a while, as if to give full power to his condemnation.

"Well, in the first place," he said, "it's an attempt to cure by talking, which to me seems a little silly, don't you think?"

I set aside my impatience with his cocksureness.

"What else do you know, or rather, I should say, don't you know, about psychoanalysis?" I asked.

"A lot of things," he replied, "that you probably will deny belong to the realm of things known, as, for instance, that psychoanalysis is a Jewish science, one of the ways Jews have found to plague the gentile world."

"That's both foolish and untrue," I said to him vehemently. "In the first place, I'm not a Jew myself."

"I didn't think so, or I wouldn't have consented to come here," he rasped. "Jews are clever enough to work on us through our own people. They've done it in the name of Christianity and Socialism and now they are doing it by means of psychoanalysis."

I have already explained in the last chapter how I talked him out of this foolish notion. When I removed his naive misconception with regard to the real meaning and functions of the new method of healing, I could feel that I had really won him over.

"And now we will discuss the preliminaries of our cure," I said to him. "Do you prefer to give me afternoons or evenings?"

"All my evenings are taken up," he announced, "but you can have, until I am too busy, as much of my afternoons as you think you can use."

"Afternoons it shall be, then." I pointed to a long couch at the wall to his right. "Will you lie down on it?" I asked him.

He followed my directions, lay flat on his back, but had no sooner put his head down than he snapped it to his side.

"Anything wrong?" I asked him.

"Not particularly, Doctor. It's just my old vertigo. I can't lay my head down even in a barber's chair without beginning to feel it swim."

"Then you could not possibly be relaxed in that position?" He shook his head.

"It's the orthodox position prescribed for the analytic interview," I said to him. "But I think we can dispense with it. You will just sit where you were, and talk with me as if we were just having a friendly chat.* When can you be here for your first session?"

He considered.

"How will next week do?"

I nodded.

"Shall we say Monday?"

He agreed.

"And how long do you think it will take to restore me?" he asked.

"I don't know," I replied, "I can't even be sure that I *can* restore you."

His hands described a gesture of despair.

"Then of what use will be these tedious interviews?" he cried.

"As to the tediousness of the interviews," I said to him coldly, "that will all depend how honest and interesting you make your answers to my questions. But no honest physician of any sort can undertake to give you any assurance of a cure. A man takes

---

* Later, when I discovered my patient's homosexual bent, I realized that his hesitation in lying on the couch was due to his unconscious dread of being sexually assaulted.

his chances with a disease when he leaves himself open to it—also when he comes to his physician for a cure."

He looked distinctly unhappy.

"You doctors do take a rather cold-blooded view of everything, don't you?" he muttered. He rose abruptly and walked to the window. There, for several minutes, he remained standing, with his back to me.

"A doctor would not be of very much use to his patient if he let himself be infected by his excitement," I cautioned him, by way of easing his temper. "You must know," I added, "that at least half of the illness a patient brings in through the door of my office is whipped up by this irritability which you are showing now."

He turned about suddenly, swiftly, and I saw traces of tears on his cheeks.

"You can't understand," he cried, "how important it is that I be kept in good health. It's not just myself I'm thinking about, please believe me. You must save me, Doctor, if only for the sake of the Fatherland which needs all the strength I can muster for it."

To me those words sounded like the ravings of a paranoic. The thought occurred to me that I might already be witnessing the final assault of syphilis on the mind of my patient, though I could not imagine how the treacherous disease could injure his brain without first undermining his body.

"If it's that important," I suggested with faint irony, "perhaps you should get yourself a better doctor."

His reaction to this was violent, and I could see him muster all of his strength of self-control. It was not a moment propitious for a quarrel, and evidently my new patient belonged to that fascinating species of madmen who know how to whittle down their natural anger to the dimensions fitted to every occasion.

"You know very well that I have no money," he contented himself with replying fiercely, "and that I can't afford to run around digging up doctors who will treat me without getting cash on the line. I have come to you because you are not only a good doctor, but a sincere and patriotic German. You understand my case, and I think it is your duty to do your best to cure me.

When I have the money, as I hope to soon, I assure you that you will be well paid."

"We'll talk of remuneration at a better time," I said to him. "I've undertaken to study your case with a view of helping you, and I want to warn you once more that it will be necessary for you to have implicit confidence in me if I am ever to really accomplish anything for you. Is that understood?"

He nodded.

"This is not an idle promise you are making," I warned him. "For the next few months nothing in your life will be more important than these examinations to which I shall subject you. An illness is a king, and a tyrannous one. All other matters in the life of a sick man are subject to it. I want you to know that there are blizzards loose in your blood which threaten to freeze you forever. If I'm ever able to quiet them, and give you relief from their havoc, you will have to submit to my ministrations without question."

"I will obey you," he declared with that stormy quiet of his. "But if I were you, I would give up trying to convince me that the ills of my meager body can be the most important thing of my life."

I stared at him.

"What ills can be more important?" I insisted.

He met my eyes with rueful alertness.

"The ills of my country," he replied unflinchingly. "What good could it possibly do me to purify myself, if my country, of which I am only a tiny unit, remains in a state of rottenness and putrefaction?"

That moment I saw my patient in a new light, and it dazzled me.

"Do you know," I said to him, "that if you wanted to, you could be quite a rabble-rouser?"

"If I wanted to," he repeated softly, and he looked wistfully into the spaces beyond me.

"You *are* a rabble-rouser," I said to him. "I think I can see it in you."

"See what?" he asked precipitously, as if he had just come out of a dream.

"I can see masses of people in your eyes," I said to him. "I don't know whether it is you leading them, or they who are leading you. It makes a grand spectacle, though."

"You're not laughing at me, my any chance?" he asked me.

I shook my head solemnly.

"No, I'm not laughing at you," I assured him. "We've gone a great distance here in Germany from the normal routines of life. But we're not yet laughing at funerals."

Strangely enough this seemed to tickle Adolf. He laughed heartily, shook hands with me as if we'd reached a real understanding, and left.

CHAPTER THREE

A STRANGE SEARCH

My Patient Does Not Keep His Appointment—Selective Amnesia—Ernst Schmidt Drops In—I Am Upbraided for Deficiency in Social Conscience—Adventure in a Beer Haus—Bertha's Story—I Find My Man—His Qualms About Me—The eturn of the Prodigal.

NEXT MONDAY rolled around, the time of the appointment with my patient came and went, but he did not put in an appearance, or send me any explanation for his failure to do so. When a whole month had passed, and I had heard nothing from him, I was prepared to put him completely out of my mind.

And then I made a disturbing discovery. I could not forget my new patient at will. Apparently he had brought more into my life than I had realized during that incalculable hour he had spent opposite me at my desk.

What was it, I asked myself. It must be a curious influence which could have the effect of chaining me to a man who had almost immediately erased me from his consciousness in a self-willed act of selective amnesia as strange as it was amusing.

As if by one of the generosities of Providence, Ernst dropped in on me one of those particularly blue days. He came to ask me what progress I was making with his friend Adolf, and when I told him what happened he just sat down and stared at me as if he wondered whether I was deliberately lying to him.

"If he hasn't been here all this time," he said dazedly, "why has he been reporting such progress to me during the last few weeks?"

I laughed.

"Your friend Adolf probably confused psychotherapy with Christian Science, and is imagining his own cure."

"You're sure you didn't say anything to drive him away?" Ernst asked anxiously.

I shrugged.

"What difference would it make, since he was bound to forget his understanding with me the moment he left my office?"

"Why bound to?" Ernst demanded.

"I'm afraid your friend is a trifle undependable," I replied.

"I don't see it. There must be a reason why he did not keep his appointment. Whatever the reason may be—and I feel sure it must be a good one—he has said nothing to me about it that might disparage you. His assurance that he not only was seeing you but getting on so well under your treatment, is just his way of not wanting to hurt you after you had been generous enough to give him credit."

"Am I to gather from the tone of your voice, and the general content of your speech, that you consider your friend Adolf almost as valuable as he considers himself?" I inquired.

Ernst let out a hearty laugh. It reminded me so much of the healthy, fun-loving Ernst I had known before the war, that it hurt me.

"Oh, then he's done a bit of bragging on his own account, eh?" he chuckled.

I smiled indulgently.

"Just a little."

It was then that Ernst showed how far removed he was from the owner of that hearty laugh. He got up suddenly, forgot that we had been speaking in fun, and faced me squarely.

"There's no reason why Adolf should brag before you!" he flung at me.

"Next thing you know," I chided him in return, "you'll be telling me that curing him is no less than a patriotic duty."

"You can be as sarcastic as you like," he said in a huff, "but it is men like Adolf and myself who are today reshaping the destiny of the German people."

"Very ambitious words," I murmured. "They display as fine a touch of paranoia as one could search for. And a messianic complex worthy of St. Paul himself. But I don't find the position of our people as hopeless as you seem to view it. All I see is that Germany has to revive her industries so that Germans may find work: as soon as Germans are working and beginning to make things with their hands again, everything will be on the upswing. There will be money once more for food and drink and pianos and trinkets—and maybe even for doctors."

He gestured despairingly in a manner that reminded me of his friend Adolf. This gesture, as I discovered later, was becoming a nationalistic trait, as if the frustration of the German people had assumed a pathetic pose in the shrug of the shoulders and the helpless flutter of the hands.

"It's easy enough for you to say that we need work," orated Herr Schmidt. "But suppose there are forces in control of Germany which make work unobtainable—perhaps for the duration of our natural lives? Would that be something for a young intelligent German like you to pass by so lightly? Why don't you stop minding your own business so closely, and take a look about you? See what's happening to the rest of the nation. Try to understand our movement which is creating men as unique as my friend Adolf. Take my word for it, if he tells you that to help him is to help Germany, it is nothing less than the truth."

"But have you any idea of how little this man knows!" I protested. "I can only guess at the meagerness of his general education from my one conversation with him. But you must know these things of a certainty. How can you possibly pin such high hopes on him?"

"Because," Ernst replied passionately, "I have lost all faith in what education and pure culture can accomplish for me. We have too much of this cultural tommyrot already, and we haven't enough feeling about the one and only thing we really need—faith in our national power, and in our ability to regain our lost place in the world."

"You talk like a blamed Spenglerian," I laughed.

"I *am* a Spenglerian," he countered, setting his jaw with an almost apelike rigidity, while his eyes flashed in an unholy, satanic fire. "We have become weak circus beasts with broken teeth. The Jew has knocked our teeth out."

"Yours seem to be quite intact," I joked.

My friend recoiled as if I had hit him a severe blow on the head. His dark eyes assumed a deeper, more fiendish expression.

"Jew-lover," he growled. "You have always been a lover of Jews."

There was no truth in Ernst's words. I was no more a lover of Jews than he. But I was not prepared to lie about them, to hate them, to humiliate them. To refuse to do these things in those days was to brand yourself a Jew-lover. A ticklish business.

"Aren't you indulging in too broad a generality?" I replied, still trying to humor my old friend. "Even *you* should be able to see the difference between a Jew-lover and a lover of humanity."

"Humanity!" he growled with a contemptuous movement of his square shoulders. "Swine! What we need in Germany right now—and in the rest of the world, too—is a bloody Caesar to put the mob in its place, ride roughshod over it, and get some good out of it."

"Have you found your bloody Caesar yet?" I asked quizzically, fingering the skull on my desk. The gesture appeared to have the effect of humanizing him, as if he had suddenly been reminded of the ultimate vanity of all human power. He smiled faintly.

"Adolf, Adolf is the man," he blurted out, suddenly regaining his Spenglerian pose. "I would gladly place the destiny of our country in his hands."

I saw that I at least had to give the appearance of considering his suggestion.

"What's Adolf's chief talent?" I inquired gently. "Outside of his marvelous faith in himself, of course," I added.

My old friend's face grew ardent, his eyes shone.

"Adolf is an orator!" he cried, "an orator in a sense of greatness the world has never really seen before. Demosthenes, you remember, was a stylist. Cicero was a scholar. But our Adolf is a mob-leader, a man whom a mob will follow straight to hell, if he shows the way. Adolf is our leader, *the* leader. Just watch him, and you'll see."

"Perhaps I'd better listen to him, and be sure that I hear."

"There's just one little thing about our Adolf that troubles me," continued Ernst. "While he was broke he was simply marvelous. But he's just got himself a job, and some money, and he already wants to leave the barracks for a place of his own, with privacy."

I did not understand.

"What's wrong with that?" I asked.

Ernst grinned.

"In any other case I wouldn't think it wrong," he replied. "But, between you and me, I suspect Adolf feels that the barracks cramps his style with women."

I remembered my patient's condition and smiled secretly.

"Then the women listen to him, too?" I asked.

Ernst sighed.

"I suspected, even in the trenches, that he would turn out something of a ladies' man," he mused. "I guess there's an air about him which lures the attention of women. But would you believe it, it never actually came out in him till the last few days. Since his first visit here he's taken on new life. I am wondering if I didn't make a mistake in getting him too good a doctor."

We both laughed.

"Don't worry," I said jokingly. "A good doctor can take care of that sort of thing, too."

"I hope so," said Ernst. At the door he held my hand in a firm grip.

"I'm sorry I quarreled with you," he said. "But it was really for your own good. I hate to see so much ability wasted when it is so badly needed by the cause. To show you that I do not think you are hopeless, I am going to ask you to make me a promise."

I laughed.

"Depends on what you want me to promise."

He still held my hand in a firm grasp.

"I want you to promise to try to understand Adolf. Promise that you'll hear him speak the first chance you get. If you hear him, no one will ever have to urge you to understand him. And if you understand him, you are sure to understand our Germany."

"You're sure he won't think I sought him out just to drag him back to my chamber of horrors?" I asked.

"Don't worry about that," Ernst assured me. "There is no danger of Adolf misunderstanding you."

With that he left.

I kept my promise to Ernst Schmidt, and in about three weeks I ran my patient down. Perhaps I would never have seen him again if I had not taken the trouble to actually hunt him up. I wonder what my life would have been like if I hadn't. But I did go looking for him through the streets of Munich, and the beer houses where the political malcontents were known to gather, and in the course of this unusual search of a doctor for a non-paying patient I ran into a queer situation which threw a further, rather unpleasant light on his character.

I was enjoying a glass of beer in one of the shadier of the beer halls when a young girl sat down opposite me and without any preamble engaged me in conversation. Despite her sensual mouth and over-rouged cheeks she struck me as a basically spiritual type. There was a deep pathos in her eyes which seemed to spread over her face and gave it a luminosity which I had always associated with Mary Magdalen.

"You're Jewish, aren't you?" I asked her, after her voice had trailed off into a titter of forced gayety.

She buckled under my remark as if I had boxed her on the ears. Her dark eyes narrowed into slits of menace.

"I see that you're no better than your patient Adolf!" she shot at me.

I couldn't have been more surprised if he had actually recommended me a patient.

"How did you know he was my patient?" I asked her.

"I followed him to your office once."

He came to me only twice, I reflected, and one of those times a woman of the streets actually followed him to my doorstep. What a life he could lead me if he really came regularly! "Isn't that unusual?" I asked her.

She met my eyes fiercely.

"I followed him because I wanted to kill him," she declared.

It seemed to me that I was beginning to partake in the opening scene of some psychological melodrama. Since it might reveal

a glimpse of the play of neuroses in my patient's mind, I decided
to see it through patiently. It was not difficult to get the young
woman with the over-rouged cheeks to talk: like most ladies of
the evening she seemed in the grip of a pathological eagerness to
unburden herself.

It would appear that Hitler's sense of sexual defeat had
already dragged him to that depth of self-humiliation where he
could only overcome his sense of shame by humiliating and
degrading the women he came in contact with. He sought out
the sort of women upon whom he could make his erotic demands,
such as were not averse to acts of sexual derangement that would
sound fantastic to the normally minded male.

Bertha (the name by which she wanted me to know her) had
become aware of my patient's eccentricities through the under-
world grapevine in Munich. She had accosted him the first time
in the very place, at the very table, where I was listening to her
story.

"You're a brunette," Adolf had grumbled to her, in passing,
"and I won't have anything to do with a brunette."

"Why not?" Bertha asked innocently.

"You might be a non-Aryan, a Jewess." Hitler flung at her,
still eyeing her intently.

"I am a Jewess," Bertha said to him. "And I'm willing to
wager I know a few things your Aryan girl friends have never
even heard about."

In Hitler's mind a moving landscape of lust must have suddenly risen up out of the welter of his frustration. Dark fires of
passion must have lit up the horizon, and burned brightly over
him, up till the very moment they reached Bertha's private flat.
Once there, he made a dash for her like a young buck, or a satyr
enamored of a nymph.

Then came the insult which my patient would never forget
or forgive. Instead of betraying as much as a gesture of the
surrender expected of her, this dark Judith of the streets merely
raised her right arm as he advanced, greeted him with a stinging
slap on the mouth which instantly drew blood, and hurried out
into the street.

The outraged Lothario had been too stunned to try for

immediate retaliation, and for the ten days which followed the
incident must have gathered venom in his mind. When he finally
acted, his vengeance was swift and terrible. One morning he
broke into her flat with eight or ten of his cronies, and at the
point of a gun compelled her to go through a routine of degreda-
tion, while he stood aside and looked on in grim silence. The
beastly melodrama over, he hit her a blow on the chin with the
butt-end of his revolver, clicked his heels military-fashion, and
marched out with his gang.

I ran into Hitler late one afternoon, quite by accident, in a
beer hall in the heart of the city. Attracted by the sound of a
voice that was both familiar and awesome, I realized that I had
reached my mark. If I remember rightly, I shrank from it a little.
Ordinarily, I could not possibly have been terrorized by a phenomenon the existence of which I was already aware of. But
Hitler's voice was something different: it was weird and com-
pelling like a Delphic oracle, filled with an earnestness so strange
and piercing that one simply could not listen to it without feeling
the inner erupting of menacing changes.

He was shouting, as I remember:

"The trouble, gentlemen, is not with our laws or even with
the edicts of our conquerors. We could do things even with the
Weimar Constitution (pause) if we got rid of the Jews and the
Communists. Let us throw the enemy like a sick cat between
two buckets of blood."

Another pause. An uncanny sensing by the speaker of the
exact reaction of his audience to what he had already said, before
he will trust himself to continue with his harangue. Yes, that
was my man, I decided, even before I got near enough to him
to see him.

He went on talking, and I forced myself to stop listening
to him, so as to be able to examine my surroundings. There were
several people sitting and standing about my patient's table, and
though they had probably heard him express similar sentiments
dozens of times before, they were taking in his words both seriously and intently. His was the sacred voice of the oracle, the
voice that gave expression to their inner torment. On the table

itself stood a few beer mugs, still wet but empty. Not too much
drinking was being done; it was not beer but delirious oratory
that had filled them to the point of intoxication.

My patient gave me not a single hint with his eyes that he
knew of my presence, that I had ferreted him out, cornered him,
at last. But I caught a new sudden tension in his speech, and I
realized that he was abbreviating remarks he had intended to
expatiate on at much greater length. It seemed to me as if I were
witnessing the sudden, unexpected freezing-over of a waterfall.
When he was through, my patient stepped away from his table,
caught my eyes and strode toward me—as though he were
alarmed lest, left to myself, I might betray him in something,
as if he dreaded that I might come up to him and say so that
all of his disciples might hear:

*"I say, young fellow, do you know that the price of salvarsan
is going up every day, and that if you had any sense you'd lay
up a stock of it to take care of that dose of yours?"*

I could not feel sure whether my presence pleased or displeased him, but I had steeled myself for the worst.

"You see I've caught up with you," I humored him as he
came up.

He took my outstretched hand rather limply.

"Thank you for being patient enough to listen to me," he
said in a swift undertone. "Can we go somewhere, just you
and I?"

"I don't know why not," I said, and not too soon. A crowd
was swiftly gathering about us, and most of them looked as if
they wanted to question him on several points in his diatribe.

Hitler pushed them aside.

"Another time," he said brusquely. Almost against my will,
for I was very much interested in those painridden people, he
spirited me out of the beer hall.

I could not help being piqued by his extraordinary secrecy
about me. Did he secretly suspect me of being a Jew or a spy?
Or was he just naturally cold to the people who befriended him?

"Since you haven't been around to see me for nearly three
weeks," I suggested, "how about just walking me back to my

office? It's quite a way, and may give you a chance to answer some of the questions these boys seem to be itching to ask you."

My words disturbed him. He looked at me with pained animation.

"Then you, too, have questions to ask?"

I laughed. I had thought all stump speakers liked to be heckled.

"Anyone would think you don't like questions," I said to him.

"I don't," he replied simply. "I just like to tell people what I think. That should be enough."

"Suppose it isn't?" I asked.

"Then you were not convinced?" he shot back at me.

"I don't think I heard enough to be sure that I wasn't. I'm positive of one thing, however: An argument is more logical when you have managed to hear most of it. I don't like the amount of venom you manage to get into most of your words."

I could almost see him flare up.

"How about the love I get into others?" he countered.

"Love, Adolf?" I jibed him. "Why, that word is meaningless to you."

His hands described a gesture of belittlement.

"That's not my fault," he rumbled. "If you must blame something, blame the *status quo*."

"The *status quo* is the easiest thing in the world to blame," I reminded him. "If a man is wrong you can imprison him, fine him, or kill him. But what can you do to this *status quo?* And if a thing cannot answer to responsibility, how can you even pretend to hold it responsible?"

"Just watch me," he said.

There was a pause.

"About your failure to show up," I resumed. "Was there any real reason for it?"

He hesitated, and looked shy, as if he had the matter on his conscience.

"Am I to take it," I asked with real pique, "that you only feigned your confidence in my ability to cure you?"

"It's not that at all," he replied. "I know that you're not a quack, but a real doctor. Perhaps you won't believe me, but the truth is I don't feel that I should give up valuable time to something so purely personal."

"You're quite wrought up about our national troubles, aren't you?" I mused.

"Is there anything else in the world worth getting wrought up about?" he demanded.

"I can think of only one thing—your health."

He laughed at me.

"Always tending shop, aren't you?"

"Never mind shop," I objected, "wasn't it yourself who called my attention to the fact that on your health depended the recovery of the whole nation?"

He was silent.

"It's very queer," I continued; "when you came to me the first time it seemed to me as if your whole life were at stake. That was why I undertook to treat you. I had no sooner got fairly interested in your case than you did a disappearing act. Is it possible that you have lost faith in your personal value to Germany?"

He still hesitated.

"I am sorry, of course, Doctor," he said after a long pause. "I meant everything I said to you during those two visits to your office. And I didn't feel so good about disappointing you, either. But I simply have no patience with giving explanations, and that's all there is to it."

"That's all right with me," I said to him. "I have even less interest in listening to explanations. I am now concerned only in your promise that if I resume treating you, you won't wander off again like a lost sheep!"

He looked up hopefully, and I could see his eyes brighten.

"I didn't mean to abandon your treatments, Doctor," he reassured me, "and it's wonderful of you to be so understanding. If you'll agree to forgive and forget, I'll promise never to break another appointment with you."

"Good!" I exclaimed.

We shook hands on it, and I want to say with regard to this particular avowal that he never broke it during the fifteen years of our association which followed.

"And now there are some important matters we have to take up before we get back to my office," I said to him. "I must know a few things about your way of living. They are general questions and I don't think you will have any qualms about answering them. For instance, I must know what your regular occupation is right now."

He looked at me.

"That's not as easy to answer as you think. Will it satisfy you to know that I am in the employ of the Reichswehr?"

I learned later that this was true, and that his particular work for the Reichswehr was to spy, on all the little agitating groups which were laboring, for different reasons and toward different ends, to do away with the infant Republic.

"The question is," I resumed, "are you compensated well enough to enable you to live satisfactorily? Do you eat regularly, for instance?"

"I can remember when I lived much worse, Doctor. But I've no kick. As a matter of fact, my economic status has improved several hundred percent since the Reichswehr deigned to take notice of me."

I remembered an issue raised by Ernst Schmidt.

"Do you still live in the barracks?" I asked him.

"Yes. But I am looking for quarters of my own. That is, with the consent of my superior officers."

"Very interesting," I murmured, for his answer had brought me to the brink of my most important questions, those having to do with his relationship with women. Since we had already reached my office, I decided to defer those queries till we were seated comfortably in its interior.

"Come in," I urged him at the door. "I promise not to hold you too long tonight."

But before I go on with my introductory talk with Hitler, I must give a review of the information regarding this phase of the Fuehrer's life as it has been treated for the world by the leading journalists of our time.

CHAPTER FOUR

HITLER AND HIS WOMEN

On the Limitations of Present-Day Reporting—The Loves of Adolf—John Gunther Sees No Evil—Wyndham Lewis Speaks No Evil—Otto Strasser Sees, Hears and Speaks Plenty—Hitler and His Fifteen-Year-Old Niece.

IT HAS been established for a long time that journalists are creatures of the moment. They are expected to describe only what they see, but they have to see not only what is before them, but also what they are expected to take note of by the powers that be, if the latter are to consent to let them continue to notice anything. In an age of power reporting, the surge of power is in many directions, so that the reports of our correspondents to their eager millions are limited by the desires of their masters as well as by the natural and unfortunate bars to human vision.

Hitler must have been on his best behavior when he was interviewed by the celebrated John Gunther, whom I admire among the five or six most brilliant living journalists. I opened his *Inside Europe* with a feeling amounting to fervor, for, in spite of exile, it was still my Europe. Imagine, therefore, my astonishment to read in that admirable crackerjack of contemporary debunkers the announcement that "he (Hitler) is totally uninterested in women from any personal sexual point of view."

"Is it possible that Gunther met dear Adolf in church?" I asked myself, and suddenly I remembered that my ex-patient no longer attends religious services.

" 'The life of our people must be free from the asphyxiating perfume of modern eroticism,' " he quotes the Fuehrer as writ-

65

ing in *Mein Kampf,* and he accepts these words as a full characterization of Hitler's attitude toward the fair sex. But what about the definitely erotic passages in the very book he quotes?

"His personal life," continues Gunther, "embodies this concept to the fullest. He is not a woman-hater, but he avoids and evades women. His manners are those of the wary chevalier, given to hand-kissing—and nothing else. Many women are attracted to him sexually, but they have had to give up the chase. Frau Goebbels formerly had evening parties to which she asked pretty and distinguished women to meet him, but she was never able to arrange a match. The rumor was heard that the coy Leader was engaged to the grand-daughter of Richard Wagner. It was nonsense. It is quite possible that Hitler has never had anything to do with a woman in his life."

This about a man who has been photographed with more women than Clark Gable. But let us run along with John. He is interesting, if not always well informed.

"Nor, as is so widely believed, is he homosexual. Several German journalists spent much time and energy, when such an investigation was possible, checking every lodging that Hitler, in Munich days, had slept in; they interviewed beer-hall proprietors, coffee-house waiters, landladies, porters. No evidence was discovered that Hitler had ever been intimate with anybody of any sex at any time. His sexual energies, at the beginning of his career, were obviously sublimated into oratory. The influence of his mother and childhood environment . . . contributed signally to his frustration. Most of those German writers and observers best equipped to know think that Hitler is a virgin."

That would have sounded just as plausible if the author had written "blessed virgin." But is it possible that John Gunther never heard of Hitler's several years' courtship of his niece, Grete Raubal, which ended in her scandalous suicide? Or of Hitler's frustrated wooing of the sister of his erstwhile friend, Dr. Ernst (Putzi) Hanfstaengl? Or of the many other instances in which the public was let in on the Fuehrer's private life? Ignorance of these matters might have been considered a possibility if Mr. Gunther had not proved by his many quotations in his book that he has gone thoroughly through Konrad Heiden's biography. The probable answer is that Mr. Gunther, having once enjoyed the privilege of interviewing Hitler, planned to enjoy it at least once more.

Abject as are the kowtowings of journalism to power, its obligations to personal ambition are comparatively despicable.

"Whenever I think of Hitler," writes Wyndham Lewis, in his *The Hitler Cult* (1939), "I think of a flower—the violet. This sounds absurd. He is a human violet, however; his bashfulness is real if nothing else. He is almost a monster of shyness; and to account for the brazenness of my strange violet—for its pushing itself forward so rudely, as if it were a sunflower or something, and absorbing the attention of the world in its struggle for 'a place in the sun,'—requires some accounting for. A paranoic violet! A strange variety indeed. But this male Joan of Arc is a strange man." And lest you begin to draw the conclusion that perhaps our violet is not a man at all, only that his English biographer is too bashful himself to admit it, Lewis adds a little later: "He is *not* a homosexual, like most Germans." The emphasis belongs to Mr. Lewis, as does his picturesquely bad English, as can be guessed even by a German with an alleged racial taint of homosexuality.

On what authority Mr. Lewis condemns the greater part of the males of Germany to homosexuality and excludes Herr Hitler, he does not attempt to divulge. Mr. Lewis again seems to me a journalist who tells us what he sees by what he some day hopes to see. Maybe this is good journalism. By the simplest standards I know, it cannot be good reporting.

We now come to the report of a German, himself once a Nazi leader, now, like myself, a poor refugee, and immediately the atmosphere begins to clear.

Kurt G. W. Ludecke (whose *I Knew Hitler*, 1937, was more the work of a journalist than that of a statesman) reveals what he knows of Hitler's relations with the fair sex through a conversation he said he had some years ago with Magda Goebbels, wife of the evil little Minister of Propaganda. You have only to read what he has to say to realize that this man has no favors to ask for or to give.

" 'So you're on your way to a great position in Germany,' I chaffed her. 'Surely you'll be *Frau Minister*—with myself and the others courting your favor. But tell me, Magda, how did it come about?'

"Lightly and amusingly she told me that her interest in Party work, for which I have been responsible, had continued until at last she began to work in the Berlin office. There she caught the eye of the leader—Joseph Goebbels. She became his personal secretary, he her ardent suitor. (And why shouldn't he, I thought, as her story unfolded. She was beautiful, cultured, intelligent; her home was luxurious, and her alimony from her former husband provided a very respectable income.) Goebbels, head of the Party propaganda machine, began to do some propagandizing on his own behalf, and eventually she yielded. 'The proposal was most intriguing, and I thought it just as well to make certain of my Frau Ministership in good season,' she explained with a mock demureness.

" 'But since you were bent on marrying into the Party, why on earth didn't you set your cap for your boss's boss—for Hitler?' I asked.

" 'I might have,' she admitted with a suggestion of a blush. 'Before I said *yes* to the Doctor, I let him take me up to Munich to meet Hitler and show me the Braun Haus. Hitler was perfectly charming, but somehow' . . . She looked at me and smiled. 'At any rate, when I was married soon after that at my son's country place, Hitler was the best man while the Doctor was only the groom.'

"I had been told that one of the most appreciated services Frau Goebbels rendered Hitler was the preparation of special meals, difficult to get elsewhere. Hitler was by now a confirmed vegetarian, finicky to exasperation over carrots and spinach, and Goebbels, by baiting his hospitality with a tasty vegetable-plate, so to speak, had managed to get and hold the Fuehrer's ear as no one else had before. His efforts to consolidate this influence by another stratagem had failed, however, because of a baffling quirk in Hitler's character—as I learned with some amusement and secret satisfaction when I chanced to ask why Magda did not find a pretty friend for the lonely Alf.

" 'My husband asked exactly the same question some time ago,' she replied. 'He was most anxious to get Hitler interested in some nice girl—it would have done him good to be able to relax and pour out his troubles to a sympathetic woman. Alas, I was no good as a match-maker. I'd leave him alone with my most charming friends, but he wouldn't respond. Putzi tried, too, but he didn't do much better than I. In some ways Hitler simply isn't human—he can't be reached or touched. My husband was terribly disappointed when we couldn't get him to choose a confidante.' "

I come now to the opinions of two giants among the German emigres: the scholar Konrad Heiden, and the fighter, Otto Strasser. Konrad Heiden has written the most comprehensive biography of both Hitler and the movement, and he comes closest among the students of Hitleriana to understanding those sexual phobias of his that border on the fantastic. I quote:

"There is documentary evidence which throws a surprising light on Adolf Hitler's relations to women. This evidence places it beyond a doubt that Adolf was particularly enslaved to the women he loved.

"Considerations of every kind make it impossible to describe in more detail either this disposition or the above-mentioned documentary evidence. We will merely mention that the Reich treasurer of the party, Franz Schwarz, who helped to free Adolf from the clutches of the blackmailers, is connected with the case.

"The fact of Hitler's enslavement to women supplies the missing component which fits correctly into the total picture of Adolf Hitler's character. It is the secret contrast to his exaggerated, affected brutality in politics and business and towards friends and fellow-workers—a contrast which is well known to authorities on sexual science.

"And now the peculiar nature of Hitler's relations with women becomes apparent. They are all obscure and mysterious; he gives himself, contrary to the reality, the air of a man without a private life. These relations, almost without exception, snap off suddenly at some place or other, and in many cases it is obvious that Hiler is not the forsaker but the forsaken. One of the women mentioned here, when questioned regarding her relations with Hitler, gave it to be understood that she had experienced a disappointment, which had made her regard him as not altogether respectable.

"So the often expressed conjecture that Hitler's emotional life is not normal is correct. Only the conjecture has generally taken a wrong direction: Hitler is not homosexual or bi-sexual: he is merely subject to sexual enslavement. Many psychiatrists ascribe to people with such a disposition a peculiar suggestivity— an unusual type of look or gesture, which is intended to fascinate. It is for the expert to answer the questions raised here."

But the final conclusive testimony is that of Otto Strasser, who was a friend of Adolf Hitler and helped him build the National Socialist movement. Strasser saw two brothers of his, Gregor and Paul, succumb to the bullets of Hitler's paid butchers, but he writes calmly and dispassionately, with the authority of an eye-witness. His testimony is so vital to the understanding of the character of Hitler that I have arranged to let him tell it his own way in another part of the book.

CHAPTER FIVE

MY PATIENT ASSERTS HIMSELF

The Nature of Authority—Hitler and I Reach an Agreement—Eating Origins—Sexual Beginnings—A Significant Spanking—The German Workers Party—Schicklgruber into Hitler.

"IT HAS been suggested to me," I said to my patient after our walk, when we had finally settled down in my office, "that you have an even more interesting reason than one of policy for planning to abandon your Spartan barracks for the luxury of private quarters of your own."

He flushed.

"I'm not sure that I know what you mean, Doctor," he said petulantly. "But I suppose I can guess. Is it necessary for me to remind you that in all this excitement I am also human?"

"Ah," I grinned, " 'human, all too human.' "

My habit of fingering the skull on my desk seemed at this moment to be disturbing my patient profoundly.

"Please don't do that," he snarled.

"Why not?"

He was silent.

"I suppose you dislike it because you suspect that it's my subconscious comment on the vanity of all earthly things," I said. "Pomp, power—and even the desire to be human."

He smiled faintly, readjusted a little.

"What is your objection to my desire to be human, Herr Doktor?" he asked.

"None," I assured him. "But has it ever occurred to you that even the business of being human can be overdone?"

When things did not go quite his way, my patient could

71

become unbearably cross, and one witnessed the sudden miracle
of the lamb transformed into the lion.

"I suppose you got all this from Ernst," he growled. "He
knows more than he understands, and maybe a little more than
is good for him." His face darkened into menace, the somber
cloud that swamps the features of the manic depressive when he
feels himself balked. "I have very good reasons for what I am
doing," he barked, "and whether you approve of them or not I
insist on their being kept free of that sort of carping criticism."

"I am as good an obeyer of authority as any German," I said.
"But I always want to know its source. Since you claim the right
to act without curb, will you tell me once and for all why you
are entitled to such consideration?"

I expected another outburst from him, but it did not come.
Instead he became quite calm and imperturbable.

"I ask for this authority," he replied, "because I have already
assumed it in my spirit, and I do not intend to play the game
by halves. You will either be with me or against me."

"I thought that sort of authority disappeared into the Netherlands with our thoughtful Kaiser," I joked. "I believe that
for the moment it is chopping trees at Doorn."

"It will be chopping *heads,*" said my patient ominously, giving me a Medusa-like stare that forced me into a stony silence.
During the embarrassing pause, I examined his face closely.
It had the look of a man in the throes of a monomania, some
terrible power-complex that would sweep aside all opposition
with fire and sword. Such an expression, I thought, must have
ravaged the face of a mad Caesar, who put the world in
chains that he might have the freedom to indulge his madness to his heart's content. Would this man overcome his sense
of inferiority by "a masculine protest," as Adler put it, a psychic
stampede into national and international violence?

"The Kaiser went," declared my patient, resuming his trend
of thought, "because he was free to go. Authority did not go
with him. It remained here, because authority is essentially German and belongs on German soil."

"I don't like to quarrel with authority," I mused. "But I hope you won't object if I suggest that you'd give it a better start by curbing its fury a bit."

My patient knotted his face in suppressed anger.

"I know I'm not your father confessor," I continued, "though I have an idea that you'd listen to me with even less attention if I were. As your physician, however, I am duty bound to warn you that if you don't care what effect your love-making has on the objects of your affections, you must take heed of the effect it may have on you. You can suggest to me, if you like, that I'd do better to mind my own affairs, but I am doing precisely that. As my patient you are strictly my business, and every time you take it into your head to begin a new courtship, you are jeopardizing everything I have done for you up to that time."

I could see that my words made a profound impression on him. He understood that I was really engaged in guarding his most precious interests, yet, as he understood the values in his own life, there were liberties even more important, which he had to protect.

"I can only assure you," he said, charging every word he uttered with a tremendous feeling of sincerity, "that I do not go about making love to women as an idle sport, and that I realize instinctively the dangers in which I place myself. I make love to a woman out of a biological necessity as authentic and undeniable as breathing and eating. Beyond the point of mere love-making I do not go, and I have no intention of changing my direction in this respect. That's my promise to you, and you can depend on it."

"We will leave it at that, then," I agreed. "For the present we are both on our honor. You are to observe the bounds you just described to me, and I am to stop being unduly suspicious. And now we can get down to business."

He fidgeted in his chair as if he could already feel the ordeal that was to come. "You understand, of course," I said soothingly, "that the questions I am about to ask you will be of an extremely personal nature. The healing process to which I am subjecting you is a sort of subtle surgery of the spirit. You must look upon my questions as the probing of the doctor's eyes for the exact spot in which to make a vital incision. But in this medication, the actual surgery is done not by the doctor but by the patient. The incisions will be made by yourself as you rise honestly to every occasion and give truthful answers to questions you do not like to hear. You must reveal to a stranger things you have always been afraid to acknowledge even to yourself. For a patient to take offense at a question is as if he tried to step off the operating table before the operation has been performed. Do you understand?"

He leaned forward on his fists in a gesture of resignation.

"I understand," he muttered.

"Very well, then. Man is a multiple force of a variety of different diversions. He reaches out, under certain stimuli, for food, for possessions, for love. He gradually becomes aware of himself, as he repeats these motions, in the name of the many forces which motivate him. Now can you remember," I quizzed him, "how long you have been an omnivorous creature?"

My patient suddenly assumed a sitting position, wove his fingers on his chest and knitted his brows in acute remembrance.

"I guess I've always been that."

"You don't understand. You've always been everything from the very first day of creation. But how long is it since you have been aware of yourself as an eating creature?"

"I honestly don't think I can remember," he finally said to me.

"Why not?" I insisted.

He hunched his shoulders and stared blankly at the wall.

"I guess I never thought it was of much importance," he thought aloud.

I couldn't help laughing.

"We'll get back to that later," I told him. "Perhaps you will do better if I ask you whether you can remember when you first became aware of yourself as a sexual being."

He grinned.

"Isn't that the question you should have asked me in the first place, Doctor?"

"I'll tell you when you have answered it correctly."

He considered.

"I guess I must have been about four years old," he said.

I nodded to him approvingly.

"You understand, of course, that you have really been a sexual being since the day you were born?"

His eyes lit to the meaning of my words.

"I think I know what you mean. I suppose so."

"Don't merely suppose so," I chided him gently. "This is the sort of thing that you must take my word for, as an acknowledgment of *my* kind of authority. It is so because I *say* so."

"Have it your way," groaned my patient, throwing up his hands in a mixed gesture of defiance and defeat.

"And it is your considered conclusion," I continued, "that the feeling of sex came into your conscious nature when you were about four. Can you possibly remember the occasion?"

He gave a faint smile.

"I remember it quite clearly," he said, sliding to the edge of his chair and almost sitting on his spine. "It was at a time my mother was recovering from some sort of illness—what illness I could only guess at. She was quite weak, so weak she could not do much of her own housework. To help her out, my father called in a peasant woman of the neighborhood to do some of the rougher work, such as washing the walls and the floors. The woman fascinated me from the very first moment she stepped through the doorway into our house.

"I see her now as clearly as if she were standing before me," he mused, "a big powerful woman with a large handsome flushed face, white arms and red hands, and the most enormous thighs I have ever seen in a human being. She had a way of drawing her skirt up above her knees when she lowered herself to the floor to scrub, and the act of lowering herself was like the launching of a boat or something monstrous on wings swooping down to the earth. She came several times, and I could not let myself wander out of sight of her while she was there.

"One Friday afternoon, my eyes devoured her as she moved about like some giant fish on the floor of the ocean, and my ecstasy reached a new height. My eyes settled on the small square sector of white thigh left bare by her raised skirt, and such a fever settled on my limbs that I realized something was happening to me which I had never experienced before. The sense of that fever—about which I knew nothing definite—remained with me for days, weeks, months. I could not even make up my mind whether it was a pleasant feeling, or something it would be best to get out of my system. But I could not help holding to it as if I treasured it, and many years later it came back to me so forcibly as a memory, that I have never since had any doubt of its origin, its nature, and the part it has played in my life."

Those last words appealed very strongly to me. When you get a patient talking that way, you're getting along. You've got him under control.

"I don't suppose you can tell me much more about this primal sensation of yours?" I prodded him.

He shook his head grimly.

It was my signal to resume.

"Suppose we try. You underwent a rising tide of your blood which you remember as a sensation, both dizzying and confusing. Can you remember what it was in your mind to do as you watched the bare thigh of this peasant woman of yours?"

He appeared to consider carefully before answering.

"I'm not sure," he said.

I leaned forward toward him intently.

"Perhaps I can help you," I suggested. "Suppose you try to remember exactly where you were when it happened, and in what position?"

He remembered easily.

"I was sitting on the doorstep of the house, exactly where my mother herself had placed me bodily."

"And you remained sitting dutifully on that doorstep while that emotion kept sweeping through your body?"

He nodded.

"You're sure there wasn't something you wanted to do besides continuing to sit dutifully on that doorstep?"

"I remember, I wanted to creep forward toward her on my hands and knees and—"

"Why do you hestitate?" I snapped at him. "Why don't you say it? A surgeon isn't much good to himself or his patient if he hasn't the courage to make the incision, once the spot for it has been discovered for him."

"I suppose I wanted to find that sector of white flesh and put my mouth to it."

"Good, we are getting on," I encouraged him. "Don't be surprised if we get back to this business more than once in our inquiry. But set this firmly in your mind, for the present. You made the first movement to achieve love with your lips. From that point we'd better get ahead and quickly. We are safe in presuming that incidents such as your enslavement to the thighs of the washerwoman continued to occur to you without arousing in your blood anything like the scandal of the initial fixation. But a time had to come when the sensation of libidinous awareness came to you through the medium of the sexual channel. Can you remember when that happened?"

He fought against the question with a nervous twist of his head.

"I don't understand," he protested, "please make yourself plain."

"It's plain enough," I badgered him, "but you refuse to answer.

"When did it happen?" I insisted.

He remained discreetly silent.

"That's not so easy," he grumbled at last.

"You'll find things easier when we arrive in the province of your more definite pleasures," I taunted him. "In the meantime, think back courageously, as if your life depended on tracing this thing back to its source."

"I can only guess," he faltered.

"What do you think God was doing when he threw his first mud ball at the sun? Guessing is long-distance thinking. It is the least idle of the predispositions of man."

"But it might have been in connection with something so outrageous that you may think it a little funny if not downright vulgar," he suddenly blurted out.

I knew that I had hit it.

"Don't worry about me," I assured him. "A doctor who can't afford a wife certainly has no place in his life for a sense of humor or burlesque."

He began like a man who talks out of a state of confusion:

The words rolled out of his mouth in a head-long torrent sweeping along the sediment of his mind.

"It happened, I think, in school, of all places, in my ninth year. The heroine of the occasion was one of the homeliest teachers I can remember. It was late in the afternoon, and the time of the year must have been in March or April. It had something to do with an interrupted lesson. I remember now that it was geography, one of my favorite subjects, because I liked to draw maps. A boy sitting in a chair behind me had asked me to pass on a caricature I had made of the principal of our school, and as I complied with this flattering request (nothing like having one's art in demand), our blue-nosed harridan, with gray eyes like gimlets and long, dry, skinny, withered hands, caught the motion.

"She stepped forward quickly, appropriated the bit of paper, and sentenced me to remain after classes. By the time the rest of the pupils had been dismissed, she seemed to have made up her mind on what form my punishment was to take. I was to stretch myself out over her lap, and submit to a good old-fashioned spanking. She was going to give me twenty-five strokes of her hand, she explained, as a lesson in good behavior. This should have immediately aroused my suspicions, because the way she usually did it was with a ruler. In the midst of counting the blows, it began to insinuate itself into my mind that they were becoming fainter and fainter, and when a sudden descent of hair made a ticklish shower on my neck, I began to realize for the first time the delightful pain of being a man."

He stopped as if to catch his breath.

"And the aftermath?" I pressed.

"When I reached home I stretched myself out on a little cot that was always carefully decked out in our front room. I lay on my back as a puppy does in the sunlight, without any more idea of why I was doing this than we may suppose a puppy has, and after a while I began to experience that painfully delicious expansion which is the epitome of man's emotional journey through life. Only that which I felt was not so much expanding as demanding. It took an infinite amount of time, maybe an hour, to realize that the only thing in the world capable of making any answer to this strange gnawing want was my hand."

I nodded approvingly.

"You're learning candor by the minute," I said to him. "It'll be a great help to us as we proceed. But there is something else you'll have to learn if we are to make any really genuine progress. It is very vital to our surgeon-patient relationship. The surgeon, who in this case is also the nurse, may cut in the right place, and yet if he is not careful, the patient will bleed to death."

"That can only happen if the nurse is not along at the right time with the bandages," he reminded me.

"True," I said. "And that's exactly my point. Let your nurse handle all of the bandages in this case. If there's to be any philosophizing in this business, leave it all to me. Understand?"

"Perfectly."

I rose, as a signal to him that we were through for the time being. He looked disappointed.

"As you say," he shrugged. "And now that we've got this part of our meeting out of the way, I want you to know that I have a still better reason than the one suggested by Ernst for wanting quarters of my own. Are you interested?"

"Excited."

"Have you heard about Anton Drexler's *German Workers Party?*"

"No, but it sounds like socialism on a blotter."

"It's not socialism raw," he assured me. "It's a kind of special German socialism, and some day not only you but all the rest of the world will hear about it."

"Give me one good reason why," I challenged.

"Because," he replied with what to him was inexorable logic, "it is going to change, first Germany, then Europe, and finally all the rest of the world. It's already changed *me,*" he added as an afterthought.

"That's a beginning," I murmured.

"Don't be so cynical," he threw back at me. "It's a darned good beginning. And now that you've got yourself into that high and lofty position, there's something I've got to beg you to observe. If you ever again find me in the sort of crowd you discovered me in tonight, forget that the name I gave you is Schickelgruber."

I looked at him with amazement. Here was a brand new turn I had not anticipated.

"What is your name in that case?" I asked him.

He replied firmly and unequivocally:

"Hitler, Adolf Hitler. Do you think you can remember that?"

I promised I would try.

CHAPTER SIX

FIRST SIGHTS AND SOUNDS

Goatee Displaced by Mustache—My Patient Takes an
Apartment—Beer Halls Differ from Saloons—Forms
His Own Party—First Color—First Sound—First
Touch—More History.

IT WAS not difficult to remember the name of Adolf Hitler. And
many things have happened since then to cause me to wish that I
were able to forget it.

I note first, among the most whimsical of these events, the
sudden complete transformation which came about in his personal appearance. One afternoon, when he arrived for an interview, my patient's wispy goatee was gone, as if it had been blown
away by one of his own explosions. And not long after that, an
abbreviated growth of hair began to show several inches higher
up on his upper lip. The people who had laughed at the goatee
were to get down on their hands and knees before the "dropped
eyebrow."

Would I try to remember the name Adolf Hitler?

To try to do so would have been equal to trying to remember
your own shadow. It was impossible unless you had lost it, like
the unfortunate creature—Peter Schlemiel. But as time passed it
began to appear that Germany was full of Schlemiels who had
mislaid their shadows and replaced them with Hitler's.

The shadow of the future Fuehrer was already casting its
dark rays upon the minds of Germans. Before I could seriously
make an effort to get used to that dreadful name, it grew with in-
creasing popularity among people whom I met every day in the
course of my work, and in my reading of the local press. After
a while it was not unusual to see it crop up in minor headlines

on the front pages—in connection with street riots and broken heads.

Adolf Hitler. A man with only a recollection of manhood and a devouring appetite for buttermilk and raw vegetables. A man who loved things for the most fantastic reasons, and hated others for no reason at all. Yet people spoke that name with more and more thoughtfulness and high-minded gravity in connection with the most important problems of the day. It began to look as if to forget it would require an herculean labor of the imagination.

He had succeeded in exchanging quarters in the local barracks for a private one somewhere in the city. His plans expanded with his enormous personal conceit, but his chief political efforts were still concentrated in the beer halls in the heart of the city.

It should be explained to the non-German reader—who is likely to confuse these purely German institutions with the American saloon or the English tavern—that the beer halls of Munich are by no means mere drinking resorts. In fact, they serve a variety of public ends, and offer spacious accommodations for every sort of festivity or gathering. Unlike the saloon and the tavern, they are frequented by all classes of the population. Every beer *haus* has its own peculiar patrons, and every table therein serves as a nucleus for one of a dozen informal clubs and groups of like-minded acquaints. The adult German population can be reached through the beer halls as easily as they can be propagandized on the radio. And the cost, of course, is cheaper. It is important to remember this in connection with the story of my patient's rise to power.

His frenzied speech-making in the beer halls went on night after night, arousing all the time a deeper and more fanatic attentiveness. It was a species of rabble-rousing which had not been let loose in Europe since the days of Peter the Hermit. The comparison is apt, because both Peter and Adolf whipped up the medieval demon of intolerance that engulfed Europe, leaving only death and terror. Hitler became the Peter of the vast modern crusade against the Jews, and Jews and Communists as well as the Peter Schlemiels walked in the shadow of his terrible wrath.

Hitler's violent hatred of Communism, which he believed to be entirely Jewish, made him almost as many friends in Munich as his assault on the Versailles Treaty. I can understand, now, in my exile, better than I did at that moment, the nature of this fierce inner wrath of Hitler's. He was one of those people who are born all eyes. Everything he saw in the first formative years of his life seemed to him good, beautiful and desirable. It was only natural that he should have conceived a fundamental dislike for a system of thought which debunked all things he had come to look on as precious, and even announced its determination to make those rare baubles the common property of all, as if they merited no real personal ownership. To Adolf, Communism was *transvaluation of all values,* to use Nietzsche's phrase, and therefore to be opposed with all the force of his demoniac being.

But he was not satisfied with just rejecting and hating. He also had in him the artist's inner need for constructing in lieu of the things torn down—of building. There had been some satisfaction for him in becoming Number Seven in the ambitious little Drexler group. But it was a satisfaction it did not take him long to exhaust. It was not long before he secretly came to an agreement with his ego. The only thing capable of really satisfying him was a program and a party entirely his own, a platform on which he could stand in the center, and from which he would be able to tell Germany what to do and how to march, in order to redeem her rightful place among the nations. What is called the "Messianic Complex" had completely taken possession of his being. He was ready to build the world into his own mad dream, even if it involved the destruction of a continent and the sterilization of European culture.

I had a feeling that some such thing was going on in his mind, when he appeared in my office for the next analysis. But I determined not to let it color our proceedings. I plunged into my own program with him.

"You have had," I reminded him, "a whole month in which to digest the several aspects of your subconscious which we uncovered during our last session. It is possible that things may have occurred to you in this interval which might modify the picture as I have it here in my notes."

He shook his head.

"Perhaps during this interval, some tickling doubts have

arisen in your mind which you would like to take up with me before we go ahead?"

He grinned sheepishly.

"How about a complaint?"

I was not certain that he was entirely in earnest, but decided to encourage speech in him as much as possible.

"Complaints of a serious nature are always in order," I told him, "until I ask you to put them aside for scientific reasons."

"I don't know how serious you'll think this is," he said hesitantly. "But I wonder how it happened that you managed in such a short session to tangle my life with two such undesirable people: one as ugly as sin, and the other more irretrievably vulgar than repentance."

I was tempted to laugh, but managed to repress myself.

"You seem to forget," I reminded him, "that I only ask the questions, and that it is you who furnish the answers. I am no ventriloquist's dummy having ready replies to the most abstruse queries. Besides, since when have ugliness and vulgarity graduated from their status as descriptions into solemn measures of value?"

"Forgive me," he said with an apologetic grin. "It seems I've been playing with the bandages again."

I waved the incident aside as unimportant.

"In the matter of the washerwoman," I confessed to him, "I may have been more at fault than you. She brought us deeper into your subconscious life than I should have led you at our first interview, and I must be as strongly on my guard to ask you the proper questions at the proper time as you must be to find in your memory the most honest and effective answers. But no damage has been done."

"I hope so," he grinned, letting his face relax in good humor. "You doctors have a habit of curing your patients by killing them off."

"I shall try to avoid such a disastrous cure," I assured him. "A dead mind—"

"Please don't talk about that," he interrupted harshly, his face turning rigid with suppressed emotion. It was obvious that, like all neurotics, he had a fear of insanity, the mind going hopelessly dead.

"Tonight we're going back—back to genesis and to first principles," I said, seeking to jolt him out of his morbid mood. "We're going back to those first impressions and sensations on which the greater part of the fabric of a human life rests. The only danger is that you might try to see yourself in your answers as something which you are not. Resist any temptation in that direction, because there is danger of your innocently frustrating any good we may have achieved for ourselves up to that point. I now want you to look back into your primary impressions and see if you can remember the first color you ever noticed and thought of by the name the world knows it by."

He considered a long time, brightened, and said:

"I think it was black."

This is a very delicate point and people rarely hit it off right on the first try. I required evidence.

"By what token do you remember that?" I asked him.

"It's very simple," he replied. "My mother had a habit of referring to the night either as black or as blackness. It was something I have never heard anyone else do. The first thing I ever saw her admire was a black hat, and I remember her referring to it by the same word. In that way the color impressed itself on my mind by its own name. The night and a hat are wedded in my mind forever."

"What about red?" I suggested.

He shook his head.

"It couldn't have been red. I never could have got so bright an impression in my father's house."

"Blue?" I insisted.

He shook his head again.

"I know it could not have been blue either, for the simple reason that I could never have distinguished it from black."

That was something.

"Then blue and black have always been the same for you?"

He nodded.

"As far as impression goes, yes."

"All right, then, we accept black as your first color. Now try to recollect your first sound. Not necessarily the first sound you heard, but the first one you remember having heard."

He thought and thought, then looked up helplessly.

"I remember the first thing I ever broke, and with it the first sound must have etched itself in my memory. It was a glass from which my mother was feeding me some liquid. Because I had violently pushed her hand aside when she was not expecting it, it fell from my mouth to the hard floor with a shattering crash. I can still hear the sound of the breaking glass, and I can see the scared look that dawned in the eyes of my mother as she calculated the damage of the cost of the glass."

"But at that time you couldn't possibly have known the meaning of such a look," I insisted.

"Maybe not as a conception of monetary damage done," he said. "But in terms of terror, I understood perfectly. Already terror and I were brothers."

I was convinced.

"That takes care of sound. Now we come to smell. Can you remember the first smell that registered itself on your consciousness?"

"I'm afraid it was a purely personal odor, my own," he admitted falteringly, after a slight pause. "I must have been out of my swaddling clothes only a little while, and I'd been left to myself for a longer time than children of four or five should be left, for all-around comfort. When my mother came back she had to change everything on me, and I could feel the befoulment in my nose for days thereafter."

I was puzzled, and even a little afraid that he might be secretly making sport with me.

"You're quite sure you remember that?" I asked him.

He shrugged.

"It was the first thing that occurred to me when you put the question. Anything wrong with that?"

"Just that people rarely distress themselves with the remembrance of their own odors."

He gave me a shrewd look.

"Maybe with me you ought to be prepared to depart occasionally from the procedure of ordinary psychiatry," he suggested.

"In psychiatry," I said to him, "you turn corners only when you come to them. We'll let the matter of odor go for another time. Can you remember the first thing you were aware of touching? That's the most complex of all sensations to try to recall, so you must be very careful. Think carefully along the variety of surfaces you have encountered, and it may come to you."

He remained wrapt in thought for a while. Then he said:

"I'm afraid I can't remember exactly, and perhaps I never shall. But I have a real conviction that the very first thing I felt consciously was a hand—a human hand."

"Why do you place such emphasis on the word *human?*" I asked him.

"I don't know, I guess, unless it is that the hand always seems to me the most human of our members. Or maybe it's just an aberration of speech."

"In that case it certainly is not to be lightly treated. An aberration of speech is an aberration of the mind, a possible cerebral lesion which we may be hunting. But tell me: Why must it be the touch of a hand?"

He thought.

"Maybe," he finally announced, with a faltering of the voice, "because my mother's hands were the most beautiful I have ever known."

I nodded.

"You remember them?" I asked.

"Distinctly," he replied.

"That's something to go into in closer detail some other time," I suggested. "For the present, we have to return to the first question I put to you at our first sitting. Can you remember what it was?"

He grinned.

"You asked me if I could remember when I first realized myself as a devouring creature. There is a wall between me and the answer to that question which must exist in the life of most people—all people, in fact, except those brought up on a bottle."

"You're playing with bandages again," I reminded him. "But this time you've done it so skillfully that we will let it pass without reprimand. You're probably right, but we'll have to get at that first impression, nevertheless. Leap that wall of sweet flesh we must and will. Do you mind if I guide you a little?"

He shrugged.

"Suit yourself," he sighed.

I leaned toward him earnestly.

"Try, to begin with, to remember some of the dishes which were favorites in your father's household."

His face brightened.

"That's comparatively easy. Pigs knuckle was my father's favorite delicacy in meat, and plain baked potato in vegetables. I remember hearing him say once that he thought the Irish had proven themselves a race of kings on the simple evidence that they subsisted almost solely on a diet of potatoes and dishes derived from it."

"How about your mother? Didn't she have any favorite dishes?"

"At the table my mother shared both of my father's culinary enthusiasms. But secretly she had a taste all her own for hard candy—and she indulged it quite frequently, usually when he wasn't home."

"Can you remember any preference she had in the choice of candies?"

"I certainly do. It was peppermint stick candy. One afternoon she shared her secret with me, and I must have kept sucking away at my part of the stick for hours. I could swear I still have the feeling of it in my mouth. There's the answer to your question. Nothing in my recollections of food could possibly precede that."

By the glitter in my patient's eyes I could see that he enjoyed the triumph almost as much as I did.

"One more question," I persisted. "You said that you remembered your mother admiring a black hat. Was that her favorite color in dress?"

"It was."

"Very well, then, we've completed our cycle for this sitting," I announced. "And now I'm going to do something experimental. I'm going to tell you now the question with which I intend to confront you a month from today when we resume our quest. The question will be: *What single image do your eyes recall as the one first impressed on them?* Don't give it any thought now. It will recur to you many times in the next few weeks, so that when I actually ask for it, your answer will be prepared for me by your own memory, And now you can relax and tell me if there is anything new on your fighting front, provided it is not of too secretive a nature to be told."

He grinned.

"There's no such thing as a secret, in my vocabulary. Everything open and above-board is my motto. It's the only possible preventive against treachery. If you don't want people to anticipate what you are going to do, publish your plans so that the whole world can read them."

"On the contrary," I said, "I prefer the technique of the Roman emperor who nailed the new laws so high on the wall that no citizen could read them or even guess at their content. That gave him an excuse for exacting big fines from law-breakers who didn't know what the new laws were about."

"That Roman emperor was a fool!" snapped Hitler. "He should have known that few people read laws; they are stuffed down their throats by the police. Only a few will read my plans, and of these practically none will believe them. But something has happened. Believe it or not, I am at last the proprietor of my own party and my own party platform."

I was both interested and amused, as he proceeded to tell me with an enthusiasm that had in it something of the element of personal triumph how he and some friends had only the day before completed the drafting of the platform of the new German liberating party—the National Socialist Party.

"What's your membership, as of today?"

"Exactly six," he replied.

"Including yourself?"

He nodded.

"Yes, we're still the original party," he explained, "without Drexler, whom I never liked."

"You once thought Drexler was a very good man," I reminded him.

"So he is. But from now on he will have to continue being a good man—by himself," he replied derisively.

I did not have a single personal encounter with my patient during the next few weeks, but it was not necessary to actually see him to keep track of him. With a political platform of his own to stand on, his activities increased phenomenally. The National Workers Party had remained comparatively static. The National Socialist Party increased its membership by leaps and bounds. It was only a matter of a few months when the realization came to me forcibly that my patient had created a distinctive and decidedly important group of politicos, and that the world about him, German and otherwise, would soon find it necessary to take him and his activities into serious account.

Hitler moved out of the beer halls into the open streets, out of threats of fighting into actual fighting. As he gradually and relentlessly smashed every communist effort to establish its supremacy in Munich, more and more people were drawn to him and to his words. Ordinary gatherings grew into mass meetings. Whereas before he had had only loyal followers, he now had an organized group of people who fought off hecklers and cleared the streets of anything that might disturb their leader in the course of a harangue.

Some time during that month I saw for the first time the swastika displayed in public as the emblem of his party, and I realized that the movement was complete. It had a god, an oracle, and a fetish that the primitive mind could worship in the absence of the god with a comic mustache, the last of his personal transformations. I had expected him to begin to dress up to his importance. But he didn't. Wearing defiance like a suit of shining armor, the shabbiness of his appearance did not detract from the magnetism he exercised over the crowds that gathered about him. He screamed, gyrated and shouted to the high heavens, all the while holding his audience in unbreakable enthrallment. It was difficult to believe that he was not consciously acting as he lashed himself into a fury—chest heaving, nostrils distended one instant, then, in the next moment, pleading and wheedling in a voice choked with messianic passion. The Messiah of the New Germany had arrived, and he must be listened to even at the price of broken skulls.

His power over the common people rose like a sullen tide. His words, his systematic ruthless warfare on the communist street-gatherings, thrilled the simple Bavarian people to the core. They were an easy conquest for Hitler, and not without good reason. Intellectually the masses had no idea of what was really going on about them, locally or nationally. How should they know? Every day some new demagogue would attack their credulity under the guise of a new program for local and national defense. They all cited different reasons, quoted different statistics. . . . But none affected them like Hitler. For one thing, my patient was not as evanescent as the rest of his kind. He stayed around, and as his violence increased so did his picturesqueness. His face was contorted like a gargoyle's, but the very ugliness of his gestures and the buzz-saw raucousness of his speech only focused the attention of the mob on his dynamic personality. In the same way Milton must have been fascinated by Satan when he made the Arch Fiend a more heroic character than God himself.

The bitterest element of the population continued to be the soldiers—the young as well as the old. The old were bewildered because, with all the victories they had piled up on the field of battle, they had lost the war. The young ones grumbled at having to look for a new occupation when they had had no opportunity to practice the only one for which they were already trained.

To capture the attention of a disgruntled people, you have only to agree with them. These demagogues did more than that. They demonstrated to the malcontents first that they themselves were obviously innocent of any wrong-doing; that done, they proceeded to prove to them who the culprits were. The ruse worked so well that it actually built up in its dupes a resistance against all reason.

Diplomats from foreign powers, and the representatives of purely humanitarian organizations from all parts of the world came to Germany with help and understanding. But the people would not listen to them. It was so much easier to give ear and credence to those lying, cynical voices which told them that there was nothing really wrong with Germany that a good, solid, well organized pogrom could not heal. They had merely been sold out by the Jews at Versailles.

Seeing all this, knowing all this, and understanding what was going on, how, the reader must ask himself, did I react? A confession is in order here. I acted, mostly, like every other German about me. As an objective scientist I saw the mass-hysteria that was being galvanized into a brutal movement of oppression and shame. But as a single atom in a whirling chaos of lying propaganda, I was sucked into the maelstrom of cannibal emotions, and seethed with the spirit of the mob.

The difference between me and the greater number of my fellow Germans is that I got over my illness much more quickly—perhaps because I was in a better position to see the reverse side of the medal.

CHAPTER SEVEN

My Own Conversion

Hofbrau Haus — Circus Krone — My Own Confusion—My First Visit to His House—"The Minimum Requirement."

HOFBRAU HOUSE, Munich, was the scene of Hitler's first important mass meeting, his political Rubicon. Up to that time he had done a great deal of talking: no more. Talk is cheap in any part of the world. A man must pin himself down by the written word if he is to impel the world to take him at his word. The word becomes the deed, the revolutionary mass deed that inflames the minds of the discontented millions. At Hofbrau House Hitler made his great departure, for it was there that he distributed that most revolutionary pamphlet of his in which he attacked the Treaty of Versailles, the Church of Rome and the Jews. Hofbrau House was an important meeting ground of Hitler and the world. But the most important of these meetings was, for me, the one which took place in the Circus Krone, for it was there that I myself was definitely converted to the Fuehrer's movement.

A vast, dimly lit hall, the Circus Krone seemed a very curious place for a circus performance. Instead of sawdust and tanbark, this ring contained a row of plain oak tables and long rough wooden benches. It was indeed a circus for the intellect rather than for the more orderly varieties of human freaks. The night Hitler took over the place was packed to the rafters. I understood why he had insisted on my being there, for it certainly constituted a substantial triumph for him. One could see, wherever one looked, people from every stratum of life: people from the fashionable districts, the theaters and the cabarets sat next to workingmen in soiled overalls. That was the miraculous thing about

93

a Hitler audience. There simply was no class-distinction to be found in it. A private could sit on equal terms with a general, a shoe-clerk with a cabinet minister. For all of them had put their complete hope and faith in the man, Hitler.

In front of the meeting-place a cordon of pickets stood on guard. To protect the gathering from intrusion by the "red scum," was the explanation usually given. The expression "red scum" was intended to include Jews as well as communists. Inside, on the platform, at the rear, and along the walls, stood the SA's in their plus-four knickers and brown shirts, with the swastika insignia on their arms. The air was thick from pipes, cigarettes and cheap, smelly cigars; the tables covered with mugs of luke-warm beer and paper plates with sausage and cheese, added to the odors of the dense atmosphere. And the crowd sat drinking and eating and talking in low voices, all in eager expectation of the great moment—the arrival of the leader. Yes, he was generally spoken of throughout Munich as *der Fuehrer*.

It was easy, while waiting, to strike up a casual acquaintance-ship, and swing into an animated discussion. Equally simple, also, was it to get into a fierce argument on the flimsiest possible pre-text. For these were a belligerent people who gathered to listen to the Fuehrer, every one eager to transmit the impression that no one could exceed them in loyalty and willingness to sacrifice, and anxious to make certain that there were no traitors within their sight or hearing. Yet, in spite of their eagerness, energy and earnestness, a cloud of depressive hopelessness hung over these people. Their faces were clouded and their eyes offered to say: *We are here, waiting to be told what hope there is for us. But is there really any hope? Does anyone give a damn about us, except the Jews and the international bankers whose only interest is to find out how much more they can wham out of our hides?*

But hope there must be for the sustenance of life, and so these sour, cynical people sat about in the vast, dimly lit atmosphere of Circus Krone to hear the words of the Leader—whatever they might be. Without actually meaning to, I drifted into their own humor. And it was as a part of the great crowd that I was sud-denly stirred by the following rapid succession of events. All eyes flashed fire, a spontaneous shout arose from the mob-throat, the sound of distant marching fell on my ears, and wild waves of *Sieg Heil! Sieg Heil!* thundered on all sides of me. Then followed a torchlight procession through the central aisle. It was as if I had been hit between the eyes by those marchers with their red swastika banners, and wild, grim, fanatical faces, suggestive of both sacrifice and suffering.

Swiftly the empty platform before us became crowded with luminaries of the Nazi party. The faces of the people sitting about me, the audience, were transformed like a planet in the sky after a passage of night clouds. By a magic purely theatrical, those tense, expectant faces became luminous with sky-enraptured visions, as if the power which had lit the electric candelabra had also set off the spark in their hearts. All was suppressed excitement, of a kind which you sometimes sense in church before an important mass. At the height of the eager tides of general expectancy, a man in plain civilian clothes came to the front, held up his hand and in a powerful, bawling voice demanded silence. Then without another word, as if words could not express what he felt, he turned to someone sitting behind him, and with no more gesture than that introduced him to the audience.

From a chair in the back rose the familiar slim figure, pale face and shock of hair drooping down over his forehead. As he moved slowly to the center of the platform, the charged atmosphere exploded from the thousands of throat about me bellowing forth the cries of *Heil Hitler! Heil Hitler! Sieg Heil!* Gradually the cheering began to die down, the crowd quieted, and all the energy which had been present in the thousands of people about me seemed suddenly reborn in the will, the gestures, and the voice of the Fuehrer, who was the only one to remain standing on the platform of the Circus Krone. Mass hysteria had found its champion.

Hitler began to speak, and it seemed to me that the people sat on the edge of their seats, mouths open, hungry for whatever morsels of hope he might toss them. His words cried out hatred of Germany's enemies, and limitless, undying, quenchless love of the Fatherland. He spoke of all the tragic, hopeless prayers of a people who had won a war on the battlefields, only to lose it at home, in their banks. He fiercely denounced the "red scum" and everything pertaining to communism, challenged the false statements of so-called democracy, and poured his heaviest vials of scorn on the Jews. He lashed the diabolical anti-Christ, anti-man regime of Josef Stalin, called for faith in God, and reminded the young men in his audience that a soldier's duty is to die for his country, the highest honor attainable by man. He called for the renewed sanctity of womanhood. He promised the revival of Germany, the stretching of the borders of the old empire. He demanded the strictest discipline and willing sacrifice of every element of the nation—except the Jews and Communists, whom he called its inevitable natural enemies. Denouncing the greedy immorality of the Versailles Treaty, he promised to smash the shackles which bound the living millions of Germany to it. He promised food, work, opportunity. Lastly, he spoke of unemployment as the chief source of national demoralization and ruin, and promised to abolish it.

The audience was thrilled. Every other sentence he uttered was cheered, every paragraph punctuated by a stamping of feet. But that was nothing compared with what happened when he made a very strong point. Ere the echo of the winning word had died out, they got up and yelled. They screamed till their voices made a strange fantastic pattern in the overhead rafters. The enthusiasm of the audience began to weigh on the orator's voice, on his words, and on the things which urged him on. Everyone in the audience began to feel this, and the hearts of those people naturally went out to him in sympathy; in sympathy with him against their very own oppression. His hands occasionally rose in the air in a plea for quiet, and he continued to exhort them, his voice breaking down time and again, only to rise again in incomprehensible power and splendor.

When it was all over, I knew that I had been fully converted. It was all I could do to refrain from joining the many who were scrambling toward him in order to get close enough to him to take his hand and kiss it.

As a convert, I felt that I owed him at least a visit to his own quarters. That way perhaps the relationship between us might become better stabilized. Moreover, it was high time to see exactly how my remarkable patient lived. When I made my visit, I received the shock of my life.

I found him in a dilapidated old house in a poor and obscure section of Munich, his bare rooms approached from stairs in the back of the house. I saw only one room, which was rectangular, with green painted walls, and a skylight, its only connection with the sun. I saw no bed, but there were a few stiff-backed chairs and a table loaded with newspapers and newspaper clippings. In that shabby flat he lived; there, too, his ragged, half-starved cohorts gathered around him, and planned with him step by step the manoeuvres which were to convert their movement from a local uprising to one of national proportions.

The impression he gave me there in his own atmosphere was quite different from the one you got of him on the platform. He seemed ever more humble; his manner was gentle, shy; and he spoke with a certain sense of humor, almost mocking, as if anticipating those people who thought him utterly mad.

"It may surprise you to know," I said to him as he rose from behind a stack of papers to greet me, "that I come to you today somewhat in the manner of a pilgrim who has sought out the shrine of his patron saint."

"In the hope that there might be a bone for him to take away with him?" he asked with a laugh.

"Perhaps. I still have a few mental reservations, of course. As I suppose a lot of your followers still have. Because it is one thing to passionately wish to alter the face of things, quite another to set about doing it as a practical piece of work."

"But that's where you're mistaken, that's where your conversion is still incomplete," he cried. "I assure you that we national socialists not only know what we want—we know exactly how to go about getting it. No one has begun to become a convert to a national socialism who is not prepared to pledge us every ounce of his faith and energy.

I was bewildered and must have shown it.

"But how can I do that?" I asked.

His eyes flashed.

"By deciding that you have unswerving faith in me and the idea I stand for," he replied unflinchingly. "The kind of faith the Russian Army had in the Czar, who could order a rebellious regiment to march off to Siberia, and off to Siberia, without a word of protest, it would march."

"I'm afraid I'm incapable of such blind faith," I smiled. "I'm not one of those who know how to march off to Siberia or sneak off to Canossa."

He was puzzled.

"Canossa?" he inquired, with uplifted brow.

"You remember, don't you," I said to him, knowing very well that he didn't, and fully enjoying his discomfort, "the incident of the emperor who defied the will of the Pope and was finally compelled to kneel in the sleet and snow at Canossa before the angry pontiff?"

He appeared genuinely astonished.

"What made him do such an idiotic thing?" he gasped.

"Blind faith," I replied. "The sort of blind faith you ask for. It is the only thing quite sure to make a man look utterly ridiculous in the eyes of the rest of the world." I saw that he was beginning to be deeply displeased with me, so I continued: "That, of course, was a peculiarly individual species of blind faith. It was the blind faith of the medieval man in papal magic, a magic so potent that it was capable of overcoming the dignity of an emperor. In the prevailing opinion of that time, when two wills clashed, God's and man's, it was the will of God exercised by the Pope that finally triumphed."

"Ah," cried Hitler ecstatically, "but that's my very own political philosophy in a nutshell. My will is the will of Germany— the will of every Aryan in the Reich. Not two wills but one— *mine!* I stand on the principle that what I feel about my country is not only worthy of recognition; it must also be followed to the end. I am your Leader and that must be the beginning and the end of your political faith."

His voice was tense and his eyes were flaming. The terrible urgency in his voice communicated itself to me like a tongue of flame, licking my brain.

"He is right," I seemed to hear a voice whispering faintly in my ear. "No great boon has ever come to mankind without complete faith in a leader. Why, then, should you deny this faith to the leader of your generation?"

But I had to say something to overcome the effect of the cynicism of my earlier speech.

"Is that how all the members of the Party understand and sustain their allegiance?" I asked tremulously.

He nodded.

"That is the very minimum of our requirements from a new recruit of the cause," he assured me.

The voice was still whispering in my ear, faintly but urgently:

"All of your healers need not be of the stature of the Christs and the Buddhas. This man is built in the size as well as the image of the unfortunate generation to which you belong. He is a neurotic, but are we not living in a neurotic age, shattered against the rock of reality? Believe in him."

I put out my hand and he took it instantly, as if he knew exactly what to expect, as if he were the ventriloquist who had been throwing that faintly whispering voice in my ear.

"Sieg Heil!" he cried.

I responded in what was to become the standard manner of a whole decade:

"Heil Hitler!"

The word seemed to fascinate him.

"That sounds good," he mused. "Some day I am going to have every living person in Germany saying that."

CHAPTER EIGHT

OEDIPUS DUE NORTH

*The Precipice—Hitler's First Human Recollections—
Early Antagonism to His Father—The Habit of Steal-
ing into His Parents' Bed at Night—Displacing His
Father Imagistically—The Young Man—The Cross.*

IT IS OFTEN the business of the analyst to reconvert a demi-
monster to manhood. But if he wishes to preserve all of those
subtle holds by which he manipulates his patient, the analyst had
better maintain a mental grip on his own wavering psyche which
is influenced by the pressures exerted by the driving will of the
demi-monster himself. As long as the analyst is probing his
patient, his own psyche remains open to the invading images of
the latter, so that at any time, at an unforeseen psychic precipice,
their roles are likely to be reversed, to the confusion of both their
lives.

Just as I had achieved one of the most difficult tasks of the
analyst, that of transference (by which the physician redirects
the loyalty and devotion of his patient to himself), my induction
into the National Socialist movement took place, and, without
warning to either of our psyches, reversed our roles. Whereas
he had been in a state of mental subservience to me, I had, as a
pledged follower of his, taken that very position with regard to
him. I was drawn into that charmed circle of hypnosis into which
Hitler was to pull not only himself, but many millions of credulous Germans.

It was a catastrophe, but not an insuperable one. The day I
realized our common predicament, I had an appointment with
him which I broke, and put off for several days later. I prepared

carefully in the brief interval for a retransference. When he arrived I made it a point to greet him coolly, not to shake hands with him, and walk ahead of him swiftly into my examining chamber.

"I hope nothing has gone wrong," ventured my patient, who had never seen me so stiff and formal.

"Nothing is wrong," I assured him, "and nothing will go wrong, if you remember that it is you who are sick, and I of whom you expect healing, and that the only hope of my being able to single out your thwarted energies and cause them to function again is in your submitting your will to me during these operations. You must honestly fulfill your end of this labor, which is to plunge deeply into the reservoir of your memory as I guide your mind along the important scenes of your life. Is that understood?"

He nodded humbly, and I knew that the danger between us had been bridged.

"What about the question I promised to ask you today?" I continued. "Have you had it in your mind as I asked you to?"

He smiled faintly.

"I couldn't have helped thinking about it even if I had tried, Doctor," he assured me.

"And you have found the inevitable answer to it?"

"I think so."

"Very well, then, tell me: *What is the very first of your living recollections?*"

"My first living recollection," he replied, "is my mother."

It was, of course, the answer I had expected, the only possible answer, in view of what I had already learned. But I had not asked as one does to obtain information, but to make it possible for him to touch his psychic wound, the memory of his mother, which might be the initial step in his final cure.

"You're quite sure of that?"

"There has never been a doubt of it in my mind, Doctor. My life begins with the image of my mother."

"Is it the image of a complete woman you see?"

"Sometimes I see her as a whole in full dress. But that is a later image. The one which I see mostly is just of her breasts."

"And what is the attribute of those breasts which functions most in your recollections?"

"Warmth."

"What else do you remember about your mother?"

"Her hands."

"Of course, you've already told me that. Do you think of her hands as open or closed?"

"Open, lying down."

"Do you see rings on her fingers?"

"None."

"Your mother wore a wedding ring?"

"She may have. I never noticed it."

"Is there any other attribute of your mother's that you remember?"

"Yes, the blackness of her clothes."

"And they make you think of night?"

"Yes, Doctor."

"Good. Now let us get into the second image of importance in your life. What would you say that was?"

His eyes appeared to darken.

"That would be my father."

"And you remember him as a complete portrait?"

"Mostly. But sometimes—" he paused.

"Yes?"

"Well, sometimes I seem to remember only his back."

"In full attire?"

"No, entirely naked. But I do not see it as much as I seem to feel it in my nostrils."

"That will bear explaining."

"I think this image is the result of recollections of the times deep at night when I got into bed with him and Mother and I would lie for hours doing nothing but staring at his naked back. All clothes were an encumbrance for my father when he went to bed."

"Your father slept alone?"

"No, with my mother."

"Am I to suppose that you did not have a bed of your own?"

"Of course I had a bed of my own. But until I was ten years

old I was stricken with the fear of sleeping alone. I would lie awake for hours till everything was quiet, and if I did not in the meantime fall asleep I would creep into my parents' bed, and remain there until morning. I would manage to do that at least two nights a week, and many times oftener than that."

"Would you say that you were a welcome visitor in that bed?"

"As it affected my father, distinctly not."

"You think your mother welcomed your visits?"

"I cannot say now. But I must have felt then that they were not unwelcome. I cannot believe that I could have been capable of doing anything to displease my mother."

"But you would not have cared if you knew that what you did was displeasing to your father?"

"That's a difficult question to answer—especially after such a lapse of time."

"You loved your mother?"

"Devotedly."

"And your father?"

"I must have loved him, too. But it was not all the same as the feeling I had for my mother."

"You do not remember a resentment of any sort that you bore your mother?"

"No. She was all loving kindness."

"How about your attitude toward your father?"

"During the last years of his life there was a great deal of friction between us."

"Never mind those years. We will come to them later. Let us stick to those early formative days, the days of your first recollections. You remember your father's naked back, you remember it more as something in your nostrils than in your eyes. You remember lying awake for hours staring at it. Would you say that your feeling about your father during those painfully wakeful hours was of an affectionate nature?"

"I can't say."

"We must peruse this carefully. You say that you crept into your parents' bed at night because you were afraid to sleep alone. Have you any idea of what you could have been afraid?"

"I can't say. Perhaps I was just afraid of prowlers or burglars who might steal into the house to rob and murder me if they found me awake."

"Your people were not rich during those days?"

"On the contrary, we were rather poor."

"Can you remember that there were things lying about your house that robbers might want to take away?"

"No."

"Can you remember whether you ever had been assaulted by a stranger those days?"

"No."

"Did you know of any little boys or girls who had been assaulted by robbers or just strangers?"

"No."

"Isn't it just possible that you really harbored no such fear in your mind at all?"

"Then why did I think of it?"

"That's very simple. When children do things which are incomprehensible to them as children, they invent non-existent but rational motives. Now if you had a reason for crawling into your parents' bed that you did not understand, would you not, when your parents demanded to know why you did it, manufacture the most plausible reason available at the moment? And since it's a popular superstition that children are afraid to be left alone (fear of darkness is usually suggested to them by their elders), what could be more natural than that you offer it to your parents as the reason for annoying them, and then follow it by actually believing in it yourself?"

"I understand this. But if it was not real fear, what motive *could* I have had in lying about it?"

"When the subconscious lies, it is usually to hide something," I explained.

"But what?" he insisted.

"We must find that out for ourselves. Were your father and mother of about the same age?"

"No, my mother was younger by about thirty-four years."

"Did you know that?"

"One would have had to be blind not to notice it."

"You are quite sure that you noticed it at that age?"

"Certainly."

"Since you did notice things of that nature, perhaps you will tell me whether, as you remember it, your father and mother loved each other with an equal devotion."

He brooded a while.

"I think my father loved my mother a great deal more than she loved him."

"How did you notice that?"

"It was very simple. On the slightest provocation my father would kiss my mother. But I do not think my mother ever returned his kiss."

"How would you know that?"

"By a certain stiffening of her mouth when he approached her. And there was another thing. Whenever he kissed her, it was usually followed by her kissing me."

"Do you remember that now, or did you notice those things when they actually happened?"

"I'm sure I noticed those things then."

"Your impression as a child, then, was that whereas your father loved your mother, your mother really loved you?"

"You might put it that way," he said.

"And you noticed how much older he was than your mother?"

"Yes."

"Now think carefully before you answer my next question. Would you say that you resented that your father was so much older than your mother?"

"I could not say I had such an exact feeling about it."

"You didn't really know your mother held back her affections when your father kissed her?"

"There was the stiffening of her mouth when he approached her. I am certain I noticed that."

"But people's mouths sometimes stiffen in passion. When you thought you saw your mother's mouth stiffening in resistance to your father's affections, might it not have been the expression of your wish that she hold herself as a fortress against him?"

"It could have been that. But why should I wish that my mother should be cold to my father?"

"Only if you loved your mother yourself."

"But I have already told you that I loved her."

"Before you really understood what was going on then, you will have to admit another important possibility—that you were actually jealous of your father."

"It seems preposterous to me," he exploded.

"Perhaps it does. But how else would you explain your mysterious creeping into your parents' bed deep in the night until you were ten years old?"

"It seems to me more credible that I was afraid to sleep alone."

"I disagree. If fear had been your only motive you would not have minded your father's back. On the contrary, you would have found great protective comfort in it."

He looked positively sullen.

"Perhaps."

"We'll get back to this later. And now let us have the impressions of your childhood which you would consider next in importance."

He thought a while.

"There's something wrong here, Doctor," he finally said. "You are asking me for impressions, and all I can remember is people."

"I wouldn't worry about that," I assured him. "If it is people who come to your mind instead of things, or events, let us have them. People can be very important in the life of a human being. Is it anyone in particular you remember now?"

"It's a very vague recollection, Doctor. But it is constantly getting clearer. A man much younger than my father used to come to our house Sunday afternoon. He came alone, and would drink tea, eat cake, and talk. I remember distinctly now that I liked him. I liked him almost as much as I liked my mother."

"Try to remember more about that young man. He may turn out to be an important key to our inquiry. Was he a friend or a relative?"

"I'm not quite sure about that yet."

"Did he come to see your father, or your mother?"

"My father, naturally. I think he worked in my father's department. Yes, it must have been that, because their talk always concerned some form of official routine about which my father was either enthusiastic or skeptical. Usually skeptical."

"And you liked that young man?"

He nodded.

"Quite as much as your father?"

"I am certain of it."

"Maybe you liked him better?"

"That's possible."

"How about your father, did he like the young man?"

"Oh yes. He thought him a very exemplary person."

"And your mother?"

"She'd dress up in her best finery when she knew he was coming."

"You still do not remember his name?"

"No."

"Or his relationship?"

"I feel sure now that he was not at all related to us."

"Just a friend of the family?"

"Yes, Doctor."

"Can you remember how old he was?"

"About as old as my mother."

"His height?"

"The same."

"The color of his eyes?"

"The same."

"And his hair?"

My patient hesitated. There was a pained look in his eyes as if I were seeing him in the act of grappling with an evil spirit.

"The same," he said finally in a dull, hollow voice.

"You seem to remember the young man in the exact image of your mother."

"I can't help that," he said sulkily.

I paused to give him time to return his attention to me.

"Try to remember something about your affection for this young man."

"Well, as it comes back to me, I remember that many times as I lay in bed facing my father's back, I tried to make myself believe that the back was not my father's but this young man's."

"Very interesting. And what would you say was the motive for that?"

"I guess I just liked him so much I would have felt better if I could have touched his back. If I had touched my father's back he would have growled, possibly he might have struck me. But it would have been much different, much better, if I had touched the back of this young man."

"You cannot remember his name?"

"No."

"So then when you think of him it is simply as of the young man who used to visit your house when you were a child?"

"Most of the time. But there are other times—" he paused.

I looked at him.

"That shamed feeling again?"

He met my eyes slyly.

"I suppose so," he mumbled.

"So much more why you must learn how to say it," I said to him severely. "Don't you see, the whole medicine with which psychoanalysis cures is a combination of aptness and courage: aptness, in this case, the questions framed by the physician, and courage, the patient's will to follow his doctor into those corners of his own brain which are haunted by the ghosts of experience. Now tell me: *What recollection of this young man dare you not reveal to me?*"

My patient squirmed, but he answered:

"I sometimes think of him as if he had been my real father."

I leaned toward him.

"You don't think it possible that he really was your father?"

He shook his head.

"Quite impossible. Neither my father or mother had met him till a year after my birth. In fact, he had not yet come to live in our town when I was conceived."

"Then why would you have thought of him when you were in bed with your parents?"

"I can't say, unless it was because I found the image of him pleasanter than the image of my father."

"That could be true, and still be only part of a much more

important motive: your feeling that you preferred to find *him* in your mother's bed."

His resentment welled into sudden fury.

"But why should I entertain any such stupid and indecent feeling?" he cried out.

"Perhaps we will find a reason for it later," I said to him gently. "For the present it is sufficient for use to know that you had the thought."

He was still furious and showed it.

"Well, I think it's a stupid, immoral thought!" he hurled at me.

I looked at him with amusement.

"As a scientist, I am not fit to pass on the decency of your thoughts," I said to him, "but I can assure you that there was nothing stupid about it. There can be nothing either clever or stupid in the workings of the subconscious. If you will be good enough to follow by reasoning carefully you may find in what you have told me something both genuine and important. Will you be patient?"

"It's difficult, but I'll try," he growled.

"Very well. Suppose you were in love with your mother to the extent of being jealous of your father, would it not be possible (since you were yourself too small and young to take his place in her bed) for you to transfer your emotion on someone older than yourself, someone whom you liked, who could perform this for you, by proxy?"

He considered my words a moment, made a wry face and replied:

"It sounds outrageous, but conceivable. But only conceivable perhaps."

"There is still another possibility," I said to him. "I shall warn you against the shock before I mention it."

"The idea that you could shock me now," he said with a certain bitterness, "is a little preposterous."

"Very well, then. What would you say if I suggested that the young man might really never have existed—might have been no more than a product of your imagination?"

He shrugged.

"I wouldn't say anything," he replied, "I would just laugh."

"Nevertheless, I do suggest it," I urged.

"That's something I could laugh at. But suppose you tell me the rationale of this strange conjecture."

"Your young man fits in so closely with the image of your mother, he resembles more than anything else one of those automatons with which the subconscious peoples the ethereal spaces in most of our lives."

He looked puzzled.

"I wish you'd explain that," he said.

"Will you forgive me if I don't stop to explain now?" I asked him.

He shrugged and gave way to an easy laugh.

I breathed relief. I had done very well to regain my patient's good humor at such a delicate point in the inquiry.

"We will leave this interesting young man for a while," I said, "and go on to what we shall call the fourth image of your childhood. Think carefully, now."

"The next image," he announced reluctantly, after some hesitation, "is no longer a human being, but a thing. It is the metal cross my mother hung about her neck."

"How do you remember it?"

"It was suspended on such a long chain, it actually fell between my mother's breasts."

"Then it is really a part of the image of your mother?"

"Yes, but it stands out by itself, too. I remember it not so much because of where it hung, but because once, as I rested my head against my mother, I hurt myself on it, scratched the skin tissue near my right eye."

"Then you remember the cross by its sharpness?"

"And coldness."

"What else do you remember about that cross?"

"That my mother kissed it occasionally."

"Another rival," I suggested.

He smiled but said nothing.

"Can you remember what metal it was made of?"

He thought.

"It wasn't gold, I am quite certain," he finally ventured. "It was of a greenish color. Like mine."

"*Yours?*"

He nodded.

"My mother insisted that I, too, wear a cross at all times. When we walked together, my cross hung prominently from my neck. Once I went off to school without my cross and my mother gave me a terrible spanking, one of the few times she did that to me. But the spanking did not annoy me. On the contrary, it gave me a great deal of pleasure, so I deliberately failed to wear the crucifix to school time after time, until my mother stopped spanking me, as if she guessed what was really happening. But she did not give up insisting that I wear the cross to school. She changed her tactics. Instead of spanking me, she punished me by letting me go to school at noon without lunch. I wore the cross quite faithfully after that."

My patient grinned.

"Instead of going hungry I became a Christian," he commented.

"Have you ever thought of your mother's motive in insisting that you wear the cross to school?" I asked him.

"I always took it for granted that it was a part of her extraordinary piety," he replied.

"Did many of the boys in your school wear crosses around their necks?"

He shook his head.

"Hardly. It was the girls who went in for religious jewelry."

"Then why that fanatic insistence?" I insisted.

He described with his hands a gesture of despair.

"How can I tell you at this time?" he asked.

I caught his eyes with mine, and held them for a moment with especial emphasis.

"Is it," I asked, "that your mother was afraid that you might be mistaken for a Jew?"

He paled and endeavored to steady his voice before replying.

"I asked a simple question; I do not doubt your pure Aryanism," I hastened to assure him.

"No one has doubted it, and no one had better try," he

declared with fierce emphasis. "There is no reason for any further discussion on the business of the cross. My mother wore a cross because she was a pious woman, and I suppose she made me wear it on all possible occasions because she thought it would make a better Christian of me."

"Did many of the women in your town wear crosses?" I asked, trying to twist away from my patient's sensitive spot as quickly as possible.

"Most of them, I believe. I used to make a point of looking for it on every woman I saw."

"How about your mother? Did she wear it a great deal of the time?"

"No, she would take it off at night before going to bed."

"How did you know?"

He looked down.

"I often watched her undress."

"But couldn't she have kept her cross on, under her night-gown, say, without your noticing it?"

He shook his head.

"I observed too closely. I believe I would have liked her to wear it at night."

This was a surprising turn.

"Why?" I asked.

No answer.

"Why?" I repeated.

He looked at me with a look of impatience.

"Can't I sidetrack at least one of these wild emotional detours of yours?" he snapped.

I shook my head, making my voice as tolerant as possible.

"It's my business," I reminded him, "to probe everything in your nature for a remedy to your illness. We have already made a few interesting discoveries. But the most important ones are still to be made. We may have to abandon everything we have learned till today, as well as the conclusions I am building upon them. Where is the material on which I am to work to come from if I continually find myself impaled against the wall of your pride?"

I could see him weakening, and I asked him again:

"What made you say that you would have liked it if your mother wore her cross at night?"

He looked at me limply.

"Because my father might hurt himself against it," he replied.

"Good," I cried. "Now we have a better view of the feeling you had about your father. Don't you see how important it is for you to say these things when they occur to you, and to bear with these sharp scalpel insertions I have to make in your mind?"

"I understand. But if anyone had dared to suggest to me an hour ago that I would allow anyone, even a doctor, to become that friendly with me, I wouldn't have believed it. I'd have taken it very badly, I assure you."

"You could do much worse than make a confidante of a doctor," I said to him dryly.

"As for instance," he asked, rising.

"There's the Devil," I suggested.

He had taken up his coat to put it on, but such was his amazement that he kept holding it up in his hands and staring at me, as if I had opened for his mind the door of a hidden furnace.

"You don't believe in that sort of thing?" he asked.

"Not as a rule," I assured him. "But nowadays the goings-on in Munich give me a very eerie feeling of things outside of my experience. There is no method of reasoning by which to approach it, except, maybe, to ask myself how there can be so much deviltry in the world, without the presence of the father of all evil, the Devil himself."

My patient pulled his coat on in empty silence.

CHAPTER NINE

THE WANDERING JEW

*The Fuehrer and His Astrologer—The Kapp Putch—
The Flight to Berlin—The Saga of Ignace Trebitsch-
Lincoln—The Return to Munich—Aftermath in a Beer
Haus—Hitler Sanctuary.*

I HAD OFTEN heard it told that gamblers who win great stakes
at cards usually wind up by losing their winnings at the race
tracks, and that the swindlers who amass fortunes (talking hard
working people into investing their savings in unsound securities)
end up by turning their ill-gotten gains over to unfaithful wives
and mistresses. So it did not surprise me to discover that the
blind faith the Fuehrer received from the adoring crowds of
Munich he gave up slavishly, ignominiously, to several itinerant
astrologers and soothsayers whom he has elevated, by this time,
to the eminence of pillars of state. Gamblers in men or money
squander their emotional as well as material wealth on charlatans
and tricksters.

At the end of our last interview we spent an hour or so
together in a beer *haus*. But as we rose to go my patient warned
me that he could walk only part of the way to my office because
he had a very important appointment to keep.

"A woman?" I inquired.

He looked ill at ease.

"A woman, yes," he faltered. "But the most important thing
about her does not happen to be that she's a woman."

"Impossible!" I exclaimed. "There never was such a female
born. It is possible for a man to be a hero, a politician or an artist
without being a man. But any role in life played by a member

of the frailer sex must be secondary to her natural role as a woman."

My patient listened to me with obvious impatience. Instead of trying to argue with me, he decided that perhaps the best way to settle the matter was to find out if I knew anything about the woman, to whom he referred as Frau Askaba.

I shook my head in the negative.

"And who may the good frau be?" I asked out of sheer politeness.

He looked as surprised as if I had shown ignorance of a great scientist.

"Don't tell me you have never heard of this great seer!" he exclaimed.

"Then she doesn't even bake good bread!" I cried, simulating disappointment. "But say, what does the good frau *see?*"

"What does she see? Everything!" cried my patient ecstatically. "You have only to sit down before her, and your life becomes an open book in which she reads your past, your present, and your future."

"Really, how perfectly marvelous," I replied mockingly. "As if it weren't miraculous enough for anyone to be able to see through our muddled present. How long have you known this prodigy of femininity?"

At this question he looked a little abashed.

"I only know about her," he confessed. "To be honest with you, I am on my way now to see her for the first time. Eckart is going to be there, too. He has complete confidence in her."

I smiled meaningfully.

"Then all these wonderful qualities of hers are things you know only by having heard people—people as irresponsible as Eckart—talk about them," I murmured.

He looked amazed.

"Aren't you influenced by what people tell you?"

"Of course. But I don't let it become a part of that precious department of my mind which I set aside for experience and its results."

"But I tell you that just hearing people talk about Frau

Askaba is an experience!" he declared. "If only half the things they say are true, she must be quite wonderful."

"I hope so for your sake," I told him.

This sounded like a concession to him, and he instantly brightened up.

"How about coming along with me?" he suggested. "When we get through, the three of us might go to the Burgerkeller."

I shook my head dolefully.

"I would if I had the time to spare," I assured him, "and if I had something for your prodigal Frau Askaba to read a little more interesting than the tedious past, present and future of a physician. But let me know how you make out with her."

He left me at that corner and I returned to my office, where three patients were waiting for me. I had forgotten the foolish incident, and had just turned in for the night, when I was routed out of bed by someone yanking away at my doorbell.

It was Hitler, and he was alone. If I had not known that he was a teetotaler I would have suspected him of being drunk.

"Where's Eckart?" I asked.

"He didn't come. But she—Frau Askaba—she was simply marvelous. I felt I had to get here and tell you about her."

I rubbed my right eye.

"Anything important?" I inquired.

"The most important thing in the world," he informed me in a hoarse voice. "According to Frau Askaba I am soon to receive a call to Berlin. Can you imagine that?"

"How soon?" I asked.

"Oh, she couldn't set a definite date. But it'll happen some time in the next few weeks, be sure of that."

"Then it's too soon to wish you a happy trip," I said to him, and, I regret to add, half managed to suppress a yawn.

He seized instantly on the yawn as he usually did on all trivial things in the conduct of those he associated with.

"Am I to understand that you're being bored with me?" he demanded.

"Certainly not," I hastened to assure him. "But if you gave me time enough I think I could make out a pretty good case of boredom with your Frau Askaba."

He looked positively hurt.

"That is downright ungrateful of you!" he cried. "When I mentioned your name to her, Frau Askaba had nothing but the most wonderful things to say about you. If one is to believe her you are bound to make a high mark in the world."

"That would depend on how high you intend to build your Nazi gibbets," I said to him jestingly. I realized the real reason why he had rung my bell that night. It was his awkward way of letting me know that his confidence in me had been justified by hearing from the mouth of the great seer that I was someone with whom to entrust so valuable a life. "But how does your Cassandra happen to say such good things about me? Does she by any chance know me?"

"What good would it be if she knew you!" he cried. "Her knowledge is only valuable when it comes out of divination."

"Divination! I think fraud would be a better word for that sort of guesswork," I said to him, and it angered my patient very much.

He made an angry gesture with his clenched fist.

"I won't have any insinuations against Frau Askaba!" he declared. "She's the best astrologer in all Munich."

"She might be the best astrologer in the whole world," I informed him, "and not constitute sufficient justification for dragging a hard-working doctor out of bed."

Instantly he realized what he had done, and was penitent.

"Forgive me," he pleaded. "In my excitement I lost all sense of time and everything else."

"That's all right," I said to him. "Forget it."

He apologized at least once more, and finally went off, though not without throwing this back over his shoulder:

"But you'll be surprised when I am called to Berlin!"

Somehow things work out for the prophets and the astrologers, no matter what the cost turns out to be for common everyday humanity. Frau Askaba's prediction found fulfillment in the course of a political development that culminated in what is now referred to as the Kapp Putsch, which began so dismally in Berlin, grew into such a triumph in Munich, and established for all time my patient's supreme faith in the powers of astrology.

It began in Berlin, of course, which was still the center of straight German political strategy. Berlin was the capital of the Republic, but the Reichswehr, whose influence was still greater than that of any one man in the Reich, had never acclimated itself to the idea of a republic, and continued to make its plans independently of the accredited government. Since it is easier to attack a human being than an idea, the leaders of the Reichswehr, from the very beginning, made President Ebert (the head of the Republic) the center of their fiercest spear thrusts. They created so many good-natured jokes about the intrepid harness-maker that they finally got into the habit of believing that he was really at heart the sort of simpleton they and their cartoonists had made him appear.

It was not, therefore, at all surprising when, only ten days after the incident of Frau Askaba's prophecy, news reached us in Munich that certain parts of the Reichswehr had broken into open revolt against the Republic and its President. The Berlin chiefs in this counter-revolution were General von Luttwitz and Captain Ehrhardt, and it was the latter's brigade which marched into Berlin with the National Socialist swastika on the men's steel helmets, and seized power.

No one could say where the man came from. He was a minor politician known simply as Kapp. And this Kapp was named Chancellor of the Reich; so that when the whole affair was over, and good ink was substituted for blood as the material of history, the event was referred to as the Kapp Putsch. The whole incident did not last a full week. Ebert, who was not as simple as he looked to the cartoonists and professional Berlin jokers, strangled the whole thing in a general strike. The few sections of the Reichswehr which had rebelled returned to quarters and ordered generous portions of humble pie; the rest of the army remained faithful and, when nobody was looking, even snickered.

In Munich, however, we had no means of knowing how limited was the scope of the Kapp Putsch. Optimistically we began a little putsch all our own, and decided to give it national significance by sending agents to Berlin who would establish a contact between the two wings of revolution, and pave the way for eventual joint action. The two agents chosen were Dietrich

Eckart and, of course, Adolf Hitler who interpreted this as the fulfillment of Frau Askaba's prophecy.

When he tried to convince me of the matter I gave him scant encouragement.

"In the first place, according to Frau Askaba, you were to be called to Berlin," I corrected him, "whereas you are really being sent there, which is an entirely different matter. As for the possible implications of such a journey, permit me to remind you of the old saying that many are called but few are chosen. I think we'll do well to postpone the rest of this conversation till a time when you will have got back from Berlin safely."

He made an angry noise and left me. The next morning Dietrich Eckart, the first poet of national socialism, and Adolf Hitler, its first Fuehrer, climbed into an old World War crate piloted by an aviator of experience, and they were off to snatch the first fruits of Nazi victory.

It was the first time that Hitler had entered a plane, though he has since taken to the air like a bird. His initial flight, however, was not a very smooth one, and the first fruits of Nazi victory turned out to be prematurely plucked. Something, first of all, went wrong with the plane, and at Juterbog they made a forced landing into an airdrome jammed with striking workers. Had Hitler and Eckart been recognized they would have been mobbed.

But no one recognized them. Eckart, who had a certain superficial intellectuality despite his predisposition toward beering and light journalism, walked right into the midst of the strikers and brazenly asked to be directed to a well-known printing establishment. They were respectfully shown the way, and later, after making the needed repairs, the three got back into the plane and made their way to safety in Berlin.

The foxy Eckart was for caution, for reporting immediately to National Socialist headquarters in Berlin, to make sure that the way was prepared for them. But the catlike, blitz-minded Hitler would hear nothing of this.

"Wherever I am, there are National Socialist headquarters," he declared. "If there's a revolution in Germany, the place to look for it is the Reich Chancellory. On to the Chancellory, then!"

But at the entrance to the Reich Chancellory they encountered a furtive looking little man whose eyes seemed to have long hands that reached out for them as they approached. They made their way toward him almost against their will.

"What are you looking for, my babes-in-the-wood?" he greeted them.

Hitler and Eckart eyed each other.

"Looks like a spy to me," Hitler whispered.

"And maybe not on our side either," hazarded Eckart.

"Suppose you tell us what business it is of yours what we are doing here," Hitler suggested, addressing himself to the comic-opera stranger.

As might have been expected of such a person, he totally disregarded the question.

"You're Hitler, aren't you?" he asked, pointing to the Fuehrer.

Hitler nodded; he did not trust himself to speak.

"I saw you in Munich last year. You look as good without your beard as I would without my troubles. Is the beer-keg at your side to be trusted?"

"My friend here is Dietrich Eckart," Hitler said stiffly.

"Ah, the poet! There are tubercular fires on the tips of your cheeks, my heart. It'll take half a wagonful of dirt to wipe them off. Now will you tell me, either of you—I am not particular which—what you happen to be doing this minute at this plague-spot of the Reich? Do you want to be arrested, put up against a wall and shot?"

"We're looking for General Kapp," explained Eckart.

He let out a short, mirthless laugh.

"Haven't you heard, my starlings? The revolution is over. General Kapp has skipped. If you've any sense you'll be on your way, too, and quickly."

They could hardly believe their ears.

"Who are you?" Hitler asked.

The little man bowed in a comic theatrical manner.

"I am the spirit of tragedy, mein Herr, I am your saviour, I am, in a word, Ignace Trebitsch-Lincoln."

They still looked suspiciously at him, and Eckart asked:

"How do we know that you're not lying?"

The little man grinned and genuflected again in the manner of a servile Oriental.

"Ah, my pretties, these are unkind words, and most unjustified. A Trebitsch alone might be tempted to deceive you. Even a Lincoln by himself might be misled so far as to misinform you. But a combination of Trebitsch-Lincoln—it is not to be thought of."

Hitler was losing patience with the whole thing.

"I believe this man," he declared with sudden conviction. "Let's get out of here."

"I'd even be careful where those sun-touched wings are headed for," Trebitsch-Lincoln added.

"You think something may have gone wrong in Munich, too?" Hitler asked in a whisper, for by this time he was quite unnerved.

"As I remember it," replied the little man in the big cloak, "one's beer is not all that occasionally goes sour in Munich."

Hitler and Eckart finally decided on risking return to Munich, which they did immediately, lest, in their absence, the danger grow out of bounds. But there events turned in their favor. A failure on its own home grounds, in Munich the Kapp Putsch was eminently successful. The Munich Reichswehr had actually overthrown the local social-democratic government and replaced it with Gustav von Kaahr, a bourgeois right-winger, as Minister-President. Munich paid a nominal allegiance to the Ebert government, but, in Bavaria, at any rate, the National Socialist forces were in the ascendant.

It was Hitler himself who had supplied me with the details of the flight to Berlin, the encounter at the entrance to the Chancellory, as well as the first description I had ever received of that remarkable individual, Ignace Trebitsch-Lincoln. As to what happened the following night in the Burgerbraukeller, I know first-hand, for I was on the scene in person, and drank with some of the prominent party leaders, including my patient.

Between beers in the Burgerbraukeller, Hitler showed satisfaction with recent events in Munich, yet could not help bemoaning the collapse in Berlin.

"Would you have been better off," I interrupted, "if they had caught you and stood you up against a wall?"

At this Hitler stirred uneasily and turned to Eckart.

"What did that fellow say his name was—I mean the one who warned us not to go into the Chancellory?"

Eckart scratched his forehead, and remembered.

"Trebitsch-Lincoln," mused Hitler. "Funny name, don't you think?"

"A funny man, too, I would say," replied Eckart.

At this moment Roehm, who had been sitting morosely at the opposite side of the table, broke into sudden speech.

"Did I hear anyone utter the august name of Ignace Trebitsch-Lincoln?" he asked.

Hitler was startled.

"You know him?" he asked, turning to the Reichswehr captain.

Roehm grinned broadly.

"Know him? My dear, dear fellow. And did I understand you properly when you said that it was he who warned you at the gate of the Chancellory?"

"That's right," put in Eckart. "He was a queer one, but by God he did the trick."

At this Roehm broke into one of his long horse-laughs.

"That's a good one," he cried, pounding his half empty mug on the table. "That's a good one," he repeated. He turned to Hitler, shaking the mug at him. "And the next time you're telling Munich what a terrible lot of people the Jews are, you might also regale them with the fact that one of them saved the life of their precious Fuehrer."

This was stunning news to the two agents to Berlin. Eckart was the first to recover.

"That man a *Jew!*" he exclaimed.

"Not only a Jew, but a Hungarian to boot!" replied Roehm with heavy emphasis. "Not only a Hungarian by birth but an English clergyman by practice, and not only a clergyman by practice, but an atheist by the profoundest conviction discoverable in the species of homo sapiens. But that's not the whole count, which nobody really knows. For the man Trebitsch-Lincoln is boy and girl, man and woman, satyr and nymph, all rolled into one."

"Wherever you dig in Germany," moaned Eckart, "up turns a Jew."

"As for me," Hitler announced solemnly, "the next time my life is saved by a Jew I'm going to commit suicide."

"I'll hold you to that one," blustered Roehm.

On the way out of the beer haus that night, I let the conversation slip back to the Jews in general and Trebitsch-Lincoln in particular.

"Suppose this man came to Munich while Munich was in the midst of an attack on the Jews," I asked him, "what would you do about Trebitsch-Lincoln?"

"For saving my life," replied Hitler, "I would offer him sanctuary, but no more than that."

Which brings me to what is now generally accepted in Europe as the strange death of this amazing European. Since I have never met him, I must rely upon the stories of trustworthy narrators such as Konrad Heiden and Pierre van Paassen, who enjoyed encounters with him in the pre-war night life of Paris.

Van Paassen does not consider it a certainty that Trebitsch-Lincoln was a Jew; yet who but a Jew could have played his varied and protean role? For it is true that he had been a Catholic priest in Vienna, an Anglican clergyman in London, a member of Parliament in Westminster and, during the World War number one, a German secret agent in Canada and the United States, as a result of which his English citizenship had been cancelled. He had also been secretary to Leon Trotsky, a "brain-truster" for one of the more recent Chinese governments, and some sort of personage in the Court of Afghanistan.

According to van Paassen "he always knew—sometimes months in advance—what was going to happen, but he never revealed his sources. This gave him an air of mystery, although there was nothing fundamentally mysterious about him. He was a restless soul, the Wandering Jew par excellence, who vainly sought for peace of mind in all the highways and byways of life. Personal success was the least of his concerns. He could have carved a career in half a dozen professions, and had more than once started out, only to break off suddenly, cut all his attachments and connections, and turn up on another road. . . . He blew in, left some startling announcement that left everybody flabbergasted, and went out again. . . ."

In 1930, the story goes, Trebitsch-Lincoln disappeared from his familiar haunts in Paris, and when he showed up five years later at the wicket in the *Gare du Nord,* he was buying a ticket to Berlin. He was wearing the yellow robe of a Buddhist monk, and announced that he was on his way to discuss with the Fuehrer the advisability of adopting Buddhism as the religion of National Socialist Germany.

"Buddhism," he explained to van Paassen, "is a purely Aryan religion, and if Germans really want to have done with that Jewish cult known as Christianity . . ."

As I was already out of Germany when this happened, I can only describe this adventure in the most general terms, as it was relayed to me through several minds. Whether he obtained an interview with Hitler or not, it is certain that in 1933 Trebitsch-Lincoln was arrested in Berlin, and hurried off without trial to the concentration camp at Dachau from which he later disappeared. When the German authorities are asked, they explain that whereas the Jew had not made an escape, there is no record of a transfer. From this only one conclusion can be drawn.

Hitler's sanctuary!

CHAPTER TEN

THE LITTLE GIRL WITH BLUE EYES AND GOLDEN HAIR

The Idiot and the Bottle—Hitler Learns Early How to Read Faces in a Mob—A Teacher—The Little Girl with the Golden Hair and Blue Eyes—His Antagonism to His Father.

"YOU MIGHT find it difficult to believe," said my patient at the beginning of our next interview, "but the person of next importance in my recollections is that of the town idiot."

We had reached the second stage of my patient's life, the one he lived between the ages of four and ten. Both of his parents were still alive, and it was prior to his father's retirement on a pension.

"Somehow or other, an idiot fits into the life of every man of genius," I consoled him. "I hope your idiot was a pleasant one."

He shook his head dolefully.

"I remember him first of all by the raggedness of his appearance. Everything he wore was in tatters, dirty, and of uncertain endurance. You expected his hat to be blown away, his pants to fall off, and his coat, hanging down from his neck in long, complicated streamers, to disappear into the pockets of the first breeze. The dirt went beyond his apparel. His fingers and toes (always exposed) showed themselves coal-black, his brow was a tan, darkened by the dust of the atmosphere, and wherever his chest was made visible, it was as if the vagabonds of the neighborhood had been bespattering him with mud."

"Nice work," I murmured. "Did your idiot have a name?"

My patient smiled.

"Yes, and I remember it. It was a name like the loud snap of a dog. I remember it quite clearly. Barsch."

"When did you first notice him?"

"I must have been about six years old. It was on a Sunday, after Mother, Father and I had come back from church. We had eaten and, as was my habit, I went out for a stroll. It was an old custom in those little northern towns for people to go walking about with their families Sunday afternoons. My father preferred to lie down and rest, and my mother would occasionally do likewise. Since my mother would not, under any circumstances, go strolling without my father, I made those trips alone.

"Usually this walk of mine assumed the form of a search for boys of the neighborhood, in the hope that I might be able to join them in some game, or induce them to listen to me. The Sunday afternoon in question, I came upon a group of people who gathered in front of an old house that for some reason was fenced off from the road. Against this fence stood Barsch, and those gathered around him were mostly young bucks from the neighborhood who were laughing, jostling one another, and getting more fun out of the poor idiot than he was apparently able to get out of himself. The exclamations flung at him were of great spice and variety.

" *'Barsch, you old devil, where did you find that elegant dinner jacket?'*

" *'I missed you in church this morning, Barsch. Are you turning atheist on us?'*

" *'Is it true, Barsch, that you and the Danish widow Lemke are only on nodding terms?'*

" *'How about giving us an imitation of your drinking partner, the devil, Barsch?'*

"The last question gave someone an unholy idea.

" 'I never knew you were a drinking man, Barsch,' said the prankster. 'Here, take a nip of this,' He handed the idiot a pint bottle of strong spirits, and began urging him to drink it. Barsch took a swig, made a very sour grimace, and tried to hand it back, but apparently couldn't remember who had given him the bottle. He held the bottle out so long that almost anyone could have taken it out of his hands, but no one wanted to because he looked so funny in his new helplessness. He made incomprehensible noises, which must have meant: *'Take that damned stuff away, I don't like it!'* But once they had him going, the boys were not going to let up so easily. The notion of the bottle had been a very happy one to begin with. The idea of making him consume the whole of its contents was the inspiration of genius."

Hitler's face was a puzzle in confused emotions. His mouth was caught between a grin and a sneer while his eyes were touched with a hint of pity. I couldn't make up my mind as to whether my patient enjoyed this little joke at the expense of a helpless idiot, or whether he felt a normal sympathy for the victim of young, irresponsible sadists. But I discovered later that I was mistaken. The pity I saw in his eyes existed only in my imagination.

"Someone stepped up to him and pushed the bottle back violently into his mouth," continued my patient. "*'Nein, nein,'* he cried out, but the mind of the man with the bottle had become firmer than ever. His left hand seized Barsch by the nape of the neck, and with his right hand forced the mouth of the bottle between the idiot's teeth. We could hear the stuff gurgling down his throat. When the bottle had been emptied, the master-mind flung it across the road, let go of Barsch, and we were treated to the spectacle of the poor fellow trying to maintain his precarious balance in a state of mounting drunkenness.

"I walked away before I could see him fall. When I told the story of what I had seen to my father at the supper table, he laughed, and said that it was nothing unusual. Something of the sort happened to poor Barsch almost every Sunday afternoon. Praise be to God it had occurred to someone to give the poor fellow a drink. If only someone else took it into his head to torture him by giving him something to eat, Barsch would be set for life."

"Did you keep track of the idiot pretty regularly after that?"

"Yes, he certainly stuck in my mind. I'd never go anywhere without looking about for him. I never saw a trace of him on week days. But one or two Sundays a month I would find him in some doorway or against a fence. There would always be a crowd around him, and if they were not torturing him with a bottle they would be digging at his ribs with a stick or throwing stones at him."

"Did you ever join in those festivities?"

"No, on my honor, I never did. On the contrary, I used to stand aside, and watch him agonize. I began to identify every gesture of his with certain words—words he could not utter but probably thought, nevertheless. It got so that I could almost anticipate his gestures from what was being done to him by some tough member of the gang milling about him."

"Did you ever speak to him?"

"No. But once his eyes met mine in a brief appealing look which struck me straight to the heart. It was as if he were pleading with me to scatter his tormentors, and let him return in peace to whatever places he haunted during his week day meanderings. A moment later his eyes returned to their habitual bleariness and purposelessness, and I restrained the impulse to try to interfere in his behalf."

"You returned to the scene after that?"

"Many times. But I had an understanding with myself that I was really trying out on him my system of reading in the faces and in the gestures of people the thoughts and emotions running through them."

"Was he the only one you had that sort of feeling about?"

"It began with Barsch, but after a while I had the same feeling toward almost everyone I met. It didn't matter whether people came singly or in groups. They were no sooner at rest before me than I would instinctively sense what each of them was feeling individually, and what state of mind they all encompassed as a group. The only advantage I had with Barsch was that in his case, because his emotions were constantly repeated by the actions of the mob about him, I could check upon myself, and see whether my deductions were accurate. I took a certain amount of pride in this."

"Did you ever discuss this with anyone?"

"No one."

"But you practiced it all the time, didn't you?"

He nodded.

"Would you say that you continued to practice it as you grew older?"

"Yes."

"As to the present: do you still feel that you can read the thoughts and the emotions of a mob individually and collectively?"

He wrinkled his brows in contemplation.

"I guess I've been doing it all the time without realizing it," he finally said.

"Were there any books in your house in those early days?"

"My mother's daily account book which my father insisted on her keeping, and a family Bible."

"No other books?"

"None that I can remember."

"How old were you when you began your schooling?"

"About six."

"Did you first learn to read or write?"

"I first learned to draw."

"In that case, Austrian elementary schools must have differed from those of the rest of the world," I mused.

"I guess I must have taken to drawing before I actually got to school," explained my patient. "I did it as a matter of habit when I entered my first classroom, and it was noticed by a sympathetic teacher."

"Can you remember the teacher?"

"Only that she was fat and good-natured. I guess she did not remain in charge of my class for long."

"Did you like going to school?"

"In the beginning. But as my studies grew less simple, interest in them began to diminish. After a while, if I had been consulted about it, I would have preferred to get along without any schooling whatever."

"Can you remember any other of your teachers of that period?"

"Not bodily. They are all shadows, more or less filled out, but never more than shadows. I guess school teachers are pretty poor human material."

"Among the subjects you studied at school those days, were there any you liked particularly?"

"No."

"Anything you disliked particularly?"

"Yes, I disliked fractions. I didn't see why the world could not conduct its affairs without the use of those ugly split and splintered little numerals."

I laughed.

"I hope you've changed your mind on that score?"

"I've had to change my mind on matters of far greater importance," he said with emphasis.

"I don't know," I rejoined. "You might be hasty in your judgment of the importance of such things. A resentment against split numerals could be a very important clue to the life of a man determined to affect the destiny of his country. But let us go on from here to the image next in your recollection."

He thought a while, then he said:

"I guess the next image is that of a little girl."

"That you knew?"

He shook his head.

"No. I never knew her. I just saw her."

"How old were you at the time?"

He appeared to consider.

"I can't say. Maybe I was six. Maybe I was ten. Maybe I was even older. Maybe—since you will probably suggest it yourself—I never really saw her at all."

"I don't want you to anticipate me that way," I warned him.

"All right, then. Forget it."

"Then you remember this little girl as someone you at least saw?" I probed him.

"Yes, Doctor."

"With what do you associate your first recollection of her?"

"It's a curious feeling rather than anything definite. I would not like to tell you about this feeling. But knowing as I do how you feel about this sort of thing, I suppose you will insist that I tell you, and if you insist, I will."

"I insist," I smiled.

"I associate it with a desire to urinate. Now that sort of feeling is ageless and could have come upon me in the street at almost any age. But you asked me for the association, and there it is. Make of it what you will."

He appeared eager to get the subject over with in a hurry. He acted like a man who had yielded to the temptation of opening the wrong door, and was eager to shut it again as quickly as possible.

"It's neither as strange nor as unimportant as you imagine, my dear fellow," I assured him. "A little boy must at some time in his life notice a little girl, and it is not at all unusual that he should do so just as his g——a have called themselves to his attention. How many times did you see that little girl?"

"I don't know, I can't say," he replied fumblingly. "You've just heard me tell you that I may never really have seen her at all. The best I can say is that I associate the need of urinating with the image of such a child—and that is really all there is to it."

"Then why do you regard it as an object of such importance in your life?"

"Because it is an image I see before me at least once a day every blessed day of my life. I don't know when it began to come to me. I don't know if it will ever disappear."

"Has the—the child any definite features?"

"Yes—and they never change."

"Give me a rough outline of what she looks like."

It was fully a minute before my patient answered, but when he did, he spoke as if out of a dream:

"She is a little girl, there can be no doubt about that. Her head reaches about to my waist. It has a round face with white skin, blue eyes and golden hair. It is a little girl, as I have already told you. But in one respect she is like a woman. It's her breasts. She has breasts like a woman."

"Surely you haven't seen them?"

"No. I can tell by the bulge, though. The bulge never deceives you."

"You have plenty to learn about bulges," I jibed him. "But

let us get back to the girl herself. You are not certain of having seen her? Positive?"

"I might have been before you began this examination."

"It would be a very important thing for this inquiry if we could establish clearly whether this little girl of yours is someone you actually saw during your childhood or whether it is a phantom that has insinuated itself into your brain in the process of your development as a man. It doesn't matter to me whether the child proves a reality or a dream; the vital thing is to establish which she is. Once we know that, we will be on a surer way to the sources of your sexual energies. Do you follow me?"

"Perfectly."

"Then try to answer my questions as accurately as possible. How old would you say the child could be?"

"Somewhere between eight and ten."

"How old was she when you first thought about her?"

"That age."

"And now?"

"How can I think of her differently? Phantom or reality, she cannot possibly be any older in my mind than she was when I last saw her."

"You're quite right. I was trying to make certain of something else. Have you ever seen her in any special vicinity?"

"No."

"A house, a field, a fence, with a human being?"

"No, Doctor."

"You said her eyes were blue. Have you ever actually met them; comunicated with them?"

"Yes, Doctor, I always seek out her eyes when I see her, and they always respond to mine without any particular expression. I don't know whether she recognizes me, or is surprised by the strangeness of my face. I can't tell whether my attentions are welcome or despised; she just assures me that she is aware of my existence."

"Have you ever seen her smile?"

"No, Doctor. I'd give almost anything you can think of if I could see those eyes smile only once."

"I don't think it matters any longer whether your little girl is a reality or a vision," was my verdict.

"Why?"

"Let us assume for a moment that she was a reality," I said. "How would you answer if I asked you what measures you ever took to talk to her; to get to know her?"

"I would not be able to say, because I don't think I ever took such measures."

"I thought so. Then the fact that you never met her cannot have any particular significance in your life. On the other hand, the image of her is a very important one. For a reason you will hardly approve of."

"You might as well tell me," he insisted.

"The little girl fulfills in every respect the image of your mother reduced by your imagination to a size, age and form desirable to you."

He laughed harshly.

"You can't be speaking in the present tense?"

"I am speaking in the present tense," I insisted. "It would be the present not of this moment exactly, but a sort of average present. And now," I resumed, "we're prepared to return to the most momentous issue in our inquiry—your peculiar relationship to your parents. You have had a long time in which to let the facts we elicited in our previous interviews arrange themselves in your mind in a meaningful pattern. Do you still believe that this relationship with your parents was an ordinary one, no different from the usual child-parent relationship?"

He shook his head slowly, and I could read in his eyes the forming of a strong impulse. I could see that it meant a great deal to my patient to make such a radical admission.

"You were right, Doctor," he said. "A hundred things have come back to me in the interim between our interviews—things of greater and lesser importance, which have convinced me that there is a great deal in your suggestion that I was fonder of my mother than of my father, so much more that I might almost believe that I lived in a state of latent antagonism to him."

"Can you remember instances of such antagonism?" I asked.

"More than one. But one, which I remember more clearly

than all the rest, was probably the most typical. It happened on the return of my father after an official absence of a few days. He had written that he was coming home by train at two o'clock the following afternoon. The morning of that day I could barely catch my mother's eyes at the breakfast table. She served me and my sister a cold luncheon, took up her sewing, and appeared to concentrate on just waiting for my father.

"I suppose children really feel all of the pangs of creation, only that they do not tag names to them. And I must have been jealous all of my conscious years of certain attentions which my mother gave my father and withheld from me. But that afternoon I came as closely as it is possible for a child to recognize this difference in the respective status of myself and my father toward my mother. He meant a great deal more to her, I realized. And when he arrived at twenty minutes after two (that's all it took him to get home from the railroad station), his hold on my mother was such that we saw neither of them till supper.

"I remember that I drifted into curious discussions of the matter with my half-sister Angela. Angela was older than I, and in such matters, the wiser. 'Do you know why they have to lock themselves up in that room?' I asked, when more than an hour had passed by, and we had not seen Mother. 'That's nothing to what happens Sunday afternoon after we've eaten and you go out for your walks through the town,' she told me. 'What happens?' I asked eagerly, excitedly. 'They do the same thing—go into that room, and do the funniest things,' she said. 'How do you know?' I asked. 'By looking through the keyhole,' she told me. 'If you stay over next Sunday afternoon instead of running around barking at Barsch like the rest of them, I'll let you look, too.' I stayed behind the next Sunday, and followed my half-sister's example: believe me, Doctor, Angela must have been endowed with quite an imagination, or my parents, suspecting her of spying, had moved the furniture about, because when I looked the next Sunday afternoon I saw virtually nothing."

My patient grinned, and then his face assumed a petulant, baffled expression, as if he still regretted his failure to catch his parents in *flagrante delictu*.

"Not knowing at the time what my half-sister Angela might

have seen," he continued, "and being unable to guess at even the nature of what she suspected, I began to invent for myself reasons for my father's secreting my mother from the rest of the family for hours at a stretch. I decided in my heart that he did her violence during that long, painful interval, drawing my conclusions from the fact that my mother always emerged from the sleeping chamber after such a session looking pale and worn, and even a little bleary-eyed. With a growing feeling of anger against my father came also a feeling of intense pity for her. I would turn from my resentment toward my father to fantastic plans for rescuing my mother from the clutches of her persecutor. Schemes that appeared perfectly feasible to my childish imagination filtered in painful and broken procession through my mind. I thought of running off with her to a nearby large town where I had once been taken for market-day and come back from it with a ripe vision of a hundred people praising the virtues of things nobody seemed interested in except I. Or I thought we might go away with the next caravan of gypsies that would come along in its due season to fascinate, delight and rob us. I would get sensations of wanting to cry, out of sheer bafflement and frustration, and tears would actually well up in my eyes as I thought how wonderful it would be to put my arms around her, caress her, and give her some feeling of the protection she might enjoy in my love of her.

"I ached to tell her how much I loved her, that she needn't put up with the abuse she suffered at the hands of our common tyrant. I began to feel the same loneliness while she was with me as when she absented herself with my father. Many a night, after she had tucked me away in my own bed, I had a feeling that she wanted to come to me and pet me, but was unable to do so because of my father's tyrannical will."

He paused, and it occurred to me to try to straighten out an apparent discrepancy in my patient's story.

"Am I mistaken," I asked him, "when I think I remember your telling me that you once felt your mother's affections closer to you than to your father?"

"You're quite right," he explained. "But when I spoke to you about this for the first time I had in mind only the earliest part of my life, which was quite different from the life it developed into in the next few years. I suppose in the early part of their marriage the difference in their ages still told against my father with my mother. But when she got accustomed to him she drew away from her children as she drew nearer to her husband."

I conceded that this was entirely possible and asked him if he could remember any other telling instance of the antagonism he bore his father.

"Yes," he said, "I remember another one clearly. It happened one day after the local dressmaker had come to the house. She had poured out her troubles, and, perhaps as the result of this, my mother discovered that she had not had a new dress in a long time, and ordered Frau Renckner (that's how I remember her name; it might have been a little different) to find some good materials for a dress. At the breakfast table, when my mother mentioned this matter to my father, gently and tactfully, he exploded into a tirade of wrath. Too much was being spent already—he would hear nothing about it. Not a thing.

" 'But I've already asked Frau Renckner to get the material,' argued my mother, quite calmly. 'I cannot ask her to keep it, simply because my husband is too stingy to see that it is wrong to let his wife go around in clothes meaner than those of the wife of the town's scavenger.'

" 'So now you compare me to the town scavenger, eh!' my father exclaimed, wiped his chin with his napkin and stamped out of the house.

"That was characteristic of him, Doctor. At the faintest opportunity he would announce that he had been insulted and start a quarrel that would go on for weeks. How I detested those outbursts. My mother was so distressed by them that she would invariably go to her room when he was gone, and though I never followed her on those occasions, I knew that all she did was to cry. But she never let my father get quite the better of her. In the instance I mention, for example, the dressmaker came the next day; my mother chose the most expensive material and began smiling again. The strangest part of it was the effect it would have on my father. 'I'm glad you chose such splendid stuff!' he cried, and took my mother in his arms right in my presence, as if he had forgotten that I had heard his outrageous explosion on the previous day."

Hitler frowned, as if he still resented his father's duplicity despite the passing of the years.

"My mother responded quite warmly to his kiss," he continued, "yes, even eagerly. They had made up without words, as I suspected they frequently did. I now know that my mother really loved my father, and after a while I began to feel that I could no longer bank on their quarrels, and it was a source of great happiness to me when the subject of my own personal career became a bone of contention between them, for here was an opportunity, a golden one, for me to actually hold the line of strife between them."

"I wish you wouldn't go into that phase of it till we get to it," I interrupted. "Let us get back to the antagonism you felt toward your father."

"I disliked those differences of theirs almost as much as I welcomed them," my patient resumed. "Like a sick man who takes drugs to quiet his pain, knowing all the time that he will have to pay with much greater pain for the temporary relief he enjoys, I always knew that a silent joyous reconciliation was bound to follow those violent passages of words between my parents, and they filled me with a furious sort of envy. I am now pretty sure that my mother was much happier in the state of domination imposed on her by my father than she would have been had she been married to a man who let her have her own way most of the time. There were, of course, many explosive moments, when she appeared to be angry with his petty tyranny. But I surmise now that she merely put him to the test to see whether he was still strong enough to dominate her completely, or, in other words, whether he were still worthy of her love. And my father, on his part, was happiest when he held her completely in his sway.

"It was when he felt his possession of her most exclusively that I hated my father the most bitterly. I guess I must have disliked him actively most of the time. Whether it was because I was jealous of my mother, or because I sympathized with her in the hurt she suffered on his account, I will never be able to decide in my mind with any finality. I only know that my dislike for him occasionally rose to supreme hatred. Mostly, I now believe, it was my resentment to his domineering ways about the house, and the fact is that I still resent such an attitude wherever I find it in domestic or in public life."

That was a profound reflection on the part of my patient. He recognized obliquely that his own Caesar-like complex was an effort to substitute his will for the will of his father. But whereas his father played Caesar only in the privacy of his own home, Hitler was striving to make all Germany the arena for his imperial passion.

"All this must sound very complicated to you, Doctor," resumed my patient. "But you have no idea how really complicated my emotions were. I did not want my father to make my mother unhappy. But neither did I want him to bring her happiness; I do not know whether I disliked him more when he abused her than when his conduct made her eyes shine with happiness. The point is that I wanted to bring her happiness myself, and be the only one through whom she could really know what joy meant.

"I was most contented, I feel sure, when my father was away from the house. I did not think it was possible for man and wife to be entirely separated, but if an instance of such a thing had transpired within my circle of knowledge, I feel sure I would have begun to conspire to repeat it in our household. I simply did not like to see them together. If they were quarreling, I wanted to see them apart so that my mother would have an opportunity to wipe her beautiful eyes. If they were getting along well, I prayed for their separation, because it hurt me to see my father making her happy when I felt I was the only one who should be doing that."

He paused.

"Have I told you enough?" he asked expectantly.

I rose with an obvious feeling of satisfaction.

"More than enough," I assured him. "And to show you how pleased I am, what do you say if we give your subconscious a holiday by going to a movie?"

He grinned.

"Gita Alper?"

There was no Alper picture showing that day, and I knew he was only ribbing me.

I gave him a good-natured slap on the back.

"I'm afraid," I laughed, "the beautiful Gita will never give your subconscious much of a rest."

CHAPTER ELEVEN

From the Other World

*A Strange Visitor—Posing the Problem of the Ages—
Party Preparations — Rebellion Within — The Final
Showdown.*

It was during this stage of the analysis of Adolf Hitler that a
man telephoned me for an appointment, and gave me a name so
similar to my own that I must have paused audibly as I jotted it
down on the pad before me. My prospective patient apparently
felt the pause on his end of the wire, because he hastened to
assure me that I need not worry; in spite of the similarity in our
names we were not at all related. He had simply heard about me
and my work and was very much interested in submitting to me
an important problem of his own. The problem would intrigue
me deeply, he felt. "It may involve some of your time and
patience," he added, "but I will pay you well for it."

"If I thought before that you sounded like a relative, I certainly do not think so any longer," I said to him with a laugh,
and mentioned a time I could see him that was perfectly agreeable to him. "But what makes you so certain that you're not
related to me?" I could not help asking.

I could almost fancy my man smiling at the other end of
the wire.

"Because I'm a Jew and you're an Aryan," he replied with
an accent of whimsicality that was indubitably Jewish.

I was a little taken aback.

"And how, pray, have you established the fact that I'm an
Aryan?" I insisted.

"It is enough for me to know that you are the personal

physician of the National Socialist Fuehrer," he said with an almost visible sweep of his voice.

I was not a little intrigued by this passage of arms over the telephone. It was intriguing to be asked for an appointment by a Jew, in the first place; as for this Jew also knowing that I ministered to the mental and physical illnesses of his professed racial enemy, that gave the whole thing a touch of mystic grandeur that promised even more amazing developments. When the man actually walked in through my door three days later, he did not have the faintest resemblance to any of the figures I had been comparing him with in my fancies. I had known Jews and Jewesses, but never had I seen so un-Jewish a looking Jew as this one—if he was, indeed, a Jew. He was tall, with wide shoulders and enormous biceps; he was blonde and blue-eyed, and he swung an ivory-headed cane like a French count. His evenness of features, combined with his great height, made him a strikingly handsome figure. He smiled as he took my hand, and sank into the chair I offered him with pontific grace. I observed him silently for a whole minute and shook my head slowly at him.

"I can't imagine anything I could do to you that wouldn't simply spoil you," I said to him solemnly.

He laughed with me, and his voice pealed out with such natural enjoyment that I began to wonder if I were not really the victim of a hoax someone was about to perpetrate on me.

"You're quite sure that you're a Jew?" I asked him.

"Not only a Jew, but a Zionist," he assured me. "Even your eminent patient does not object to Jews who are also Zionists."

"Provided they are prepared to carry out their Zionism as a practical policy and leave Germany," I reminded him. "I wonder if you'll be good enough to tell how you happened to know that the Fuehrer is a patient of mine?"

"What difference does it make how I came to know?" he replied. "It's only important that I know. Because his being a patient of yours is an essential part of the case which I am about to place before you. Before I pose my problem, however, I feel it's my duty to tell you that I made quite an extensive investigation of your background before getting in touch with you. I learned that you are not only a doctor but something of a scientist. You are young, and not to sure of your own vision of the world, not so sure, at any rate, that you are not open to reason. You understand that, as a Jew, especially one who does not try to hide behind a European appearance, I could not come to you unless I felt some assurance that you were not too prejudiced to hear me."

"I'm highly flattered," was my reply.

"The intention was not to flatter," he said quickly. "I belong to one of the richest Jewish families in Germany. We gave our quota of blood to the war, and we fought like good Germans. I did my own bit of fighting myself at Verdun. But we're in something of a funk now. All the things which have followed the peace, and which have made the majority of Germans poor, have made us rich. We are today infinitely more prosperous than we were before the war, and it looks like the end is not in sight."

Still plagued by the possibility that I was being hoaxed, I decided to cut in on him sharply to forestall any embarrassment.

"I'm not an economist, just a doctor," I reminded him. "Did you come here to boast? If there is something really wrong with you, I wish you'd get down to it with as little more preamble as possible."

He looked calm and entirely unaffected by my rebuke.

"I have just told you what ails me, Doctor," he said cryptically, "but I'm afraid I will have to explain myself a little better. Do have more patience with me, please."

"I'm sorry to have been so abrupt," I apologized. "But this is the first time that wealth has ever appeared to me in the guise of a positive and remediable illness."

"I was born in Germany," continued my visitor, "as was my father before me, and his father before him. I obtained my education in German and in Hebrew at about the same time, but there has never been a question in my mind that, though born into the synagogue, I owe complete physical fealty to Germany as my fatherland. In business I owe my success to a combination of luck and commonplace ability. Is it my fault that the sun seems to shine on all the enterprises of my family? Yet your celebrated patient is guiding Germany into confiscating our wealth and turning us out into exile."

He paused, but I knew that there was more to come, so I waited until he resumed:

"I'm not here because I'm frightened. There are things too big for us to see, sounds too loud for us to hear, and pains too deep for us to feel. If the debacle anticipated by Herr Hitler comes, I shall probably feel it less keenly than I would feel today a slight at my club. I come to you as a layman to a scientist. I want to understand this thing as I would want to understand cancer if it were about to strike me. I have come to you not only because you are a scientist, but because, as Hitler's physician, you are privileged to observe every day the spectacle of his fathomless rage against me and my people. For the moment you seem to me to be in the best possible position to understand what has baffled the brains of men caught up in two thousand years of alternate rage and despair.

"Coming to you with this object in view may seem extraordinary and even irrelevant. To me this seems so logical and irrevocable, so fundamentally sound and necessary, I wonder why it has never occurred to a Jew to take such a step before. It occurred to me as I overheard two people in a beer *haus* discussing the relationship between you and the Fuehrer. And in a moment the thing came to me as a flash of lightning. This great Jew-baiter is confessing himself to a doctor, a man of science. As he listens to the outpourings of this heart, to what depths may not this doctor be privileged to see?

"We have always taken our case to kings, ministers of state, secretaries of the interior and much lesser fry in the political world. How could these stupid people who bring to trivial routine tasks of state so little competence, be expected to bring the cure of understanding to an illness as complicated as ours? But here is a physician, a man forced by his education and training to observe phenomena in their related forms, situated where he can practically watch the deadly bacteria under the most powerful of lenses: who better than he is likely to catch a glimpse of the true formations of our enemies? Would it be wise to do less than to ask him what he sees?"

He paused, this time to hear what I had to say. But I was already myself the victim of a complicated set of nervous intellectual visitations. I would have to iron myself out before I could hope to be of any use to him. But I could do so by speaking tentatively, feeling my way as I spoke.

"Your visit is a very flattering one," I said to him by way of a beginning. "But I am afraid that if you really looked forward to something, I will have to disappoint you. You understand, of course, that I have never enlisted my sympathies in this cause of your people. You guessed as much when you introduced yourself, and you were right in the heart of truth when you did so. I am not a Jew-sympathizer. But as a scientist I have worked with Jews, and I don't see what harm there can be in my talking to you, if I do not have to tell you anything but what I think and feel."

He nodded.

"I have come for no more than that and no less."

"You came to me with a problem of doom. You mentioned cancer, and it seemed to me to compare admirably with the illness which we call anti-Semitism. There are doctors who feel that we simply have to find an easy way of removing cancers without killing the patients, and other doctors who think that medical salvation might be found more easily in the discovery of a way of diverting the cancerous growth into safer interior channels of flesh. There is not only a difference in methods, but also in tempers, in moods of patience. I suggest to you that it is easier to cut away malignant tissues than to study its infinitesimal structure with a view to controlling its growth. Now if you will be humble enough to accept this comparison, the gravest charge that can be brought to the doctors of National Socialism is that they train more with knives than with rays and microscopes. I do not hesitate to testify that the change in Germany in particular is largely justified. But it is not because we prefer the knife to the microscope. You yourself probably know from your experience in German universities that it is not so. It is unfortunately true, however, that in this particular laboratory of politics our tempers have reached a boiling point."

He looked perplexed.

"I could tell you a great many things simply which have always been said to you metaphorically," I said, "but I doubt if it will make you happier for having heard them. And I assure you that there is little hope in any of it."

He sat there staring at me like one fascinated.

"Please tell me what is on your mind," he pleaded. "You cannot say it too clearly or too bitterly. I haven't come for comfort, but for understanding."

"I doubt if there is much understanding I have to offer you," I told him. "But it seems to me that, by virtue of his everyday experience, any Jew should be able to make the best and clearest possible reading of the hopelessness of his position. Hitler tells me that there are too many Jews in Germany and that they exercise too much influence in German affairs. If the Germans liked Jews, it might occur to us to demand proof that the Jews are an influence for evil. But we don't like Jews and never have. So we take the evil for granted. According to his temperament, every German would like to get rid of the Jews in his own way. I think it would be enough just to take them out of the professions and force them to live, as Jehovah told them, by the sweat of their brows. But, unfortunately, Herr Hitler has conceived remedies of a much more violent nature. But that is because I only dislike Jews, whereas the National Socialist Fuehrer hates them with that bitterness which breeds homicidal violence.

"I don't know exactly what makes Hitler hate the Jews so desperately," I continued, "but I think I understand why you cannot appease him or bribe him. What you have you will not freely give him, because if you freely gave him your worldly goods he would only despise you the more, and ask of you things you would not be able to offer him because they are not yours to give. I think that the most terrible thing you could possibly try to do with my patient is to try to appease him. You might as well try to appease an earthquake."

That was all that passed between me and the Jew, whom I have never seen again since that single interview between us. And yet, in a sense, I have never completely survived him, for this Jew had done something typically, exquisitely Jewish; he had psychologically enlisted me in behalf of himself and his people. How this had the far-reaching effect of muddling my conduct in the midst of my National Socialist and anti-Semitic surroundings will now become evident.

As far as I could probe my own thoughts, I was a convinced, practicing Nazi, and was politically acceptable and sound for all except my friend and friendly enemy, Ernst Schmidt. Ernst insisted that my conversion was a surface affair which did not affect matters one way or the other. When I had argued the matter with him quite intensely for a whole hour one evening, he got up from the table with sudden violence and shouted, "You're no more a Nazi than that pig Rathenau. No German is a full-fledged Nazi till he has spat into the face of at least one Jew."

I turned to Hitler, who had been unusually quiet.

"And how many Jewish faces have you spat into?" I asked him.

He gave me a sullen look but made no reply.

I turned to Schmidt.

"I suppose the Jewish faces you spit into are those of women and children."

This was too much for Ernst. He rose fuming and stormed out of the house.

Except for such occasional differences with Ernst, the developments of the next few weeks continued to be for me as interesting as they were decisive. With Bavaria now ruled by a government that gave a free hand to all right-wing parties, Hitler's party had easy sailing, and grew prodigiously. The new Munich chief of police, a stout, florid man by the name of Pohner, sided openly with the several organizations in Munich which were secretly pledged to wreck the Republic.

We celebrated at least once a week with a public meeting. These meetings had a double effect. They not only created a solidarity among the members, but they resulted in swelling the membership rolls. Most important of all perhaps were the placards which announced the meetings, because they told for a whole week, in powerful slogans, what the speaker at the meeting could only say for a few hours. Those placards were really more devastating for their effects on the people of Bavaria than any series of mass meetings possibly could be. They showed, more than anything else, the utter contempt in which our revolutionary society held the existing order. The placards denounced the Republic, vilified the Jews, and poured vitriolic abuse on the whole government in Berlin.

I suddenly began to find myself rebellious under the low intellectual tone of those meetings and slogans. I did not attribute it in any way to the influence of my brief conversation with the Jew who bore my name, only that he spelled it without an "e." It was a matter of great relief even to me, if only temporary, when we were joined in our party labors by intelligent people like Hermann Esser, a man ten years younger than Hitler, but a very accomplished orator, and Max Weber, whose speech was as effective as Esser's, even if it was a little too literary and polished for the simple tastes of the masses. Listening to these men was an improvement on beer *haus* nights spent with boors like my friend Ernst, Rudolph Hess and the satyr, Julius Streicher, of whom it has been said that it would be impossible to understand him if one had no sense of smell. But my spiritual depression returned, more clearly than ever.

Meanwhile, things were coming to a head with Germany in her relations with the outside world. The representative of the allied powers placed the reparations bill against Germany at one hundred and thirty-two billion gold marks. The order of the day was for Germany to pay—or else. As it was impossible for my country, strangled economically, to even pay the interest on such a staggering amount, the precariousness of our place in the world became apparent even to those who had refused to see that there was any reason for unusual protest.

"Those fools are playing right into our hands," Hitler gloated. "They are delivering the German masses into our hands like so much meat on a butcher's counter."

I thought this was an odd figure of speech for my patient.

"I thought you were a vegetarian," I protested.

He grinned.

"Not in politics, Doctor. In politics my diet in meat. The heavy meat of the people is the only one that interests me."

Politically, my patient's appetite was not to be relied upon. One day he wanted a diet of the masses. The next day he was all scorn for the mob, and could think of nothing but certain rich industrialists, their money, and the favors still to be obtained from the Reichswehr.

"If only I could get the full confidence of the Reichswehr!" I heard him grumble quite frequently. This seemed to him his gravest and most difficult problem, but strangely enough it was solved for him sooner than he expected.

The Reichswehr had its own problems, its own sad vision. For with the treaty signed, and with the reparations agreed on, it began to realize more than ever that the future of Germany lay in secret organization and that it had to place most of its faith and hope in the leftist groups, of which our party was not outstanding. The Reichswehr gave us more money, however, and, as a further assurance of its confidence in Hitler and what he stood for, it one day bought him a newspaper, the *Volkischer Beobachter,* which has remained the Fuehrer's personal organ to the present day. With such plums thrown in our laps, it was natural that there should come about a certain amount of inter-party dissension, disputes as to who were the real leaders of the movement. Hitler's following began to split up gradually into two clearly discernible groups—the one led by the original leaders of the movement, and the other generalized by Hitler and his own personal brass hats—Rosenberg, Dietrich, Hess and Esser.

I discovered a curious distinction between the two groups that few people in the party or out could see. The first group, the one containing the originators of the movement, was practically proletarian. The second, the one favored by Hitler, was, by comparison, aristocratic, intellectual. It flattered me, of course, to belong to the second group. But it was not long before I realized that, fundamentally, Hitler and I had our own peculiar reasons for our choice of party affiliations. I do not mean to imply that Hitler was not sincere—but that he always knew on which side his bread was buttered.

One characteristic the movements of rebellion against the Republic shared alike, and that was anti-Semitism. One of the organizations, as old as Hitler's and in its Jew-hatred even more virulent, was the German Socialist Party, led by Julius Streicher, who was to direct one of the few revolts against Hitler. It was a fiasco from the start. And when the rebellion failed, it proved the advantage of organizing a national movement with people infinitely inferior in spiritual and intellectual resources. When he was finally slapped down, Streicher remained put, and has been loyal to Hitler ever since.

Streicher was ambitious, as are all rebels. But, uncertain of his ability to supersede Hitler in Munich, he waited till an important conference took the Fuehrer to Berlin. He then proceeded to talk a few of the home-ground imbeciles into moving the party headquarters to Berlin. Even Anton Drexler, the leader of the proletarian group, and not entirely an idiot, agreed, and for a while it looked to me as if Hitler might return to empty quarters. But Hess, who was loyal, managed to get word to Hitler as to what was going on, and in a few days my patient was back in Munich to face Streicher and his rebels and make his decisive bid for the leadership of the National Socialists.

Many of us were fearful of the consequences of this encounter, because the feeling against Hitler and his aristocratic associations had been mounting high. But Hitler showed all of us that there were cards which he alone knew how to play. He let his friends Eckart, Rosenberg, Hess and Esser create a barrage of oratory in his defense. When it was finally over, he took the platform and quietly announced that, unless he received a full and unequivocal vote of confidence, he would be compelled to resign from the movement.

The whole gathering reeled before him. He had no sooner uttered the words, almost completed his threat of withdrawal, when everyone realized that he represented almost everything that they had: the strongest friends of the movement, the men with the money as well as the police influence, and even the greatest asset of the movement, its daily newspaper. Hess got up and shouted at the top of his voice: "Whoever lets Hitler resign is a traitor to Germany!"

"Whoever said anything about letting him resign?" bawled Streicher, who was smart enough to know when the game was up.

Hitler had won without striking a single blow. He was restored to power with such acclaim that no one could doubt what had happened. And Julius Streicher made a quiet return to Nuremberg.

"What would have happened if they had accepted your resignation?" I asked my patient as we walked away from the meeting that night.

"That's a very silly question, Doctor," he replied. "I can't really resign . . . I *am* the party, don't you see, and for me to resign from it would be for me to resign from myself!"

CHAPTER TWELVE

THE FRUSTRATED ARTIST

*Father-Mother-Son Data—The Church and the Artist
—The Children Who Ran After His Father and Called
Him a Jew—Hitler's Attitude Toward Domestic Ani-
mals—The Decision of the Academy of Vienna.*

AT THIS POINT in my investigation, it is important to remind the
reader of the handicap under which I am writing. Working without the benefit of the notes I took during those interviews with
my celebrated patient, I must trust my memory as to what transpired. And yet it is not strictly necessary to recollect these interviews either in detail or in the order in which they occurred.
Many of them were of a transitional nature, and though necessary in their time, have no direct bearing on the development of
the whole. Some of our conversations were of a nature so intimate that the details would be of legitimate interest only to
physicians.

The next phase of my inquiry into the psyche of my patient
covered the period between 1899 and 1908, the latter being the
year in which his mother's death left him on his own. These were
very important years in the life of my patient for me to know
and understand. From the point of view of a developed personality, they were gestative years, the years in which many
of the most important events of his life occurred—those imperial
events which eventually founded the Germany which is today
bleeding to death under the baleful necessity of conquering every
important people in the world.

Among the first questions I asked him, I remember, was about
the immediate effect on him of the death of his father.

"I was fearfully affected," he replied. "But strangely enough,

151

the actual figure of my father had very little to do with my grief. I felt myself almost melting into tears, but when I ask myself why (since my actual feelings toward him were hostile), I realize that this ache in my heart was not for the man who lay dead before us. I was crying for some hypothetical father whom I should have had, who would have been, had things been different, the kind of father I needed. Can you understand that?"

"I understand," I told him. "We play God by creating people in our image."

"And your mother—how did she behave?" I asked curiously.

"She was much calmer. But then, in her way, she was losing something which she could find again."

"Did she?"

"I don't know and I don't think it's important."

"Perhaps you don't know, but it would be important if you did, I assure you."

"I don't know," he repeated sullenly.

I decided to switch the subject.

"Your mother outlived your father by how many years?" I asked.

"Five."

"The effect of her death, when it came, was entirely different, I presume?"

"It was as if a great part of myself had stiffened and died."

"Because her role in your life had been a much more important one?"

He fidgeted.

"How could I know?" he asked.

"Perhaps you will know as we progress in our inquiry," I consoled him. "When you realize the truth, I hope you will have the good sense to tell me. For the present, it is necessary for us to better understand the nature of the part she played in your development. Let me see now, how old was your father when you were born?"

"Fifty-four, I think."

"And your mother?"

"Twenty."

"Then your mother was thirty-four years younger than your father, and only twenty years older than you."

"That's good arithmetic," he smiled.

"But it's even better psychology," I assured him. "I want you to note that the difference in ages between your father and your mother was greater than that between your mother and you."

He was staring at me, and his eyes had very little friendliness.

"What significance could that possibly have?" he asked.

I tried to warm him back by smiling.

"A great deal," I assured him. "Don't you see that it places your mother closer to you than to your father?"

He eyed me with a faint glimmer of understanding.

"But perhaps we can determine this better by means of the actual unfolding of your life," I added. "You decided rather early, didn't you, on the career of an artist?"

"Yes, I was barely past six."

"Can you remember how it came about?"

"Definitely. I think the genesis of my desire to be an artist goes back to the times I spent in church on Sunday mornings. I must have been impressed first of all by the ornateness of the church itself. After that came the pictures in our prayer book, and the stained glass windows which used to hold my eyes throughout the services. As the beauty of these things began to haunt me, I would find myself thinking of church as a sort of Sunday home. It was so much brighter than my real home that I would wish we could go there more frequently, and one Sunday when we returned I found pencil and paper and began to copy secretly some of the illustrations in my mother's handsome prayer book."

"Was it an effort of your subconscious to bring the Church into your home?"

He shrugged.

"It could have been," he admitted.

"But it made an artist of you?"

He reddened.

"Almost."

"Who first noticed this tendency of yours to draw, your father or your mother?"

"My father. Unfortunately he discovered some scrawls I had made in the margin of my mother's prayer book. It was natural, therefore, that he recognized in it a tendency to destruction."

"What happened?"

"I underwent a severe scolding."

"From your father?"

"Yes."

"And your mother?"

"My mother's attitude was that there was no harm in my copying pictures if I found paper on which to do it. The net result was that I did more daubing than ever, drew increasingly as I grew older, and at eight, had already formed the idea that I would grow up one of those starry-eyed people who plied brush and paint for a livelihood."

"House painters do that, too," I reminded him.

He laughed.

"And so did I."

"But what was the reaction of your parents when they realized that you wanted to become an artist?"

"My father was shocked, my mother was pleased. My father pointed out that most artists were no better than vagabonds. As for my own inclinations, one only had to see the sort of things I copied to realize that nothing good could come of it. 'Look,' he said, 'women, women, women. The boy thinks of nothing but women!'"

"What did your mother say to that?"

"Mother replied by denying that the figures I drew were those of women. 'They're angels,' she insisted. 'Anyone who has eyes and wants to see clearly can see that what the child is drawing are saints and angels.' My father was never won over by arguments, much less arguments so feeble."

"Just between you and me, what did you draw?"

He shrugged.

"The truth is, I can't really remember. But I wouldn't be surprised if my mother was right."

"Your mother was usually right?"

He flushed.

"Almost—almost always," he stammered.

"Can you remember a definite instance when she was wrong?"

He thought a while.

"Yes," he said. "It was on a Sunday afternoon. The priest had been to see us, and when he was gone my father reproved my mother for having failed to escort the holy man to the door. My mother insisted that she had done so, and stuck to her argument the rest of the day. But I had been there; I had seen. She had remained in her chair at the table until the priest was gone."

"The only time you remember your mother being in the wrong was when your father was right?"

He nodded.

"In a previous interview of ours you mentioned how relieved you were, when you grew older, to be able to foment quarrels between your parents which you could keep them from settling too quickly. Do you remember that?"

"I remember."

"And the disputes created were mostly over your choice of a career as an artist?"

He smiled ruefully.

"Yes, I'm afraid it was a much greater point of dispute between them than could be justified by my artistic talent. The less my father wanted me to draw, the more time I gave to it. But the more time I gave to drawing the less time I had for the rest of my studies, which began to deteriorate into a state of real neglect. When the school reports of my studies came in at the end of the month, they were pretty discouraging; my father would literally boil over, and he would demand in an outraged voice how with such marks I could ever hope to become a civil servant, a *beamter?*"

"What did you say to that?"

"Just that I didn't want to be a *beamter*, only an artist."

"And—"

"Father stormed, but made no impression."

"Not even on your backside?"

He grinned and shook his head.

"Your father never beat you?"

"I think he meant to. He never got around to it, however. My mother saw to that."

"But your mother did beat you?"

"Only because I wanted her to."

"How about your brothers and sisters?"

"I have only one brother, Robert, and two sisters, Angela and Paula. The rest are dead."

"How did you get along with them?"

He shook his head in a gesture of indifference.

"I did not mind them, and they paid very little attention to me. I may say that I have been fairly friendly with Angela, who is a little older than I. I am not sure at this moment that I know where any of them are."

"Have you tried to find them?"

"No, I'm not sure I even cared."

"They were not the cause of any differences between you and your parents?"

"I'm positive that they did not affect this relationship one way or another."

"You attended the same school?"

"Most of the time."

"Did they excel you in study?"

He smiled.

"No one could possibly achieve a lower level than me in any study."

"You say that as if it were a record to be proud of."

"I certainly don't intend that it should sound that way. I've had good reason to be very sorry for the neglect I lavished on my school books."

"We'll get to that later. In the meantime let us make sure of this: there was no jealousy whatever in the feeling you had about your brother and sisters in those days."

"Now that you mention feeling, I wonder if I had any feeling about them at all."

"Can you think of any condition that might have been responsible for this?"

He shook his head.

"It is possible, of course," I reasoned, "that you divided all the love and hatred in your nature between your parents. But how about your classmates?"

"They made no particular impression on me, either. I cannot remember one of them."

I saw a place for an important wedge.

"Not even the little girl with the golden hair and blue eyes?" I asked.

He flushed.

"My recollection of her is not a school one," he declared.

"I know. I just wanted to make sure. How about your teachers?"

"I don't remember them at all."

"Not even your drawing teacher?"

"Now that you mention him, his image comes back to me. My drawing teacher was a a particularly odious young man. It has been a conspicuous pleasure to forget him."

"I imagined you would have retained a happier memory of the young man who taught you in your cherished art."

"Well, I don't," he declared abruptly.

"Did any of the subjects you studied in elementary school have any particular fascination for you?"

He considered.

"I was quite fond of history. Then there was geography, with which I was really in love. I would have been a great scholar if all that our school taught had been history and geography. I think that what I hate most about the Treaty of Versailles is that it so completely muddled up history and geography, especially the history and geography of the Reich."

"I wouldn't be at all surprised," I laughed.

"Now, about music?"

"Oh, we had music in school, but what we had didn't interest me any more than arithmetic. I didn't actually know music till I was twelve years old. Then I heard Wagner for the first time. I have never heard any other music since."

"Ah, the perfect Wagnerite!" I jibed.

"What!" he exclaimed in utter amazement. "You do not like Wagner?"

"We're going too far afield," I dodged. "Let's get back to

your sisters and brother. Did you share with them the usual childhood games?"

He shook his head.

"No, I was not very friendly with them. But there was a host of town children with whom I did play now and then."

"What sort of games did you play with them?"

"I believe I was fondest of military games. But there were reasons why I was not too friendly with those children."

I waited. By this time I did not have to urge him to tell me things so essentially unpleasant that their revelation hurt his sense of dignity.

"I don't know how to say this without giving you the wrong impression," he resumed. "My mother and father were Germans of the oldest and best stock. I know it because I heard my father boast frequently of how deeply, anciently German we were. For some reason or other the people in our town did not get that impression. On the contrary, they apparently thought we had Jewish blood, and belabored us quite freely with this accusation. It was not unusual for the children I tried to play with to taunt me by calling me 'Jewboy.' I needn't tell you how humiliating this was. But I don't think I was as much humiliated when they threw the epithet at me as when they hurled it at my father. I remember once seeing my father running after some children for almost half a mile because they had taunted him with the cry Jew! Jew!' at a distance."

I began to understand the fierceness with which my patient hated the name of Jew.

"Did it ever occur to you that you might really have Jewish blood in your veins?" I ventured.

He grew livid.

"Whenever you can find anyone who can successfully prove to me that I have as much as a drop of Jewish blood in my veins," he replied with slow-burning ferocity, "I promise I will, without a quiver of hesitation, cut my throat."

But I had comfort for him at this point, and I could not withhold it.

"Did it ever occur to you," I asked him, "that you were never really accused of being a Jew?"

He looked surprised.

"How do you make that out?"

"As a good German you have thrown the word Jew at many people. Were those people *always* Jews?"

He thought a while, then shook his head.

"You're quite right, Doctor," he agreed.

"Then you realize that even now and then you use the word Jew as a reproach?"

"That's right. I'll call a perfectly good Christian a Jew if he displeases me. But what could the village people have had against my father?"

"The youth of your mother," I replied emphatically. "Subconsciously they knew that that was the real reason why they hurled 'Jew!' at your father. And so the accusation was never really sincerely made. And you, in your own heart, held that against your father, too; only, of course, you were not aware of it."

"I have a confession to make to you," he said at this point. "Once when I was particularly incensed against him, I, too, threw the epithet in his face."

"Thank you for telling me that," I said to him. "And now to get back. You didn't have a very happy time of it with the little boys of your town?"

"No, not too happy. There were five towns in this part of my life: Passau, in Bavaria; Linz, Upper Austria, Hatfeld an der Traum, also Upper Austria; Lambach, in the same neighborhood; and finally Leonding, near Linz. It was the same in all places. Wherever we came they all tagged my father with the Jew label, and the children did not let me join them in their games. It might have been due, at least in part, to our almost nomadic wandering from town to town and from village to village, all inside of one childhood. Gypsies who pitch their tents everywhere are everywhere under the same suspicion of working evil. To be respectable we must take root in the soil. A fixed milieu may also be important to the shaping and sharpening of our essential loyalties. However it may be, I'm certain that our moving from town to town, as though we were really wandering Jews, could not have done us any good."

I started on a new tack.

"How about domestic animals? Did you make friends with them?" I asked.

"Not that I can remember."

"Were there any domestic animals about your house?"

"Oh, I suppose there was the usual household quota of cats and dogs."

"How'd you get along with them?"

"I only remember a dog who did not stay very long with us."

"Did the dog die?"

"No. My father presented him to a neighbor and never brought another dog into the house."

This struck me as unusual.

"Have you any idea what happened there?" I asked.

It was obvious that my question had brought back to him some painful recollections.

"It was—it was a silly idea of my father's," he stammered, "that I didn't like the dog, that I tortured him."

"It wasn't true, you didn't really torture the dog?"

"Certainly not."

"Then how did he get such an idea?"

"In a funny way. He once found me in the garden caressing a field mouse. When my father came up, I had just given it a fond bite in the neck. It was from this that he got the idea that I was inclined to be cruel to animals."

"How did your father feel about dogs?"

"He himself was very fond of them."

"Then it was something of a sacrifice for him not to have a dog around the house?"

"I'm sure it was."

"Then he must have been convinced of the violence of your instincts toward domestic animals."

"His being convinced of it would not make it true," he growled.

"No, not necessarily," I agreed. "But let me have a better glimpse of what happened. You say you bit the field mouse in the neck?"

"Playfully."

"Out of a feeling of affection for it?"

"That's right."

"Did you make a practice of that sort of thing?"

"Not on field mice, if that's what you mean."

"How about human beings?"

"Maybe I never felt enough affection for one."

I paused. It was time to change my method of attack.

"At any rate, you did not miss your father too much after he died?"

He met my eyes with livid intensity.

"I missed him as much as I missed him even while he was alive," he said.

"After his death, your mother continued to send you through school?"

"Yes, I was allowed to go on with my studies. But both my mother and I placed most of the emphasis those days on my prospects as an artist."

"And, of course, your mother approved entirely of your choice of a means of making a livelihood?"

"To my mother, it was more than a means of making a livelihood. That her son was to be an artist meant more to my mother than that he might become a titled noble."

"What happened with your prospects as an artist?"

"Mother and I decided that since being an artist was the only thing that really mattered to me, it was not important how I did in my other studies, or whether I finished them or not. So I didn't as much as wait for my final *realschule* exams, but took my work down to the Academy School of Art in Vienna by way of applying for admittance. My mother and I were so pleased with what I had accomplished in water color that there was no doubt in our minds that I would pass the art test and be admitted."

He sighed audibly.

"But I was in for quite a disillusionment. The Academy was not at all impressed with my work, and not only refused me admission, but offered me very little encouragement. I returned home completely beaten. I never again drew a picture except as a means of raising money for food. My dream of becoming an artist was definitely ended. Nor did the decision of the Academy stop with killing my ambition to become an artist. My mother survived the shock only a few years. After that I never saw her smile again. It was the first definite triumph of the Jews over me."

"The Jews?"

"Who do you think runs the Academy and all such cultural institutions in Austria and Germany?"

"Austrians and Germans, I have always thought. But I've never looked into it. You know better, of course, if you've investigated."

His eyes lit up with a fierce malice.

"There's no need of investigating. Judah is what ails everything in Austria and Germany. But don't worry. We'll soon take care of that."

I had unwittingly struck at one of the main roots of Hitler's Judaeophobia. The Jews, who had pocketed the culture of Europe, had blasted his life's ambition of becoming a Goya or a Rembrandt. They had not only destroyed him as a creative human being but they had annihilated the womb where he lay psychically during all the years of his mother's life. They had exposed him to the slings and arrows of a hostile world controlled by the cunning Elders of Zion in Palestine. Having been robbed of the impulse to create, he would henceforth devote his life to destruction. The Jews would be the first to receive the full impact of his fury because they had blasted the womb of creation, and rendered him bitter and sterile, a psychic torso tossing in the terrible winds of frustration.

CHAPTER THIRTEEN

VIENNA DAYS AND NIGHTS

One Loveless Year—Poverty—Hitler Suffers Haman's Humiliation—His Jewish Benefactor—Lice and History—Hanisch—A Fruitful Partnership—Night Life —Hitler Discovers That People Will Listen to Him— Exit Hanisch.

AT THIS STAGE of my investigation into the development of his amative instincts, Hitler made an interesting revelation: during the whole of 1909, his first year in Vienna, he could not remember ever thinking of women, feeling the need of women, or even having remotely that sympathetic inclination toward the opposite sex for which every race has found some fine word of gallantry. After revealing his virginal, angelic psyche, he betrayed a curiosity that was even keener than mine.

"What does it mean, Doctor?" he asked. "Think the old loving instinct just took a vacation?"

I could not help smiling.

"No, none of our faculties ever takes a leave of absence from us," I assured him. "They are always in our natures, and when they are inactive, it is usually because they have been submerged. Things are always happening to us which obscure one faculty while they bring another into stronger relief; circumstances of that nature are capable of atrophying temporarily almost every instinct except that of hunger. If you will keep up the good work and tell me, honestly, everything concerning this part of your life, perhaps I'll be in a position to explain that mysterious apathy of yours toward the fair sex. Suppose you begin telling me, in the simplest possible words, what you remember most about that period of your life."

He looked at me quizzically.

"That's easy, Doctor. My poverty."

"That's a little too easy," I admonished him. "If I remember correctly, you had not been particularly rich before that."

"True, Doctor. But there is poverty and poverty. You simply cannot imagine the sort of poverty I lived in in Vienna during the five years following the death of my mother."

"I'm willing to learn," I said. "Why don't you tell me?"

"I am referring," he said, "to the poverty of hunger, of raggedness, and of downright beggary."

I was puzzled.

"You had some family in Vienna, didn't you?"

"Yes," he nodded, "but they were quite as desperately poor as I was. I have heard it repeated, misery loves company. Perhaps that's true of a certain kind of misery of the spirit. But there is a misery with which even the most miserable human being will not acknowledge kinship, the misery of aloneness and destitution. It is only too easy to underrate any of these dark attributes. Hunger, for instance. There are so many kinds and degrees of hunger. A man who is hungry—as hungry as I was in those days—can stand better the company of well-fed people than of those suffering as he does. Let me tell you something about that period of my life."

He arrived in Vienna one morning at the Miedling Station, hungry, penniless, and carrying under his arm a bundle of old shirts and stockings that even a beggar would have scorned to hold on to.

"But, underneath all that, I was quite determined to make something of myself," he reminded me at this point.

(I judge from various interviews with Hitler which I have read in Europe and in America that in telling people the story of this chapter in his life, he never fails to put in this remark. It is significant of many things, chiefly of his lack of self-assurance which he has always sought to overcome by his blitz-technique of sudden, irresistible action, deeds that could not be revoked by a foggy, vacillating will.)

Vienna, like every big city, has, in the heart of its poor section, its own peculiar flophouses for receiving this sort of human driftwood. Hitler sought out one of these shelters. But for one determined to succeed he was not in too great a hurry to get away from it. Except for a brief interval, after his ejection, he remained in this flophouse all of four years. Compare this with the endless repetition of his determination to make something of himself, and you have a psychological fact of some significance! Where is the mighty *Fuehrer* given to *blitzkriegs* and purges that descend upon his enemies with the speed of lightning? The only time he left this flophouse in four years was not due to his own volition. He was kicked out.

His ejection—which he told with some hesitation—came about quite simply. With no means of buying even soap, Hitler neglected his personal appearance; did not comb his hair, or bother to shake out his clothes. The manager of even that low establishment was horrified. There are limits to uncleanliness, even in a bug-ridden dive. One day as Hitler returned from one of his idle strolls, the outraged manager met him at the door and refused to let him in.

"Why, what's happened?" Hitler pleaded. "How can you do that when you know I've absolutely no place to turn to?"

"Why is he ordered out, he wants to know!" cried the lowly hotel keeper with a show of hysteria. "Take a look at yourself. Can't you see that you're lousy, that the vermin are crawling all over you! If I let you stay on, you'll belouse my whole establishment!"

There was nothing for Hitler to do but go. In his condition, there was no place that would take him in. Things looked pretty black. But at this point—when almost anything might have happened to turn his life into a different channel—one of the denizens of this flophouse befriended him and took him under his wing.

It is now pretty well known that this man, an etcher, Reinhold Hanisch by name, was Hitler's first companion in misery.

"I began to notice him because his bed was next to mine," said Hitler. "I suppose he recognized me the same way. We almost laughed at each other the first time our eyes met, and he asked whether I knew what time it was. I told him my watch was in pawn.

" 'Bet you never owned a watch,' he challenged me, and I admitted he was right. My mother sold my father's watch right after his death. Then he asked me what I did and I told him."

"What did you tell him?"

Hitler met my eyes reluctantly.

"What was there to tell him?" he asked.

"But you had to do something, even for a few pennies."

His eyes flared up.

"I did not steal. I borrowed," he declared.

"Do you perhaps mean that you begged?" I insisted.

My patient did not answer, but I knew that my conjecture was the truth.

During that first interview, at their bedsides, Hanisch made the discovery that the young, thinly dressed man who, among other defects, was suffering from a lung ailment, could draw. Then and there he made a partnership with him, and thereafter Hitler drew picture postcards and Hanisch went about from shop to shop and from door to door selling them. In that way the future ruler of Germany was converted from a shuffling street-corner beggar into a laborer who on certain days even made more than he needed for his room and board.

For a while it was a running business. What was left after all expenses had been paid they divided equally between them. Each took and placed in his shabby, patched-up pockets, a little hoard of pfennigs, and felt rich. The sense of having this metal blood to draw upon had a marvelous effect on both of them. Hitler began to supplement the painting of postcards with more "serious" creations. Hanisch encouraged him and offered to sell, however ignominiously, anything his art-partner produced.

"It was then that you began to notice women again, wasn't it?" I interrupted.

He nodded enthusiastically.

"You think my repression was really due to my poverty, Doctor?" he inquired.

"Entirely. Man has three fundamental wants: society, occupation, love. The most important of all is society. Without that there is no motive on which to hang a steady, fruitful occupation. But he must have some remunerative occupation to balance his place in society before he can branch out into the great extravagance of love—for love brings a man outside of himself into the province of creation."

The possibilities of the idea absorbed him.

"Then it is possible for a man to miss out in love altogether just because he is poor and too busy earning a livelihood?"

I nodded.

"I would like to know some more about your poverty," I said (by way of resuming the body of our inquiry). "You apparently were very badly dressed. Where did you get your clothes?"

He made an impatient gesture.

"They were cast-offs."

This did not satisfy me as a full answer.

"But people don't drop their cast-off clothes out of windows for wandering homeless men to pick up," I pointed out to him. "They are given to those who need them, either personally or through some institution. Which was it in your case?"

My pressure obviously embarrassed him, but I was relentless.

"It was not an institution," he mumbled.

"Then it was a man?"

He nodded.

"Who was he?"

My patient looked wearily at me, too proud to beg off but obviously wanting to.

After a pause I asked:

"A merchant in the neighborhood?"

He nodded without enthusiasm.

"An Austrian?"

"You might call him that."

I remembered that he held Austrians, when they were not outright Germans, in deep contempt.

"He was not a Jew?"

My patient made no reply.

"Then he *was* a Jew," I insisted.

Still no reply.

I began to understand better the foundation of his Jew-hatred.

"Can you remember any particular article of clothing he gave you?" I asked.

He looked up.

"A winter coat."

"Why do you remember it?"

He smiled sourly.

"Because I wore it all summer."

"How did that happen?"

"He gave it to me at the beginning of the summer. It had served him two winters, he told me, and he felt he had had as much use of it as he could expect, considering that he had bought it at a bargain. It was on my lips to refuse it, but I noticed how long it was and that if I wore it, it would cover all my shabbiness."

"Then it was a Jew's cloak that covered all the shabbiness of your youth," I said to him suggestively.

He was silent.

A weariness had come over him as a result of such wearisome recollections, and it boded ill for whatever else might come along if I continued.

"Suppose we go on from here the next time," I suggested, rising.

He agreed wordlessly.

Before I continue, in the next chapter, my findings on the nature of Hitler's personal love life, I would like to simplify, first of all, the intricate ramifications of his relationship with the etcher Reinhold Hanisch.

As must be obvious by this time, Hanisch was drawn to Hitler by a feeling of pity for a sick man with no money, no family and no ambition. It was only an accident that the care of this poor fellow made it possible for him to make money for himself, too. In my opinion, it would not have lowered Hanisch in the scale of friendship if, in these transactions he conducted for Hitler, he had even taken the lion's cut of the purse. The man who labors and the man who creates must, in our society, take second place in comparative social importance. Perhaps the salesman's greater reward is for playing such a comparatively contemptible role.

With a little money in his pockets, Hitler began to find ways of counteracting in his life the dismal effects of the flophouse.

Vienna provided a poor man with one great inexpensive release, her coffee houses.

"It is simply wonderful," he reported to Hanisch, late one morning, after the night he accidentally stumbled into one of these cafes. "For a couple of pfennigs you can occupy a chair at a table, with the best of people, sip away at your coffee and tell the whole world what's on your mind."

Hanisch closed his eyes in that queer way he had.

"Did you do all the talking, Adolf?"

"Only because they let me," Hitler assured him. "Believe me, from the moment I opened my mouth they just sat and gaped at me. You should have seen it. It was magnificent."

"I can imagine," murmured Hanisch dryly.

But the next night he accompanied Hitler to this fabulous coffee house. To his astonishment, he found that his shabby friend had not overstated matters. The fellow could really talk. And people found fascination in listening to him.

"Funny how you never as much as opened your mouth at the hotel," Hanisch remarked as they returned to the flophouse.

"I guess I didn't know I could do it," Hitler acknowledged.

"You mean you had never before argued political matters with people?" I interrupted.

"I used to try to harangue the boys at school and on the way home from school," he confessed, leaning forward eagerly. "But they did not listen to me. We used to play military games, and I tried to make speeches to them a la Frederick the Great. After the first sentence I would usually find myself alone. Subsequently, I got into the habit of declaiming to back fences, trees and garden vegetables. Those experiences were not particularly conducive toward a career in oratory. But that night in Vienna in the coffee house I discovered for the first time that I could get people to listen to me."

"What did you talk about?" I asked.

"I read the newspapers," he reminded me with a flash of anger. "A man who reads newspapers learns a great deal, especially if his mind has not been spoiled by books."

I could not help smiling.

"Don't you like books?" I asked.

"I have no patience with them," he confessed. "A newspaper

tells you what is going on in the world. A book tells you what someone thinks is going on. There's a difference."

"Quite so," I admitted, "but we will come back to it some other time. What were your cafe discussions about chiefly?"

"Oh, economics, politics, the Jews—we had a good time."

I grinned. My patient was wise in giving verbal expression to his frustrated life. His mind was like a boiler that must let off steam or burst.

"Tell me more about you and Hanisch," I suggested.

He continued. And it came to this:

They both began to take their cafe careers very seriously, and as the demand for money for more coffee grew, Hitler's canvases grew. I have seen a few of these oils, and speaking as one who enjoys pictures, I did not like them. They seemed to have no color, no sense of movement, and only the faintest resemblance to the outlines of living things. I know that enthusiastic Nazis have paid as high as five hundred gold marks for some of these horrors. But Hanisch had to sell them on their merits, and it is my solemn opinion that he must have been a high-powered salesman. Any merit the pictures took on in the eyes of the purchaser, Hanisch must have supplied.

Hitler knew nothing about painting in general, and much less about his own work, as is illustrated by the incident which separated him from Hanisch. He somewhere got the outlandish idea that a picture of the town hall of Vienna, or some other public building, would sell as easily and at a good price. Hanisch did not encourage this idea. Nevertheless, Hitler went on with it, and when it was finally offered for sale, it was difficult to get anyone to look at the monstrosity, let alone buy it. Hanisch finally disposed of it for a small sum, and when he brought the money, all of it, to his "artist," Hitler hit the ceiling, called him a cheat and a Jew bastard, as he did anyone who displeased him, and so concluded his first *fertile* relationship with a human being.

Hitler certainly fitted into Schopenhauer's porcupine description of that strange animal called man. Trapped in his neurosis, he huddled in a corner and shot his quills into the flesh of humanity. Later these quills were to become bayonets dug into the body of life. Germany and the world were being gradually prepared for *The Night of the Long Knives.*

CHAPTER FOURTEEN

THE ULTIMATE IN CONFESSION

Spiritual Mining—Love Affairs in Vienna—Irate Father — Street-Walkers — Jewesses — His Relations with Captain Roehm—Consolation.

THE BUSINESS of the psychoanalyst is to dig into the lower layers of his patient's subconsciousness for the solid rock on which to rebuild his character. He works with a broad shovel, and, as in all excavational work, the shovel throws up many an interesting and precious curio of other times and other passions.

About some of these things I feel that they are safely left to the imagination of the reader. Others, however, point so severely to the heart of my inquiry it would be negligence of duty to leave them undisclosed. How, for instance, with his libido fixed on his mother, did Adolf start out to have normal relations with women? Where, when and how had this normality of his been defeated and compelled to take a back seat in the directive imagination of his life?

Both of these questions had to be answered before I could begin to have any real understanding of the man's psyche as it presented itself in the course of my investigation. All of the questions I asked him during these sessions were, therefore, directed with these solutions uppermost in my mind.

"During the first years of your stay in Vienna you had, as I understand, very little to do with women?" I began our next interview.

"Nothing at all," he assured me.

"The desire for women was, of course, already known to you?"

"Yes."

"Especially in the image of the little girl with blue eyes and golden hair?"

He nodded.

"And your psychological withdrawal from women was really due to your poverty?"

"I'm now convinced of that, Doctor."

"Then the fascination had never left you, but was sleeping all the time on the floor-bed of your blood and your brain?"

"That's right."

"About when would you say that you resumed noticing women—as females, of course?"

He searched himself.

"I think it was about the time when they began to notice me, when they began to listen to me in the cafes."

"Did any of them invite you to their homes?"

"One of them."

"And how did you make out with her?"

He made a sour grimace.

"I would have done better with her if I had not done so badly with her father."

"No mother?"

"I thank God for that. Fathers only throw me out. Mothers usually call the police."

"What was wrong with that particular father?"

"Everything. He was a Jew."

"We don't seem to be able to make much progress without running into the Jew business," I complained. "But didn't the father's being a Jew make his daughter a Jewess?"

"I suppose so."

"Well, how did you even get as far as her front door?"

"I had not noticed her Jewishness. Once I realized where I was, of course, I abstained from going there again."

"But that was after the unpleasantness created by her father?"

"I'm afraid so."

"Would you say that the father's objection to you had something to do with your resolution to keep away from that particular girl and all other Jewish girls?"

"I suppose something of it did get into my attitude. But the real objection to my association with Jews came out of my own inner nature."

And I could get no more out of him about this unfortunate phase of his Jewish adventure. Whatever I learned later came from other sources, and I go into it in one of the later chapters of this book. I look upon this as another one of the several instances in which my failure to break through my patient's obstinate refusal to get on his hands and knees before his past, contributed to the failure of the whole analysis.

The next question I levelled at Hitler was calculated to dig deep into his life without his knowing it.

"What was the nature of your relationship with women those days?" I asked him, and he replied:

"Oh, quite normal."

I almost gasped at this, for it gave him away completely, and supplied me with the deep insight into his life that eventually made necessary my fleeing from the Reich. If the man before me had never been abnormal, I realized instantly that his answer would have been, "As usual." But his mind was aware of a difference between two distinct divisions of his love life, and, because a man cannot calculate such matters every minute, he, without meaning to, revealed his division to me. To make the best of my triumph I decided not to take advantage of it immediately.

"They were mostly women of the cafes, the women you carried on with in these days?"

He shook his head mournfully.

"No, none of them were women of the cafes."

I pretended to be disappointed.

"Really?"

He smiled a smile of profound weariness and disillusion.

"No, nothing ever came of these flirtations," he told me.

Instinctively I knew the reason, but it was important to get him to utter it.

"Why not?"

He shrugged.

"You know women, Doctor. I was a poor man, just barely

able to pay for my own coffee. Those female leeches rarely could pay for their own, or wanted to. The man who paid for their bills at the end of an evening, not the most interesting or the most eloquent man, was the man they granted the pleasure of taking them back to their lodgings."

I was tempted to laugh, but resisted.

"That must have been quite a disappointment to you," I mused. "What did you do?"

He smiled grimly.

"The next best thing, Doctor. I picked women off the streets."

"You had to pay them, of course?"

"Yes, but in the long run it was cheaper than trying to pick up the checks of the girls in the cafes, where it would take at least three checks in succession to earn the right to kiss a girl's hand. Then there was something else. If you contracted a clandestine relationship with a Jewish girl from a cafe you never knew what you might expect from her friends or her family. A Jewish streetwalker was a pearl you could afford to forget the next morning."

"Then you preferred Jewish street-walkers?"

He nodded.

I leaned forward and looked at him intently.

"How could you tell a Jewish street-walker from one who was not Jewish?"

He made a grimace which engaged only the upper part of his face and his eyes.

"I could tell, Doctor, never fear."

I would not let him off so easily.

"But how?"

"By the eyes, Doctor," he said thoughtfully, "but mostly, I think, by the smell."

"Come, come," I objected. "That sounds a little like horse-play."

"I am very much in earnest, I assure you," he declared.

"Were many of the Vienna street-walkers Jewesses?"

"Quite a few."

"You noticed them particularly, didn't you?"

He nodded.

"One might say you were actually on the look-out for them?"

"That's right."

I leaned over toward him.

"Why, in your searches along the sidewalks of Vienna, were you so careful to pick up Jewesses?"

He grimaced.

"In those days I felt that the whole sex business was an unclean act, best consummated with a member of an unclean race."

"You thought of them in those days as an unclean race?"

"Yes, Doctor."

"And today?"

"I have not changed my mind. I never will—about them."

"You do not care any more about Jewesses?"

"I have no more traffic with them," he said stubbornly.

"You have decided on that as a measure to keep yourself morally clean?"

"And spiritually."

"Worthy resolution!" I murmured. "But suppose you came upon that decision a little late?"

"I don't understand."

"Suppose—as is possible—that your years in Vienna have tainted you forever?"

He shook his head with fortified certainty.

"Whatever taints I may have acquired in Jewish Vienna I have managed to purge from my body completely in the fires of the World War."

"That's a comforting thought," I mused. "A little too neat, don't you think?"

"I believe it, Doctor," he declared. "It's enough for me."

"Then you have not had relations with a Jewess since your return from the wars?"

"No, Doctor."

"Nor with *any woman?*"

"You know that, Doctor," he said resentfully.

I looked steadily at him and held his eyes.

"I don't know anything of the sort," I told him.

His face became deadly white.

"Are you insinuating," he asked, "that I am faking my impotence?"

"Certainly not. I am suggesting that whereas you cannot have a normal relationship with any woman, you might find no difficulty whatever if you knew that the object of your passion was a Jewess."

"Preposterous!" he cried. But he was interested, fascinated.

"How do you make that out?" he asked breathlessly.

"You know," I said to him, "that our bodies are the tools of our minds. We walk not with our legs but with our minds. The same with eating, sleeping, digesting and rutting. If you will only listen to me very carefully, you will understand, for there is much for you to learn about your psyche. Suppose your preference for Jewish women in your Vienna days was something deeper than your feeling of a fellowship of uncleanness with them? Suppose your deeper nature really preferred Jewesses, as seems possible from your confession that you could practically tell a Jewess by sight and smell? Would not your decision never to have further intercourse with one of them have at least helped to thwart your sex vitality? And, conversely, might not your reversal of this unnatural order release your vitality again?"

He squirmed visibly.

"If I granted your premise, yes. But I don't."

"My premise is the premise of your doctor," I reminded him sternly. "And while I do not at this moment insist that it is the very premise from which we may effect your cure, I suggest to you that some day, in the near future, perhaps, when I do recognize it as such, I will expect you, my patient, to follow me step by step like a little child."

He shook his head.

"I would not touch another Jewess if it were my remaining hope of happiness on earth," he declared.

I was stunned.

"You know that you are unnecessarily obdurate in this matter."

He met my eyes firmly.

"I must be."

"In all important matters, one has to learn to make a gracious compromise."

"Not in such a matter."

"Why not?"

"Because," he declared, "in such a matter Germany's interests are above my own."

"What have your country's interests got to do with this?" I demanded.

"Plenty," he replied. "I am teaching racial purity to my people and by God, I intend to practice it!"

"You would prefer to remain a eunuch in order to give Germany a consistent Fuehrer?"

"Whether or not I remain a eunuch is not of the faintest importance to my country. I am submitting to the humiliation of these conversations of ours for my own good entirely. I limit their scope to the confines of my private life, but where the interests of my country are involved, my private life doesn't even exist."

"We will return to this later," I said to him, making still another fatal compromise with my patient. But I made him pay heavily for it, for then and there I decided to open up the pathway indicated by the indirect confession that he had been guilty of homosexuality.

"Suppose you tell me how you have fared with your own sex?"

This was a direct blow, aimed clean between the eyes, and he staggered under it.

"My own sex?" he repeated.

His face flamed and paled in turn.

"I don't know what you mean, Doctor," he stammered.

"You know exactly what I mean, Adolf, or you would not be coloring so desperately. But perhaps I should point my question a little more sharply. How do you get on with your friend, Captain Roehm, nowadays?"

He was flabbergasted. It was a whole minute before he would open his mouth. When he did, it looked to me as if he were foaming.

"It is a most outrageous question!" he cried out hotly, rose from where he was sitting, strode up to the window and remained there for a while with his back to me.

I let a long pause mollify him, then said to him gently:

"You have allowed yourself to become inordinately excited by just an ordinary routine question."

He turned to me, glared, and spluttered:

"Routine!"

"That's the only word to cover the situation," I replied. "A doctor who analyzed a man living in an army barracks and did not ask him such a question would not be even a good fool of a doctor."

I could see him quiet down gradually.

"If you will be good enough to sit down," I pursued, "I will tell you one or two things which should interest you, and convince you that there was nothing unusual in my question; that it was just ordinary psychic medicine."

He sat down without a word.

"A man," I said to him, "is born with only a little more of masculinity than a woman. Some with more, some with less, but the whole difference is so small it may be said to be almost entirely social. The real areas of sex in us, the big ones, are neither male nor female, but what an Englishman of wit has named intermediary, and there is actually more differentiation of sex in our clothes than in our bodies. I could not tell you right now where the boundaries between our true sex zones are violated. But in the regions of femininity or masculinity in us, we cannot, really, ever be violated. And so, how much offense could there have been in my question?"

He still looked cold and hostile.

"If it was of no importance, why did you ask it?" he demanded.

"I wanted to measure its full effect on you, that's all. Whatever good there is in that question has already been accomplished, and if you prefer to do so, you may forget all about it."

He looked at me shrewdly, calculatingly.

"It was not because of any little bits of gossip of the barracks you picked up that you asked that question?"

I shook my head solemnly.

"You did not know as a matter of fact that anything had transpired between me and Captain Roehm?"

"I knew that he had singled you out for his favors," I reminded him. "Everybody knows just what kind of a man he is, and under no circumstances would anyone think of attributing to him a simple kindness without a selfish motive behind it."

He nodded somberly. I could see that he was steeling himself mightily against any further inroads into this department of his privacy. But I already knew all that I needed to know, and there was no reason for needlessly distressing him further.

"I think we've done very nicely tonight," I said, getting up as a signal that our work for the time being was over.

"Thank you, Doctor," he muttered, rising, also, and nothing was so apparent as the depth of his relief.

CHAPTER FIFTEEN

THE FIRST DARKNESS

*Hitler's Youngest Sister—Goebbels' Wife—A New
Putsch Is Planned—Hitler's Impatience—The Fearful
Young Volunteer—The March Itself—Debacle—Hit-
ler's "Heroism"—I Lose Faith.*

I WAS SITTING by myself one evening in a cool corner of the
Burgerbraukeller, smoking and drinking leisurely, when a middle-aged man swaggered up to my table, looked at me good-
humoredly for a while and, without a word, sat down at my
table, pulled out a tobacco pouch, and smoked.

"I suppose you're wondering at my audacity, Doctor," he
murmured, puffing his pipe into a blaze.

In reality this sort of intrusion had never been practiced on
me before. But as this man did it, it was difficult to find any
offense in the gesture.

"If you promise not to think of it as an audacity," I said,
yielding to him, "you have my pledge not to think of it at all.
But how did you know I was a doctor?"

"Only because you're more than a mere doctor," he grinned.
"Because you're our Fuehrer's doctor. Or is that supposed to be
a secret? Knowing that he's having his troubles right now in
Vienna, I thought you might like the temporary society of an
old man."

So that was where Hitler disappeared to on those occasions of
mystery. It occurred to me that there might be something for
me to gain in things my patient would not tell me if I pretended
I knew about these visits. My man looked as if he needed very
little encouragement to talk.

"With the Vienna police feeling about him as they do," I

commented, showing the proper anxiety about the Fuehrer's safety, "it seems to me a little foolhardy for him to risk so much for so little."

"Exactly what I tell him!" enthusiastically agreed my companion, giving the table before him a faint slap. "Especially that younger one—whom he'll never win over, I can assure you. If you listened to her you would imagine street-walking was a profession—and a cherished one."

I guessed that he was talking of Hitler's sisters, but I had to make sure.

"I like the older sister better myself," I murmured.

"Of course, of course," he agreed. "And as soon as he can afford it, he's bringing Angela over to keep house for him here in Munich."

So at least one of Hitler's sisters had been a street-walker in the Vienna of his poverty. No wonder he hated this poverty. No wonder he called all street-walkers Jewesses! It was part and parcel of the regular Nazi practice of dragging the world down beneath its own shabby level. When Goebbels' wife for instance handed on to her husband a venereal disease contracted in a passing affair with a Nazi comrade of theirs, Clubfoot took the rostrum and cried out to the world that any German prostitute was better than the most respectable Jewish mother. How else could he continue to live in peace in his own house?

I planned to introduce this vital information into my next interview with Hitler. But when my patient returned from his secret trip to Vienna he announced to me peremptorily that all other business between us would have to be suspended for a while during the operation of an important development in the Party.

"Believe it or not," he said to me breathlessly, "we are about to take over."

These were not idle words, I knew. Hitler was no longer a potential *Fuehrer*, but a leader *de facto*. The Party itself had grown beyond bounds and limits. No longer confined to Munich or even Bavaria, it had made some additional stalwart converts in men as nationally famous as General Erich Ludendorff and Captain Heinrich Goering. As his party grew, so did my patient's soaring ambitions. And the greater his ambitions, the less his

fund of patience with the *status quo*. With all Munich hailing
him as a conquering hero, the seizure of the local government
never looked to him more dangerous than a swift, sudden for-
mality, and once he was in possession of Munich, the march to
Berlin would be easier than Mussolini had found the march to
Rome. Hitler's heart was full of the lust of possession in those
days, and because greed warped his judgment of time and place,
his ultimate triumph was postponed by a whole decade.

Our assets were, as I have already indicated, valuable, but
by no means limitless. Besides the easy friendships of Herr
President von Kaahr (imposed on Bavaria by the Kapp Putsch),
we had, what was even more important, the active sympathy and
cooperation of Lossow and Seisser, the heads of the Bavarian
police. Officially, however, the government of Bavaria was still
loyal to the Republic. The existing tie between Munich and
Berlin was not a strong one, but it existed. Hitler scoffed, railed
and fumed at it. But he could not laugh it out of existence. Irony
is a heat that dries its object without breaking it.

Day by day the opportunity appeared to ripen in Hitler's
eyes. As he saw it, it needed only the daring of three men, Kaahr,
Lossow and Seisser—and the Revolution would be on.

Lossow apparently was not so sure about it.

"Have you forgotten our friends, the Prussian generals?"
he asked Hitler once, when the Fuehrer had got through raving
about lost opportunities. "How do you think we will get on with
them?"

Hitler was a man with a mania for cure-alls, and at the time
his favorite cure-all for anything under the sun was General
Ludendorff. Ever since Ludendorff had joined our ranks there
was nothing too big for him to plan. Didn't he have the hero
of Tannenberg to back him up?

"Perhaps we can't count on the old fogies," he replied. "But
the young officers, the live ones, can be counted on to join us, and
more than that we do not need. Besides Ludendorff is with us,
and with him on our side, where are the lions who will dare to
oppose us?"

Everybody thought Hitler's conception of Ludendorff as a
sort of "heroic monument on wheels" which he could direct in

whatever way he wished, was ridiculous, and yet it was not long before it began to appear as if he had really managed to reconceive the old gentleman in his own image.

As I got the story from my patient, upon his return from Austria, Hitler, Goering and Ludendorff, all three, agreed on the organization of a putsch that would oust the subservient Bavarian government and make possible the setting up of a purely National Socialist government in its place. They hoped to be able to achieve this with a minimum of opposition. But if opposition would come, Hitler was confident of the power of his followers to subdue it.

All orthodox conceptions of him to the contrary notwithstanding, Hitler was never a gambler. Certain of his ability to overpower any force brought against him by the local government, he preferred to play for a guarantee of personal victory. Between himself, Goering and Ludendorff, the date for the putsch had been set for November 12th. But when he learned in Vienna, strangely enough, that, at the request of several business organization, Herr von Kaahr was to deliver a programme speech on the evening of November eighth at the Burgerbraukeller, the closeness of these dates made a profound impression on Hitler. It gave the event a new meaning in his eyes, and without as much as consulting his colleagues, he decided to take time by the forelock, and advance the date four days.

Von Kaahr kept his date. He was only about halfway through his speech, when he was surprised by the sudden appearance of Hitler in front of him with the Fuehrer motioning him frantically to stop. Von Kaahr looked about him. There was no one anywhere. What did that idiot in the trench-coat mean by trying to interrupt him? Von Kaahr spoke on. The Fuehrer stopped gesticulating, leaped to the platform. He held out his arm in the familiar salute, and in a thunderous voice cried out: "Fellow Germans, the Revolution is on! Don't think of resistance. The house is surrounded!"

He had six hundred of his men, all armed, on guard at all entrances, he proceeded to explain, that no violence was intended. He only wanted their excellencies Von Kaahr, Lossow and Seisser to confer with him in an adjoining chamber. If he did not get perfect cooperation he would have a machine-gun posted in the gallery. The rest they could imagine for themselves.

The next crucial hour Hitler divided between wheedling the Bavarian triumvirate and fooling the waiting audience into believing that the government had been won over. When he brought back to the three sweating officials in the adjoining chamber the news that the crowd was with them and ready to lift them bodily on their shoulders, Von Kaahr, Lossow and Seisser pretended that they were giving tacit consent to the putsch.

Instantly, and again without consulting his colleagues, Hitler began to form the new government. In the midst of designating names and offices he was interrupted by word that in a certain barracks of the Reichswehr there was rioting. "Rioting indeed," cried Hitler, and he promptly drove out to the luckless garrison to re-establish order. He expected, on his return, to find his generals and civil appointees planning the march on Berlin, but found instead that they had all left without such a march being mentioned. At the garrison he found no revolt; back in the hall, no generals.

On the morning of the crucial day that followed, a party messenger brought me an urgent note from the Fuehrer. I must present myself, without fail, as quickly as possible at the Burgerbraukeller. Like most party members I knew what had happened the night before, and like them I was all perplexity. It was common talk among several of the party members I met on the way, that the three chiefs of state who agreed to support the putsch had recanted and might, after all, be considered as possible opponents. Especially since that favorite of cartoonists, Ebert, had endowed one of the government's faithful generals with full executive powers, and had sent word to Munich that the rebels were to be met with full force. On the other hand, it was not to be taken for granted that Hitler had been pushed aside. He was probably that very moment preparing the way for the putsch, in spite of the obvious risks. The best proof of this was that we had been summoned to appear.

There were only a few hundred people at the Burgerbraukeller when I got there. But I decided on a strange move. Instead of joining the rest of the party members along the lines where they could be seen waiting for instructions, I chose to sit down among the ordinary habitues, drink beer and talk. If anything happened that morning there would be plenty of people to report the proceedings from the inside of the party. I would be one of those who had watched from the sidelines.

To the tune of excited voices and the click of emptied beer mugs I strode down the central aisle and took my place at a small table at the far end of the hall.

I looked around and studied the situation. A hundred people or so were seated at beer tables drinking. One could judge from the nervousness of the conversation and the swiftness of their side glances that they were expecting something—though something as yet indefinite. The brown-shirted men were in lesser force, but they had taken their places strategically along walls, near doors, so that, in the event of trouble, they would enjoy complete command. Not a single higher-up of our Nazis was as yet visible.

When I fully took in the situation, I found a very young man seated at my table. He was dressed as those dress who wear their clothes threadbare; his brow was drawn, and he appeared to be in a sweat. I thought I would talk to him and, if possible, ease him.

"I see you are all ready," I said to him by way of a beginning, because he was obviously one of the younger Nazis one saw at meetings. My words afforded him great relief.

"I am," he replied quickly. "But I wish something would happen quickly."

I smiled.

"At your age," I said to him, "you need not be in a hurry for things to happen."

He gave me a quick look.

"At my age, I am told, people die almost without provocation," he replied swiftly.

I was taken aback.

"Nervous?" I asked.

He nodded, and looked about him apprehensively as he did so.

"Then you must know more than I do," I said, laughing. "Are you perhaps one of the inner circle?"

He flushed.

"I didn't mean to imply anything of the sort," he said hastily. "I probably know less than anyone here. Only—I'm not used to this sort of thing. I was not even a soldier in the last war. And if it's really dangerous perhaps I should have warned my mother."

I saw that he needed pacifying.

"It may not be dangerous at all," I suggested.

Apprehension grew large and gaunt in his eyes.

"Still I feel I should not have gone away without telling my mother," he insisted firmly. "She's quite alone in the world except for me. You see, my father was in the big war. I don't know what my mother would do if anything happened to me."

"In that case, why did you enlist in a cause about which you were warned in advance and which might require you to place your life in jeopardy?"

"I had to. I've been listening to the Fuehrer whenever I could. I know in what a terrible plight our country is. My father, who gave his life, would be pleased if he knew that I have pledged myself to redeeming the international status of my country."

"Perhaps he would," I murmured. "But it is possible," I could not help adding, "that he would have required better guarantees on fundamental issues."

The young man stared at me strangely.

"You sound like a spy!" he said with a naivete credible only in the young.

"You will find this spy fighting side by side with you—if they are considerate enough to give me something to fight with," I reassured him.

At this moment an upheaval broke out in the far corner of the beer hall opposite where we were sitting. In its wake followed swiftly a great swell of excited voices as of people suddenly risen to a violent decision. The number of brown shirts present had suddenly, mysteriously been greatly increased and from where I sat I could see that a large majority of them had gathered about one person, as smoke gathers closely about a flame. The flame was, of course, Adolf Hitler himself.

"There's your action," I whispered to my young neighbor.

Hitler leaped on top of a table adjoining the excitement, raised his arms in the air and clamored to be heard. In a moment the whole attention of those present was riveted upon him with nervous expectancy.

"If anything happens," I whispered to the young man next to me, "just stick at my side."

He nodded, still staring at me in that strange way of his. A fearful silence had grown about us.

Hitler broke the silence abruptly.

"Comrades," he cried, "the National Socialist Revolution of which we have dreamed is now at last under way."

He paused as if to get his bearings in the crowd. A wave of uneasiness broke out and ran through the assembled people, followed by some sporadic shouts of excited laughter. Obviously not all those present were National Socialists.

Unworried by the reception accorded his announcement, Hitler resumed.

"This is not a speech. The hall is filled with hundreds of our men. No one will be allowed to leave."

A few of the people who had begun to edge toward the doors stopped short, and waited as if they had suddenly become petrified.

"The Bavarian government and the government at Berlin have been declared overthrown by our National Socialist Party," the Fuehrer continued, his voice rising to a scream. "The police have rallied to our banner, and we're about to march out in a body to take possession of the town hall." He paused and added significantly, "Make no mistake, any of you. There is going to be no running out of this for anyone. You are all going with us, whether you like it or not."

I saw one man duck unseen behind the bar, where he crept about stealthily as if searching for an exit not covered by Hitler's men. There was a certain cool method in his movements, and I was just beginning to wonder whether I ought not to step forward to stop him, when he appeared to reach an exit and disappeared entirely from my view.

He it was, I learned later, who had found the telephone booth from which he informed the police of the imminence of the descent of the storm troopers.

In the meantime, unaware of what had just happened, Hitler

gave the order to march and we followed him out of the beer hall in the direction of the town hall.

At the head of the procession, as I remember it, marched Hitler, Ludendorff and Goering, Ludendorff being in the center and moving forward like a statue on wheels.

Behind them I saw Roehm, Hess and Streicher. But it is my impression that Streicher dropped into the ranks some time after we had gotten started. However, I'm not sure of this.

That the Satyr of Nuremburg was not with us at the Burgerbraukeller, I felt certain. In the colorful language of my celebrated patient, I would have smelled him if he had been present.

There was a heavy formation of uniformed storm troopers behind the leaders, a shabby formation of the innocent drinkers coerced into the march, sandwiched in between the storm troopers in front and the equally formidable section which marched behind. Among the latter I marched with the nervous young man at my side. We looked a little clumsy with our allotted muskets.

The park through which we marched was already deserted. Here and there we could catch the occasional glimpse of a man or woman hurrying by on some petty personal errand. Otherwise the whole area seemed empty and deserted. We were cautioned to march silently, which we did. But within twenty feet of the town hall, we were halted by the sudden appearance of a company of police who stood with drawn bayonets, as if they had been waiting for us. I remembered suddenly the man I had seen sneak out through the unguarded doorway.

Hitler's face turned into a scowl, as if he were prepared to attack. But the hand of Goering shot from behind and held him. A whispered conference ensued between them, at the end of which Goering stepped forward. He said to the commander of the troops:

"The first man dead or wounded on our side will result in the shooting of all our hostages."

The police did not shoot. We marched on.

Goering shot Hitler a look of triumph, as if to say:

"You see, it's that easy when you know how."

Our next run-in with the police was the final decisive encounter. It was destiny—for to the amazement of those who expected not to be opposed too strongly, we saw the whole road was covered by police all waiting with rifles and cocked guns.

Undismayed, and encouraged by the easy capitulation of the previous array, Hitler stepped forward and in a voice heavy with insolence shouted:

"The government is ours, you fools. We've taken it. Out of the way!"

The words made a weird impression on the slowly enveloping ranks of the police. Instead of moving aside to let us pass, they broke into an outburst of laughter.

Enraged, Hitler gave his men an order to fire, and faithfully the young storm troopers raised their rifles to obey. Before a trigger could be pulled in behalf of the Fuehrer, however, the trained militia opened on us with a storm of bullets.

In the first barrage of flying lead about a score of the Nazis fell, among them the young man who stood right at my side. I saw Ludendorff, Streicher and Hess move forward into the ranks of the police, who made them prisoners, but when I looked for Hitler, he was down on the ground swiftly crawling away from the carnage!

Those of Hitler's followers who were not killed or wounded had thrown themselves on their faces to escape possible repetition of the fire. There was no need to ask for their surrender. They had done so without firing a shot.

I took another look at the disappearing form of my Fuehrer, then got down on my hands and knees and felt for the pulse of the young Nazi who had been so anxious about his mother. There was no pulse. He was dead.

But something had died in me, too. The voice which had demanded of me a slavish obedience to the Fuehrer. It had been silenced by the hail of bullets. I was no longer a Nazi.

CHAPTER SIXTEEN

PRISON TENSION

*Justice Blackmailed—I Get a Letter from Landsberg—
The Interview—Roehm and Heines—First Word
About Mein Kampf—His Message to the Outside
World—My Miscalculation.*

HITLER's arrest and trial follow each other dismally in my recollections. His capture—behind some dresses in Eva Hanfstaengl's clothes closet—came only two days after his spectacular escape. The trial itself was postponed till the March of the following year. Once they had bagged Hitler the difficulties of the authorities only began, as I learned from exultant party members who had escaped arrest. The accusations brought against him, it turned out, were applicable not only to his part in the unsuccessful rebellion but against some of the most formidable members of the prosecution too. Had not von Kaahr, among other little matters, actually negotiated the putsch with him? For a while it seemed as if the Fuehrer might manage to escape the penalty for his resistance to the state by the simple threat of involving his judges in the very same charge.

The machinery of justice, too heavy to be entirely stopped, was stalled. I watched the amazing spectacle of a poor, penniless man against whom were proven some of the gravest charges the state can possibly bring against a citizen, stand calmly before the bar of justice and demand considerations for himself that could only belong to privileged royalty. With an insolence incalculably shrewd, Hitler set out to prove that the very people who sat in judgment upon him were the real criminals and that he and his followers were mere dupes. And when his guilt had been decided and assessed, I heard the judge refuse to pronounce the mandatory

sentence of five years' imprisonment until he first received from
the Berlin state authorities the solemn promise that the prisoner
would be pardoned at the end of six months.

As if all that had been needed was to rid the scene of the
presence of the chief of the National Socialists, the whole air of
the Reich appeared to clear on all important fronts right after
Hitler and his partners had been bundled off to Landsberg prison.
The mark became stabilized and desirable. The French moved out
of the Ruhr as suddenly and mysteriously as they had entered it.
The great bankers, led by the American Dawes, took the settle-
ment of the reparations problem out of the hands of the politicians
and placed it in the hands of the economists who had been responsible for it, in the first place. The economists settled on a
plan of payment by which the installments of a more reasonable
total would be turned over to the Allies only as the Reich itself
grew and was able to manage without a breakdown of the national
economic structure. And the needed capital from foreign lands—
where, only, it was obtainable—began to flow into German enterprise. Business became so good that even the pay of workers for
the state was raised.

Perhaps I should not have used the word *even* in the last
sentence, since the solemn truth was that the economic status of
the masses of workers in the Reich was not in the least improved.
About them, no one seemed to know what to do, with the result
that their drift into communist sympathies grew in impetus, and
darkened the outlook of the nation as such.

In his elaborate cell at Landsberg Prison, Hitler saw none of
the good things which were happening to the Reich, and all of the
bad ones, if one is to judge from the substance of his prison
memoirs. In his own frenzied vision, it was as if everything had
become so much worse by his own forced withdrawal from the
scene of the struggle. Nothing could alter his conviction that his
own personal struggle was the most important of all things going
on in the Reich. As for myself, I was getting myself accustomed
to the idea that, for the time at least, I was quite free of my
remarkable patient, when, one morning, one of those mornings on
which the only letters I expected were those containing bills for
equipment not yet paid for, I received a note from the authorities

at Landsberg Prison that was both formal and pointed. I was free if I wanted, it informed me, to visit my patient, Adolf Hitler, within their domain. All I needed was to notify the prison office seventy-two hours in advance of the time I planned to arrive.

I was first shocked, then outraged. However I looked at it, a trip to my patient in Landsberg Prison seemed out of the question. But when I had almost decided to disregard the whole business, and pretend the message had never reached me, my nature turned against my own conclusions, and I reconsidered. In those times there was no telling what real significance attached to such a message. Maybe my being asked to visit Hitler was part of a larger plan into which I was to be initiated only after I had shown sufficient interest to make the trip. The letter came from the prison authorities, but it was still a question who might have instigated it. Under any circumstances, there was nothing lost in going, and in failing to heed certain dark wishes I might incur for myself insuperable enemies.

I arrived at the prison nine o'clock of a Wednesday morning, and was informed that I would first have to submit to an interview with one of the prison officials in charge of visits and visitors. Besides, prisoners could not see anyone before one in the afternoon.

Everything seemed quite usual and routine. But I was still suspicious.

"Can you tell me what it's all about?" I asked the man in uniform to whom I had been referred—a tall, faded individual with a manner brusque, yet not at all offensive.

He nodded good-naturedly at me.

"Every Landsberg inmate, especially an honorary prisoner like your patient, is entitled to at least one visit from his own physician," he said to me. "But naturally, before we let anyone, even a doctor, meet an inmate, we must make sure that we are not dealing with an impostor."

Luckily, I had remembered to bring my army discharge paper, which identified me not only as a citizen but as a physician. It completely satisfied the Landsberg prison office that I could be trusted to meet their prize guest. The rest of the conversation with the official, such as it was, remained entirely good-natured and social.

"Anything particularly wrong with Hitler?" I asked, rising to go.

"Nothing that we can notice," was the answer. "But all of man's physical troubles do not show on the surface, as you know, and since he seems so anxious to see you, maybe you can be of some service to him."

I could not help smiling inwardly at the anxiety in the man's voice. It would have done credit, I thought, to a first class reformatory. I waited the rest of the time in the prison library, and when the visiting hour arrived, I was conducted to a chamber on the second floor of the prison which looked more like a waiting room in a third class hotel than a place designated for such interviews. It was true, then, all of it, about how the prisoners of the putsch were being pampered. I noticed that my patient was looking better than I had ever seen him look—as a matter of astounding fact, he was actually getting fat.

"You're doing all right," I murmured as I sat down. "Do you think you could arrange additional accommodations for your doctor?"

"Why not?" he cried. "Nothing can be too good for the doctor of Germany's future."

I would probably have more fun if I were its banker, I thought, but said nothing about it.

"I put some important matters aside to make this trip," I reminded him.

He was silent for a while.

"As a matter of fact, Doctor," he said to me at last, "my well-being, in a certain sense, is in a delicate balance these days, and I had to see you."

"This looks to me like the kind of prison that would have a particularly good visiting doctor," I murmured.

"No doubt," he said hurriedly. "But I needed you."

"Flattering," I acknowledged.

He smiled.

"You cannot possibly have any idea *how* flattering, my dear

Doctor. But I'd better come to the point. Do you remember that last talk of ours?" His voice suddenly fell, thickening just a little.

I remembered, and nodded.

"Did you know," he asked, "that Roehm, who was so prominent in that talk of ours, was sentenced to this same prison?"

I shrugged.

"I didn't know, as a matter of fact. But it is not surprising."

He paused a moment.

"You are not at all anxious on my account, because of that, Doctor?"

"Why should I be, since I was careful enough to inoculate you in advance against such an eventuality?" I replied.

His eyes brightened.

"That's what I thought," he said thoughtfully, more as if he were reassuring himself than as if he were speaking to me.

"Besides," I continued, "of what use would be such anxiety? It is the business of the doctor to indicate a cure. He does not need to actually administer it. I thought I could trust you to manage that."

"You are right, of course," he said. "And up to now, circumstances have been fairly favorable to me."

"What circumstances?" I inquired.

"Did you ever hear of Edmund Heines?" he countered.

"You mean the homosexual murderer?" I inquired.

He nodded.

"Don't tell me that he is also a guest in this delightful hostelry?" I exclaimed.

"That's right, and a good thing it was all around that for the last three months Roehm has been completely taken up with him and their cells were next to each other. With the guards napping, they had quite a time of it together, but Roehm was discharged a few days ago, and Heines, whose discharge may be held up for months, is beginning to turn evil eyes in all directions, including mine."

I laughed.

"Where is he lodged?" I asked.

"On the floor below, for the present, but he knows how to get himself moved when he wants to."

"Don't tell me Heines has money with which to bribe anyone."

Hitler laughed.

"He doesn't need money. He makes himself so obnoxious to the guard on watch that he instantly recommends his removal. That way he keeps getting himself moved till he lands where he wants to be."

"Are you afraid of him?"

"Not exactly."

"Perhaps you think I should advise the prison authorities of the character of Heines?"

He laughed.

"As if they don't know. There is really not much left for you to do. I only wanted you to come here and let me tell you about it. That seemed to me all I needed. And now that I've done it, that I've talked to you about it, I do not think I need any further protection against Heines or any other pervert who might turn up to disturb the last few months of my stay here."

"Glad to have been of use," I murmured. "What do you do to while away the busy hours?"

He leaned forward and his face took on a new animation.

"Haven't you heard?" he asked. "I'm writing a book."

I tried to seem interested.

"Good, what about?"

His face clouded.

"What is there for any man to write about? I am writing a book about my life."

I pretended shock.

"What, before you have properly lived it?"

He made a trifling gesture with his right hand.

"That depends on how much of a man's life you consider important enough to write about, Doctor. But my own adventures are only a minor part of my projected work. The chief actor in the drama is the heroic German nation itself. Surely that is worthy of a book."

"Anything is worthy of a book," I said to him. "But it is a good book that proves itself worthy of any subject, however minute the subject may be. But I wonder if you realize how important a part such a book may play in the healing of your own life?"

He looked puzzled.

"How?"

"In writing such a book," I said to him, "you are continuing, ex officio, the treatment I have given you, except that, since you dictate as well as work, you are both doctor and patient."

"But how can it affect your treatment of me?" he insisted.

"Every word you write will count in the exposure of the energies you are trying to free," I explained. "You are undressing yourself naked before the world and me—and—what is more important—your own conscience. Take my word for it and be careful what you write in the book."

He looked resentfully at me.

"Have I given you any reason to believe that I intend telling you anything but the truth?"

I waited until his anger was gone, and then asked:

"I presume that you intend to try, by the medium of this book, to extend your theories of national socialism into new spheres of influence?"

"Of course."

"Isn't that propaganda?"

He nodded.

"What about it?"

"Just that propaganda is a very poor substitute for the truth."

He rose and paced the floor for a moment.

"There is propaganda and propaganda," he informed me. "This is the propaganda of eternal truth. Just wait till you see what I have to give to the world."

"I am waiting," I assured him.

"It's not just a book I'm writing, Doctor," he assured me. "It's a plan of campaign. For here, in the deathly stillness of this room, the whole past, present and future of the world are at my command. I am forming my ideas, but more than my ideas, I am forming my lines of battle. This looks to you like a humble prison, doesn't it? You would not believe it, would you, if I told you that the very outlines of a new world are being drawn here."

"God created the world out of nothing," I reminded him.

"Talking of nothing," he said, "reminds me that there is something else you can do for me, something most of my doltish Nazis wouldn't know how to go about. I want you to tell my people outside what is really going on in here. Tell them that I am only imprisoned, not dead. Tell my followers not to listen to the crazy people who say I am an abandoned leader. Anyone who has left me since my arrest has never been a follower of mine to begin with.

"More than ever, though, I want you yourself, Doctor, to believe in me, to work with me, and for me. I need men to be faithful to me, to fight for me, to carry on where I have left off, so that when I am released I will not have to begin building all over again, from the ground up. Wouldn't it be a pity if the cream of my following were misled in looking about for another leadership? The other parties are doing nothing for us, I assure you. I am still Germany's man of the hour."

I was silent.

"You don't believe all the rubbish which is being repeated against me?" he asked anxiously.

It had been faintly in my mind to tell him that I had lost my faith in him, that it was useless to appeal to my loyalty for him. But I realized that it was not the sort of thing to do, even to a man as brutal as my patient. Let him be as conscienceless as he liked in his dealings with his fellows, but I was not going to tell a man in prison that I thought he was a complete failure even if the man happened to be as essentially unattractive and as lacking in simple humanity as Adolf Hitler.

"I wouldn't spend any time worrying about that," I said to him soothingly. "After all, what do you care for the opinions of a few turncoats? All mobs are full of them. Write your book. Put your whole heart into it. When it reaches the world there will be plenty of new turncoats to take the place of those who have abandoned you."

He seized my hand gratefully.

"Believe me, I will never forget this consideration of yours," he cried. "And when I come into power, I will remember you with all the others."

Inwardly I was laughing at him, for I felt that his critics were right. He had already outlived his usefulness in society. When he was freed, he would be enjoined from speaking for at least a year, and that would help to drive him down the road to oblivion.

Hitler's imprisonment lasted much less than the five years to which he had been sentenced and nearly twice the period of his sentence as pronounced by the court. He stayed in Landsberg Prison a little more than eight months. During that time the Nazi movement dwindled almost to nothing, and only a fraction of what remained of the movement remained faithful to him. Of this I was glad, chiefly because, in the state of party decadence, it was not noticed that I no longer took any interest in meetings and party celebrations which, when Hitler was about, I had been known to patronize extensively. Perhaps I would be able to forget it, as one forgets a bad dream.

But I was trusting in a very trivial god, the god who governs human appearances. The reverse of all my anticipations came to pass, as the world knows only too well.

CHAPTER SEVENTEEN

A Dream Comes to Life

The Death of His Niece Geli—Murder or Suicide?—
The Advent of Hugenburg—Hitler Sends for Me—His
Dream—Alternate Night Visitations—The Consolation.

FULLY A MONTH passed after the suicide of his niece Grete Raubal had scandalized the living world, before Hitler sent word that he would see me. It was six years after his release from Landsberg Prison. During this period our interviews had been few, far-between, and inconclusive.

The impending interview would be an ordeal for me. The newspapers had accepted the story of the suicide. But there were a great many murder whispers, in which Hitler figured as the betrayed lover. And there was talk of a secret session of police officials, in which a murder indictment was discussed outside the record.

How was I to confront my patient? What attitude was I to take? Was I to accept the suicide story as a fact? Would he tolerate my probing him? Under any circumstances it would require very careful handling.

Our original arrangement had, in the meantime, undergone fluctuations commensurate with the changes that had come about in the Fuehrer's personal and party fortunes. It had been perfectly natural that he come to my quarters for the analysis, when his own apartments were still mean, and cluttered defiantly with a ceaseless flow of human and newspaper debris. But all this was now changed. There came upon the scene Alfred Hugenburg, leader of the Nationalists, one of Germany's most influential newspaper owners. He had agreed with Hitler to furnish all the money needed to run a socialist nationalist movement, if Hitler turned over to him, Hugenburg, the support of the won-over masses to whatever measures he favored for passage in the Reichstag. The result was that money began to flow through Hugenburg into the National Socialist coffers in a veritable torrent, with the Fuehrer in full, undisputed charge. Whatever the Party owned in real or movable estate was registered in his name. The *Volkischer Beobachter* (then and now the Party's official organ) was turned over to him as the legal owner, as, also, all Nazi buildings and enterprises. Hitler maintained for himself the right to receive and dispose of every donation to the party funds as if it were something handed over to him for his own personal use. His private offices grew into a suite of regal magnificence. Costly orchids lay on his gold-encrusted desk. His home became like that of one of the Rothschilds whom he professed to despise. The beggar on horseback was riding into power, waving the sword of kingship over his prostrate minions.

Apparently a man had been stationed at the door of his apartment for no other purpose than to receive me. This man conducted me immediately, without any hesitancy, to Hitler's study, where I found my patient pacing up and down the room in a state of pitiable mental agony.

"Forgive this mood of mine, Doctor," he rumbled, forgetting that hitherto he had always gone through the civility of shaking hands with me. "The truth is," he went on, without looking at me, "that I almost decided to let matters lapse between us. Your remedies may be cures, but they do not seem to accomplish very much. I am still overwhelmingly tied to myself. Trapped!" He stopped in his tracks suddenly and faced me with a desperate gesture. "Trapped, you understand, caught like an animal in the Berlin Zoo. Things happen to me which probably never happened before to a living being."

I knew, of course, to what he was referring. But I felt that I stood in such need of regaining his faith in my therapy that I could enter into his troubles only by the aid of his own conscious direction.

"As to whether you wish to go on with these consultations," I said to him dryly, "you will have to please yourself. In the meantime, I am not only a doctor. There may be nothing more wrong with you than a normal need of someone to talk to with perfect freedom."

He circled the floor again, paused in the middle of the room, and turned to me a pale, tortured face.

"Can talking ever really do anyone any good?" he asked bitterly.

"It's the only medicine that will not give you a sour stomach," I assured him. "What do a man's troubles consist of, I ask you? Is not mere words their very essence? Here, for instance, is an animal whose mother was sent to the butcher, and there is a child whose parent came to one of those horrible ends we refer to as a natural death. Which of these will sooner get over the grief of its loss?"

His face was a mask of confusion.

"You don't have to think much on the matter," I assured him, launching into a psychological explanation. "The brute instinctively grieves on the sudden loss of a familiar friendly presence, but the memory dies out, and in time there is nothing left of its grief. For the beast it is as if it had never had a mother or a father. But the human child never stops grieving. Why? Because in its case violence has been done, not so much to a relationship, as to a word. A relationship is a physical tie which dissolves with the dissolution of one of the two connected bodies. A word has thousands of inter-relationships in the memory. If it is not reawakened by one word today it is bound to be prodded into the wounded consciousness the next day by another. Most of creation seems concerned with physical bodies. Human beings, however, are entangled in an infinity of undying words."

His eyes lit up with a growing interest as I spoke.

"Yes," I continued, "we build a Babel's Tower of words against which we lean until we find it crashing over our heads. Then we are buried beneath a mountain of woe. But our grief is made up of words, the one composite of our nature we usually forget to look into when we are in trouble."

He stood listening to me and shaking his head wonderingly.

"Is it your point, Doctor, that the prolongation of grief by the association of words is not really proper, should, and can, be done away with?" he asked anxiously.

I nodded.

"You have hit on my very thought," I replied. "There are of course some drawbacks. The chief of them is the regard in which we are held by the world, and which affects an ordinary man."

My words puzzled him.

"It's very simple," I explained. "If a man treated his private griefs with the brevity of a domestic animal, wouldn't his attitude arouse horror in those of his kind who noticed it, to whom his neglect to suffer would take on the callousness of a person who had no feeling whatever for the finer things of life? And now, of course, we have thrust ourselves into the midst of another tangle of words!"

A long pause.

"Maybe so," he mumbled. "But it doesn't really help. That child was my niece. I loved her, and she loved me. Now she is dead as a stone somewhere in a cemetery in Vienna."

At this point the prospect of my being able to raise the question of how Geli died began to fade. I would continue to be on the lookout for internal evidence, but as for the active assistance of my patient I could not count on it.

"You could have buried her in Germany," I suggested.

"That's right," he agreed. "I thought of it. But my sister made all the arrangements, and I did not have the heart to interfere with anything so close to her. Maybe Geli's being taken to Vienna was all for the best. After all, a good deal of my life belongs to the shadows of Vienna. I am always there in the humbler part of my spirit. But the thing which led her to this terrible deed—how am I going to live the rest of my life with it, how shall I continue doing my work with this perpetual gnawing in my heart?"

I sought his eyes and held them firmly.

"If I were your judge," I said to him, "I might think: *Since you have earned your doom, live with it, Adolf Hitler*. But I am not your judge. I am your doctor. As your doctor I can only say to you: Since you cannot live with the accusation of the death of your niece in your heart, the charge must be eradicated as if it were a cancer. It can be."

His voice was full of despair.

"Tell me how," he pleaded.

"It's very simple," I assured him. "Words make up your grief. The words can be eliminated. We can talk the matter over carefully, quietly, reasonably. We must learn to understand it. When we understand it, it will have become a part of the province of your accumulated wisdom and experience, and it will no longer congest your heart, but flow freely and triumphantly through your blood."

He sat down in a chair opposite me; his voice had become calmer, steadier, more self-contained.

"How shall we begin?" he asked.

"It doesn't matter. The best way is at random. How long before her suicide did you last see your niece?"

He bowed forward, his face in his hands.

"The night before the morning she killed herself."

"Did you quarrel with her that night?"

"No, Doctor."

"Did you have any disagreement with her at all?"

He shook his head.

"All our disagreement had come before. It had been disposed of."

I nodded.

"I understand. How long did you actually know your niece?"

He thought.

"About four years."

"You never saw her as an infant in Vienna?"

"Never."

"Nor as a child?"

"No."

"How old was she when you first saw her?"

"About fifteen."

"Can you remember what was your first thought when you saw her the first time?"

He considered. When he answered his voice was a little tremulous.

"I thought of my little blue-eyed girl with the golden hair."

I nodded again. I had rather expected this.

"You're quite sure of that?"

"I have the best of reasons for remembering it. Physically, Geli did not entirely resemble my little girl. Geli was blonde and blue-eyed, but she was quite a big girl even at fifteen. Yet the comparison inevitably came to my mind the very first time I saw her."

"I do not doubt that that is what you thought the first time you saw your niece. And it's a great pity. Because, actually, your niece must have borne resemblance to a woman much more important in your life. If you had thought of her instead, what transpired between you and Geli might have been of a tenderer and safer nature."

He stirred uneasily.

"Whom are you thinking of?" he asked.

I looked at him.

"Can't you guess?"

He lowered his head.

"I can, of course; you mean my mother. But I swear to you that I did not think of my mother at all when I first saw Geli."

"I believe you. Where did you see Geli for the first time?"

"In my own house. I had sent for Angela, my half-sister, her mother. When Angela came, she had Geli, too. There was nothing to do but accept her in my household."

"You loved her as soon as you saw her?"

"Yes, Doctor."

"Didn't your sister notice this?"

He hesitated before replying:

"I'm afraid that my sister was never very much of a mother."

"Did you ever discuss Geli with your sister?"

"Any number of times. School matters. Little home problems. I acted more in the capacity of a father than an uncle."

"Perhaps you assumed that role so as to deceive your sister into having complete confidence in the integrity of your conduct toward her daughter when you were alone with her?"

He shook his head fiercely.

"I deny that," he declared.

"You mean that you deny that you acted the father role with the role of a lover consciously in view," I corrected him.

"Yes," he admitted shamefacedly.

"When did you first make advances to your niece?" I prodded him.

"Advances?" he repeated. He was sparring for time.

"When did you first kiss her?"

"I don't remember."

"You mean you *refuse* to remember," I reminded him. "Haven't I already pointed out to you that we choose to forget what is painful?"

"But," he said, in a voice almost like a sigh, "that kiss was not in the least painful. It was bliss itself. My subconscious is very cruel to me if it is conspiring to make me forget so much heaven."

"Yet the memory of it haunts you because it led to this tragic climax, isn't that so?" I insisted.

"I'm afraid that it is so," he admitted sadly, his voice drooping again.

"You do not really think of her?"

He stared at me, shook his head.

"No, I do not think of her," he admitted.

"And yet she haunts you. How?"

He bowed his head.

"In the form of a dream, Doctor."

"A recurrent dream?"

"Yes, Doctor, it comes upon me night after night. Every time I am caught in it I feel as if I will never wake again. If I do not somehow rid myself of it, I think it will be the end of me and everything."

The reader will notice that Hitler identifies his own end with the end of everything. In no other patient have I ever noticed such a poignant consciousness of personal importance. His messianic complex was already assuming alarming proportions.

"When did you last have the dream?" I asked.

He looked at me with those drab, melancholy eyes of his.

"Last night."

"How many times has this dream come to you previously?"

He figured for a moment, then announced:

"Nine. Last night was the ninth."

"And after you lost your nine cat-lives," I humored him, "you decided to call me, your Daniel, for advice."

My patient refused to get into the spirit of my levity. His brow wrinkled into a frown, his eyes bulged suddenly, as if the mental disturbance was trying to push its way into the light.

"Suppose you tell me about it," I suggested gently.

He clasped his hands in his lap. He spoke slowly, graphically, as if he were trying desperately to recall every detail of the scene of horror.

"I dream," he mused, "that Geli floats toward me like an angel through a cloud, seeking me in the darkness of my bedroom and kissing my mouth. I try to kiss her in return, but as I do, her head suddenly disappears from her body, and a stream of blood begins to pour from her headless torso upon my bed.

"The blood continues to pour, and as the torso vanishes I find myself sliding down a crimson cataract into a whirlpool whose mouth gapes open like that of a huge shark. Sometimes I see a mammoth shark opening its jaws to devour me, and howling with terror I swim in the darkness. I find myself on my bedroom floor foaming like an epileptic with my arms making frantic motions to get away from the nightmare."

As my patient completed the description of his dream, beads of sweat stood on his face, which he wiped off with his handkerchief. Despite the evident torment, I could see that making his dream oral was a great relief to him. It is in this spirit that an assassin rushes into a confession of his crime in order to lift the burden of guilt from his conscience. He fell into a chair and looked at me with begging eyes. He was waiting for the magic words that would bring about his redemption.

"It is obvious from your dream," I explained, "that you are plagued with a feeling of responsibility for your niece's death." I purposely did not use the word *suicide,* in the hope that it would betray him into as much as a gesture of surprise. No such thing. I continued:

"Mentally you're a pagan like your father, but physically you are the child of your mother, molded from her simple puritanic conscience. In the eyes of the law your little niece-mistress committed suicide. But in your heart, you murdered her, isn't that so?"

A dark cloud seemed to drift over his face, befogging his true emotions. His tormented mind was being crucified between the two thieves of guilt and innocence, and he strove desperately to hide his inner anguish.

"You feel like an assassin, don't you?" I insisted.

"Yes, Doctor," he admitted without flickering.

"Now let us look into this dream of yours," I continued. "According to it, I am bound to tell you, she was not the innocent child you picture yourself as having wronged."

He gave me a swift look.

"How do you make that out?"

"In the first place," I said to him, "she floats into your bedroom. If she were really an angel, as you imagine her to be in your dreams, she would not be floating into your bedroom, but you would be seeing her in her own. She must have been a little less than an angel, quite human, in fact, and it was because your mother-image of her was shattered that you began to think of her as Eve the mistress, rather than as Eve the mother. Am I correct?"

My patient sat back in his chair, kneading his hands as if he were struggling against a terrible admission.

"Am I right?" I pressed.

"How could I know whether your conjecture is right or not?" he demanded petulantly. "I never knew her."

I knew that he was lying, so I sat and looked at him.

"Oh, God!" he cried out suddenly, and covered his face with his hands.

"Then you knew that she once even loved another man?" I asked pitilessly.

He nodded.

"Did you ever feel that she loved you?" I pressed.

"Yes," he sighed, relaxing his tension. "Once when I was asleep in my room, I felt in the dark a movement over my brow as gentle as the stir of a butterfly's wings. Something sweet and tender touched my lips, and as I sought to embrace her I found myself clutching at emptiness. I awoke, switched on my light, looked about me, but saw nothing to verify my suspicions."

"You mean you suspected it might have been your niece?" I asked him. "Why?"

He leaned forward.

"Because by that time I had begun to look at her as a desirable woman, and I felt that she was consciously making herself desirable."

"A very apt conclusion," I remarked encouragingly. "Even the most innocent girl might play the harlot if she finds it is the only way to win the object of her affections. But she must be a consummate actress, making the pretense of pure innocence, if she is to win the man to whom innocence and chastity are the great lure that draws her to his heart. How did you finally assure yourself about these suspicions?"

"I had her watched and caught her red-handed with my chauffeur."

"Did she seem frightened when you revealed yourself?"

"That's it. She seemed glad."

"As if she had expected that it would mean something to you?"

He nodded.

"And what did it mean?" I asked.

"Well, it altered considerably the delicacy of my original attitude toward her."

"I understand," I smiled. "The chaste Diana became Venus in your eyes; and since you feared the kisses of Venus, you assumed the role of the puritanic father and scolded her for trying to storm your chastity. Right?"

"Right," agreed my patient rather sheepishly. "I gave her the scolding of her life, and actually *spanked* her. That started the whole thing. I suddenly found myself swept by an emotional hurricane. Her crying ran through my blood. Her hands pinched my thighs, and her legs appeared to me to be kicking wildly in a deliberately lewd rhythm. For the first time in my life I was conscious of feeling a violent passion for someone of my own flesh and blood."

"Did you try to take her?"

He shook his head despondently.

"Are you sure?" I asked.

"I am sure," he replied. "A little voice in the inside of me kept telling me that the fallen angel of my dreams should not be dragged down much deeper into the slime. I who was her protector must force myself to protect her against herself."

"You realized also, of course," I reminded him, "that you were at the same time protecting yourself against your inability?"

"Yes," sighed my patient. "I had occasion to realize it only too soon."

"How?"

"The angel who floated into my room soon found me floating into hers."

"In your dreams?"

"No, in reality. In my night clothes," he added, and we both laughed. As we laughed I realized that my patient was well on his way to rid himself of his murder complex (he might even have been her murderer): he was beginning to look upon the tragedy of his niece in a comic light.

"You paid the angel a return visit, as it were?" I resumed. He nodded.

"And how did it turn out?"

His face clouded again. Beads of perspiration reappeared on his brow. He opened his mouth to talk but remained silent.

"I know that this is the most difficult part of your confession," I suggested to him soothingly. "But you'll never rid yourself of your recurrent nightmare unless you tell me exactly what happened. Unless it is removed the event will continue to stick like a sharp piece of metal in your brain, and is as likely to be the death of you as if it were a real obstruction in your blood."

His hand went to his head automatically. It seemed as if he actually felt the metal lodged there. He tried to dodge.

"You can imagine for yourself what happened," he said furtively.

"I can," I agreed, "and if *I* were suffering any inhibition, I would be cured. But it is you who happens to be in distress, not I. It is you who must utter the words. the words must actually come from your own mouth. Believe me, as you speak, the metal obstruction in your brain will loosen and dissolve. You'll feel like a new man."

He nodded and I saw that I had won. "I'll tell you," he began, and the words came tempestuously, as if his pent-up anguish had found an exit, and was breaking down all the artificial levees in its course. "I approached her in the darkness of her room that night like a passionate lover. I clasped her in my arms and kissed her eagerly on her lips. She reciprocated as if she had been waiting all of her young beautiful life. My bliss mounted to almost unbelievable heights. Then suddenly—" My patient shuddered and paused.

"Go on," I urged.

He forced himself to continue, and I could feel the fearful strain in his voice.

"Suddenly when I most needed the strength of my lust, mountainous waves of erotic emotion were swept away. Out of some strange fountain came a soft tenderness that cleansed my body of desire. Have you any idea what it could have been, Doctor?"

"The fountain was the maternal womb," I explained. "You were plagued by your mother-image."

"Yes," he sighed. "I could only kiss her body tenderly, kiss it like a child, caress its nakedness in a holy act of love. Her flesh became too sacred to be possessed as a man possesses a woman. I felt a terrible profanation. . . . I begged her—she refused. . . . It was as if she were struggling to remain a harlot while I wanted her to resume the role of an angel. . . . I—I—" He could find no words to express his horror. "Don't you understand, Herr Doktor?" he finally pleaded with me.

"Of course I understand," I said. "But you must tell me yourself."

"There is little more to be said," he sighed, like a man deflated. "I wooed her in desperation all night. When she finally surrendered to my strange mood of love, the only way open to a man like me, it was only because she had not the strength to continue the struggle. To her the surrender must have seemed abject, just as dreadful as the other thing would have seemed

to me, even if I had been capable of it. And now I finally understand why she killed herself. She couldn't go on living with the
memory of what had happened. Removing herself from life
seemed to her the only exit. She felt degraded, because Geli
thought I was some sort of god. I was right, wasn't I, Doctor?
There was, really, no other way for me to live through that
night?"

"You were entirely right in your way of living," I assured
him. "It was either her life or yours, and the stronger element
conquered."

My patient lunged in his chair as if he had felt the fatal
bullet enter his brain. Then he relaxed, uttering a great sigh
of relief, and I knew that the bullet had been extricated!

"The metal has disappeared," I said to him suggestively.
"You know now that you're not responsible for your niece's
death."

He looked at me wistfully.

"Who then is responsible?"

I shrugged, perfectly at my ease, for a doctor's gesture at
such a moment is, perforce, the steadiness of a surgeon's hand.

"God, fate, nature—anything which represents the universe
controls," I said to him. "But not you. *You are not guilty.*"

"No, I am not guilty," he echoed me. "God knows I am not
responsible."

In the light of Otto Strasser's revelation, that Hitler shot
Geli in a jealous rage, the above is a good instance of the power
of hypnosis to soothe a guilty conscience.

CHAPTER EIGHTEEN

BLOODY LAUGHTER: FARCE AND VIOLENCE

Nazi Triumph—I Am Given Notice—Hindenburg in a Night Shirt—Herr Goebbels and His Comrades Celebrate—A Fair Nocturnal Visitor—The Red Bathrobe.

ON JULY 31st, 1932, the Nazis polled 13,700,000 votes, running far ahead of every other party in the field. Munich went wild. "I don't suppose I'll see you for another month," I protested to my patient, and he replied, "Maybe not for a year." A few days later I learned that he had gone to Berlin to bargain with destiny and Von Hindenburg for the Chancellorship of the German Reich. I think he waited a little to be called. But when the call failed to come, he went of his own accord.

The bargaining did not go well with Hitler in the beginning. I knew this to be the case, because the derisive stories which used to be told exclusively of Hindenburg now began to be connected with the name of Hitler.

"Let Hitler mend his manners, or I will appoint him postmaster some place where he can lick my backside on postage stamps," was one of the boldest of these jibes.

I did not know that Hitler was back in Munich until I received a note by messenger. The note requested me to present myself at the Brown House within the hour.

"I may be leaving for Berlin any hour," he said to me rather peremptorily. "I would like, when I am settled there, that you transfer yourself also."

"You don't expect me to live in Berlin," I objected.

"If I get the Chancellorship, why not?"

"Well, you know that both Doctor Sauerbruch and I think it is important for your health that you keep as much as possible in the rarefied atmosphere of Munich," I reminded him. Dr. Sauerbruch was a consultant in all matters connected with his physical well-being.

He shrugged.

"I will live in Berlin as long as it will be necessary to make my leadership nationally effective," he declared.

"Do you expect this to happen soon?" I inquired.

"I hope so," he said fervently. "The day after my appointment is made public, I want you to follow me to Berlin and notify my secretary of your whereabouts. If anything goes wrong—" he began to say, but immediately corrected himself. "Nothing can go wrong," he announced, and smiled his most self-confident smile.

Realizing that it would be useless to argue such a matter with him seriously, I smiled in return, and asked him if it might not be a good idea to take a poll among my patients as to whether I should remain among them, or accompany their Fuehrer on his higher adventure of state.

He gave a contemptuous snort.

"Those swine wouldn't know how to vote even if I let them!" So the subject was closed.

Swine as an expression of contempt has always been popular among Germans, but the Nazis have given it a vogue in the general uncritical association they established between it and the Jews. Hitler's reference to my patients as *swine* therefore aroused in me a repulsion which I could hardly suppress.

"Some of my patients are good party members who not only obey me but pay regularly for their services," I reminded him.

He gave me a savage look.

"That does not prevent them from being swine, and swine they are, as far as I am concerned, if they threaten to obstruct me by as much as a thought." He got up as a sign to me that our interview had reached an abrupt termination.

"When shall we meet?" I asked him, taking his hand, which became limper and limper as he rose to the heights of his Caesarian power.

"In Berlin," he snapped, and gave me a significant look.

Berlin it would be, for him, I became certain.

It's a curious thing about these great clashes for power which occasionally embroil the world; they involve picayune forces of the most trivial and innocuous nature. In this case, Hitler's seizing of the Chancellorship, which eventually resulted in a bloodbath for the whole planet, meant no more than the routine of coaxing a tired old man into doing something which seemed to him indecent and detestable.

Hitler had earned the Chancellorship by the mere preponderance of the Nazi vote. Yet the law said distinctly that the Chancellor had to be appointed by the President. There was governmental intelligence behind that law, which foresaw the possibility of a rabble attempting to sweep into power a faction whose tendency might be a complete dissolution of the spirit of the laws. Because Von Hindenburg as a President of the Republic considered the Nazi leader such a danger, he considered him poor material for that high post, and rejected him.

When the President's slight of the Nazi Fuehrer became known, the storm broke loose in and about the suburbs of Berlin. More than fifty thousand brown-shirted storm troopers marched to the city in force, and began to form an iron ring about it. More troops were flowing toward the capital from all parts of the country, with the same end in view. When it appeared as if Berlin might be isolated from the rest of the country, and, that way, starved into submission, the Nazi trick was sprung.

Oscar von Hindenburg, the President's son, who had been won over by Hitler, broke one midnight into his father's sleeping quarters, accompanied by the minister von Papen and the Fuehrer. In reply to the old man's protestations against such an unwarranted intrusion and disturbance of his rest, Oscar told him that a matter of great importance necessitated the act. General von Schleicher had decided to meet the emergency by calling out the Reichswehr, and he thought his father should know about it.

The old man's head snapped, and all traces of sleepiness vanished.

"What does von Schleicher think he is, a field marshal? As far as I know he is no more than a civilian, and as a civilian he has no right to give orders to the army. It is I who am field marshal."

"That's what I thought," murmured Oscar, and smiled. Things were at last coming his way.

Von Papen now played his part.

"There is really only one way out for your Excellency," he said. "You must displace von Schleicher with a civilian chancellor, which will leave you in command of all national forces."

"And you know what non-military man will be acceptable to the majority of the people," added Oscar smoothly.

Von Hindenburg knew, and made one last gesture of despair. "I suppose it is you, Herr Hitler?" he said.

The Fuehrer bowed.

"What's to be done must be done," sighed the old general. He sank down in front of the desk near his bed (where the papers had already been laid out for him) and signed. When he got up and faced the intruders, his voice was almost mechanical. "I proclaim Adolf Hitler Chancellor of the German Republic," he announced. "You're no longer a corporal, but a minister of state," he said to Hitler. "God help us," and went back to bed.

When I reached Berlin two days later the Nazis were still celebrating, and the forms which their holidaying took illustrates more than anything the peculiar humor of our people when they are in power. Finding themselves in the saddle at last, the Nazis in Berlin rode roughshod over every civilized restraint, and broke into an orgy that turned the gayety of the German capital overnight into a place of terror. Berlin is never too delicate a city, from any point of view. It is cleaner than London, but lacks London's great poise. It is more ceremonious than Paris, but gives no evidence of the French capital's aesthetic sincerity. It compares best with New York, but New York is so essentially a city that it always appears to tone to a human level the behavior of its denizens.

I was staying at a large hotel in the Alexanderplatz where many of the triumphant party functionaries had taken residence during the impending crisis. The scenes I saw in the lobby, and at the crowded bar, appear in retrospect a fantastic nightmare, crowded with shapes of delirious madness and grotesque horror that leaped into a spine-chilling farce born of sadistic violence.

A group of communists had been rounded up by the S.S. and dragged into the lobby of the hotel to serve as bait for the amusement of the Nazi functionaries. There were nine or ten in the group of prisoners; four were young women, obviously girls of culture and refinement. As they were herded into a corner of the lobby, I noticed a burly Nazi stagger out of the bar and weave his way toward the terror-stricken group of prisoners who were being guarded by the S.S. men. He crashed his fist into the face of a short, anemic-looking youth, and would have struck him again had the little fellow not slipped to the floor. The attacker howled with laughter.

Meanwhile a crowd of Nazis had gathered about the prostrate youth, one of whom I recognized as Herr Joseph Goebbels himself. I had met him at the Munich Artists House, where, as usual, he was busily engaged in propagandizing an actress into sharing his bed with him for that night.

As the youth dropped to the floor, one of the male prisoners raised his hand as if to strike the drunken Nazi.

The bully noticed the gesture, and the hesitancy which brought it to a halt. Brushing aside the S.S. men who stood about with their revolvers cocked, he strode to the lad and spat into his face.

"That for you, you Jew-swine!" he hissed.

The blonde-haired young man wiped his face calmly.

"I'm not a Jew," he replied. "I'm as Aryan as you." This elicited general laughter.

"That can be easily corrected, eh, men?" the aggressive one cried, turning to his fellow celebrants.

"Sure thing!" cried back a drunken chorus.

The big one turned to the communist who had dared to interfere in behalf of the little fellow who had been knocked down.

"I'll make you a Jew in less time than it took your mother and father to beget you," he declared. "You're going to be circumcised according to Talmudic law."

With this, he seized a dagger-of-honor from one of the S.S. guards, overcame the youth's resistance, and in a brief struggle proceeded to emasculate him while his audience of party members roared with glee.

I heard this bloody laughter all through the night as I lay in the darkness of my hotel room. I tried to find some explanation for the obscene violence of those people on the grounds that Germany was facing a frightful emergency, and that perhaps, historically, the technique of terror might be justified by the national unity eventually to be achieved. The Nazi students who yelled *Wir scheissen auf die Freidheit* spat upon freedom because liberty of conscience only led to political and economic anarchy. Perhaps Germany must be drilled into unity through an awareness of blood that would drain out the humanitarian conscience and revive the glories of Frederick Barbarossa, who made the Roman Empire holy because he forged it into a grand whole, a divine organism designed to withstand the ravages of time.

I sought to follow Hegel and subdue my own private conscience to the needs of the state, but my simpler human emotions got the better of me, and the laughter hurtling through my mind prevented me from falling asleep. The hotel seemed to rock with gay, festive noises, shouts of hilarity mixed with female screams, coming, no doubt, from the communist girls who were being subjected to torture and abuse. A sudden piercing yell of a woman in pain drove me out of my bed to the door. As I opened it, a blonde girl, entirely nude, staggered into my room in a drunken hilarious state, throwing herself upon me in a violent nymphomaniac gesture.

This was hardly what I had expected.

As I extricated myself from her embrace, I noticed that she was wearing Hitler's honorary S.S. badge around her neck as a lavalliere—so she wasn't entirely naked!

"You can't escape me," she laughed hysterically. "I'm an S.S. Black Guard and I have orders to sleep with you tonight!"

"Orders?" I asked, wrapping my bathrobe around her naked shoulders. The touch of clothing seemed to have a soothing effect upon her; she wrapped the robe tighter around her slim body, and gave a little shiver, as if she were suddenly a bit frightened by her escapade.

"Red pajamas," she smiled, looking at my underclothes. "I simply adore men in red pajamas."

"Do you really?" I said stupidly, trying to think up some way of getting rid of her without causing a rumpus. She seemed to guess my thoughts, for her face suddenly grew dark with anger

"I think you're positively unpatriotic!" Her features assumed a strange savage beauty. "You must be a communist!"

"Why?" I asked her, amused.

"Because you don't join our strength-through-joy movement. Here I am ready to offer myself to you as a dutiful member of the League of German Girls and you act like a cold marble statue!"

"I'm a married man," I lied.

"We have a great many married Nazis," she said soberly. "But they are too busy doing party work to have relations with their wives or to romanticize over their sweethearts." She plopped on the bed and hugged a cushion with a passionate gesture. "That's where we come in," she smiled coyly. "We are Hitler's instant-duty girls ready to serve the party by giving ourselves to party members on call."

"I didn't call you," I reminded her.

She threw the cushion at my head.

"Oh, Herr Doktor," she pouted, "you almost make me blush with shame."

"How do you know I'm a doctor?" I asked, surprised.

"Herr Goebbels pointed you out to me in the bar," she explained. "He said you are Hitler's private physician. Is that true, Herr Doktor?"

"Yes and no," I dodged. "I sometimes give him medical advice, but he never takes it."

She laughed bawdily.

"Tell me," she demanded suddenly, "what is wrong with Hitler?"

"How do you mean?"

"There are rumors," said the blonde darkly, and then burst into a giggle.

"The rumors are false," I lied. "Herr Hitler is a man like any other man."

Suddenly a scream pierced the tense air of my hotel room, and my uninvited guest leaped to her feet, wrapping herself in the bedcloths.

"Oh, he really shouldn't do that!" she cried. "It's too much!"

"Who is he?" I asked.

"Herr Goebbels. He's got one of the communist girls in his room. He ordered one of the S.S. men to strip her and lash her with a horse-whip, when I left. But I didn't think he'd really let it happen."

"Is that why you ran out?"

"Yes."

"Then you didn't expect it to happen?"

"In the beginning I was in on the fun," she said shamefacedly, wrapping the bed-sheets snugly around her breasts and thighs. "Goebbels kept urging me to do something that would humiliate the communist girl. But she kept kicking with her legs until the S.S. men pinned them down by placing a heavy trunk upon them. When I saw the terrible pain in her face, I couldn't stand it any longer and bolted without my clothes."

"Then you're not so completely drunk and abandoned?" I asked her paternally.

"Wish I were!" she declared, and burst into tears. A minute later she squirmed back into my bathrobe, rubbed her eyes with a sleeve and dashed out of my room. Had she been frightened by her humanitarian emotions, which interfered with her patriotic duty as a member of the League of German Girls?

A week later Hitler came to see me at my hotel. A great deal of the jubilation in Berlin had died down, and with it the stampede of instinctive urges that had turned the capital city into something like one of the orgiastic nightmares which my patient had revealed to me during one of our interviews. Hitler's neurotic dream-life was becoming social reality, and he seemed to be in an exultant mood, the rapturous state of the manic-depressive slid into an abyss.

"Shame on you, Herr Doktor," he laughed, slapping me on the back. "I went over to Munich for the weekend to see Goebbels and I saw his mistress wearing your red bathrobe."

"How did you know it was mine?" I asked.

"She told me," said Hitler, digging me in the ribs.

"Hasn't she a bathrobe of her own?" I asked.

"She wears yours in memory of that night."

"What night?"

"Don't play the angel," my patient ribbed me. "I know what happened. You are now officially a part of our strength-through-joy movement." He laughed.

I pretended a mock gesture of despair.

"What next?" I asked.

He gave me a sly look.

"Get your coat on," he said, "and I'll take you to a shotgun wedding."

"A shotgun wedding?"

"One of my lieutenants, who aspires to be Gauleiter, has seduced the daughter of Max Hof, tavernkeeper in Hamburg. I am forcing him to marry Bertha to give her child a name."

"But doesn't that put a damper on your strength-through-joy movement enthusiasts?" I questioned.

"How?"

"If rape and seduction are to be punished by marriage," I explained, "the patriotic fervor of your followers will lessen considerably."

"You are making sport of the movement," grated Hitler. "I must show the masses that I respect the chastity of a tavern-keeper's daughter. I can never rule Germany if I don't place sexual morals on a lofty pedestal."

"What happened the past week doesn't exactly fit in with your ideas," I said.

"What happened the past week had my full approval," was his rejoinder. "Bestiality (*bestialitat*) is a necessary technique to drive out that Jew-feeling of humanity which is the cancer that is devouring the strength of too many German men and women. In a few months there will be concentration camps all over Germany that will be turned into torture chambers for Jews and communists. I must train my followers, even to the most stupid storm trooper, not to flinch at inflicting pain. If they show a trace of humane feeling, they will turn the concentration camps into hot-beds of bolshevist activity. I must drown Germany's enemies in a wave of terror, so that they may not bring the Reich to the brink of ruin with their humanitarian slogans." Noticing my revulsion he added jocularly: "Would you like to witness a flogging, Herr Doktor?"

"No, thank you," I said.

"Perhaps you would like to give one of the beaten swine your professional attention?"

"That's more in my line," I replied. "Where is she?"

"How do you know it is a woman?" asked Hitler.

"Your storm troopers seem to prefer women as guinea pigs," was my reply.

"How do you mean that?"

"I mean it is easier to work yourself into a beast with a woman than with a man," I explained. "A man who can break

a woman's spine, or force her into unnatural relationship with
another woman at the point of a gun can run the whole gamut
of *bestialitat;* is it not so, Herr Hitler?"

"Quite so. When I speak of *bestialitat,* I have reference to
psychological terror more than physical torment. To break a
woman's spine is not half as effective as breaking her mind and
spirit."

As he spoke there was a loud uproar outside my hotel window. I looked out and saw a common sight during these days of
high jinks, orgiastic behavior and calculated sadism. A sensitive
Jew, wearing a top hat and a Van Dyke beard, was being paraded
through the streets in his underwear. There was a rope around
his neck and he was being led in the manner of a trained bear,
while the mob that surged about him laughed incessantly.

"What is that noise?" asked Hitler, showing a trace of fear.
I told him what I saw.

"Oh, that's one of the Jew professors."

"And the usefulness of that?"

"Ah," cried Hitler ecstatically, "it is this sort of force that
will do for the street-mobs what the hotel scene did for our
leaders. Suffering must be made shameful, ludicrous, idiotic, before it will lose its halo of Jesus, its pious sanctity. That Jew
will probably go home and shoot a bullet through his pig's head,
but the mob will live on, an eager instrument of my will." He
paused. "How about that shotgun wedding?"

"I prefer to see the young lady you mentioned," I said.

"It's no use," laughed Hitler. "She's a Maedchen in Uniform,
a Lesbian."

"A Lesbian? Why did your storm troopers pick a Lesbian?"

"As the headmistress of one of the largest private schools
in Berlin she was known for her perfect contempt of the masculine mind. This handsome young woman—she's no more than
thirty-five—looked upon all men as inferior beings."

"Especially upon Goebbels?" I asked.

"How did you know Goebbels was involved?" he laughed.

"Goebbels is always involved," was my rejoinder.

"Yes, the infernal idiot! But listen to this. He was telling her how much he was concerned with the state of feeble-mindedness in Germany, and he pointed out that we had a million feeble-minded, a quarter of a million hereditary mental defectives, ninety thousand epileptics, and God knows how many thousands more hereditary bodily defectives. 'I feel responsible for all these unfortunates,' he insisted.

" 'No doubt you are,' smiled the girl, looking down at his clubfoot."

Hitler and I had a hearty laugh at Goebbels' expense.

"But would you allow a girl of such wit to be mistreated?" I asked him.

"I didn't know what happened until it was over," explained Hitler. "As soon as I discovered her condition, I came here to tell you about it. That shotgun wedding was just a ruse to get you to her apartment."

In a few moments I was in Hitler's Mercedes driving into one of the Berlin suburbs. As the car stopped, Hitler suddenly decided to let me go in alone.

"I must not let my private conscience interfere with political policy," he explained, quoting Hegel without knowing it. He drove off with his chauffeur and two S.S. guards while I walked up the few stairs to the door of an old-fashioned brick house.

Contrary to my expectations, I found the young woman in an optimistic frame of mind despite her harrowing experience.

"They thought they could break me that way," she said, smiling wanly. "But a woman can suffer greater humiliation than that of being attacked."

"You mean, not being attacked," I humored her.

She laughed, showing a set of even teeth that added lustre to a light oval face framed in a severe boyish bob.

I found her body in a badly lacerated condition, the wounds on her breasts, thighs and legs still bleeding.

"You must go to a hospital for immediate treatment," I told her.

"It isn't necessary," she smiled, "I've taken curare."

Despite my efforts to revive her she was dead within a few minutes.

CHAPTER NINETEEN

The Fuehrer Hunts a Wife

One Reason for Marrying—Comparison With the Kaiser—The Duchess into Cook Evi Braun—Jenny Jago—Frau Wagner—The Perfect Wagnerite—Gita Alper.

It must now be recorded that in the first months of his chancellorship my patient underwent a profound (if temporary) change with regard to his feelings about remaining a bachelor. "It seems odd," he confided to me, "that I should be advising the whole Reich to marry, and remain myself in unwedded bliss. I could marry, couldn't I, as a matter of form?"

This seemed to me a very interesting and desirable development, and I decided to encourage it as much as possible.

"It could be more than a mere matter of form if you pick the right kind of woman," I assured him.

"What would you call the right kind of woman?"

"One who would be careful to see that you get for your table only the precious vegetables of which you're so fond," I suggested. I was getting tired of the rumpus he raised every time there was the faintest change of policy in the Chancellory kitchen.

"You're not suggesting that I marry my vegetable woman," he snapped.

"Not exactly."

"If I marry," he said, "I know precisely the kind of woman I want."

I was soon to find out just what his idea of such a woman was. One afternoon, as my patient was relaxing on a couch in my office (he had shown signs of fatigue throughout the interview), I noticed something particularly feminine slip from his trousers pocket and fall to the floor. It was a ladies' garter. Adolf retrieved the telltale bauble with a flip of his hand and stuffed it back into his pocket, making an heroic effort to look unconcerned. His fierce nonchalance was so amusing that I laughed. He joined me in the merriment.

"A very interesting hobby you have," I grinned, "collecting ladies' garters. Now, at last, you have something in common with the royal woodchopper at Doorn."

Reference to the Kaiser did not please him.

"At least," he said proudly, "I make a fair exchange. The Kaiser's diamond bracelets were usually nothing but paste. I give my actresses the genuine article."

"So that garter belongs to an actress, I am to presume?"

"On the contrary, it graced the leg of a duchess."

"A duchess," I gasped. "Aren't duchesses a little new in your line?"

"My interest in this one is purely marital," he said solemnly.

"You want to marry a duchess?" I exclaimed.

"It didn't begin that way," he assured me. "I merely went to ask her advice. You see, Doctor, I grew tired of those indefatigable matchmakers, Frau Goebbels, Frau Goering, and Frau Himmler, who shove pretty actresses into my room, shut the door and let nature take its course. Nature never takes its course." He broke into a broad grin. "The pretty actress leaves disappointed, and I leave with her garter. Sometimes I only do so when I want to reciprocate with a valuable gift, like a necklace."

There was an awkward pause.

"I know what you are thinking of, Herr Doktor," he grinned. "This garter hobby of mine is some sort of fantastic perversion. I pay too great a price for my feminine trophies."

"How old is this duchess of yours?" I asked obliquely.

"Old enough," smiled the Fuehrer.

"You've still to tell me how you came by the garter," I reminded him.

"You have a man's curiosity after all, Herr Doktor," he chaffed me.

"Quite right," I assured him. "But the garter interests me more as a fetish than as an article of feminine allure."

At the sound of the word "fetish" he suddenly grew wary, like a cat arching its spine at the approach of a dog.

"Do you know what a fetish is?" I asked him.

He shook his head.

"It is simply a tendency in human nature to aggrandize the value of one thing. Some men feel about women's shoes the way you feel about garters. Other men spiritually bend the knees to a corset, a toothbrush, a glove—any one of a thousand humble objects. To prove to you what a fetish is, and that yours is a garter-fetish, I will make a wager with you, Herr Hitler," I added, suddenly shooting in the dark.

"A wager?"

"I'll bet my future as a doctor in the Reich that you are in love with one of your twenty-seven cooks!"

"What made you think of a cook?" he gasped, paling.

"The thing that made you think of a duchess," I replied.

He recomposed himself.

"Perhaps you can also tell me which one?" he laughed obscenely.

(My memory came to my rescue here, for it must have been the memory which prompted me in the first place.)

"The one whose stocking slipped to her ankle when you took me to the kitchen of the Chancellory," I said quietly.

"You're better than Sherlock Holmes," he rasped, seeking hard to hide his embarrassment. "I should have put you at the head of the Gestapo instead of that pot-bellied ape Himmler."

"That garter belongs to your favorite cook, does it not?" I asked, pursuing my point with a terrier-like tenacity.

My patient remained grimly silent. I could see his face flush in a confession of guilt.

"And now you're in love with her?"

He hid his thoughts behind a fog of silence.

"I know why you can't live with your Austrian cook," I continued on the hunt. "It would be a political error and a sexual crime. It would be like—"

"Stop!" he barked, leaping from the couch with a gesture of panic. "Don't identify that stupid woman with my mother!"

"It is not I but your own mind that identifies her as such,"

I corrected him. "When you grew ecstatic about the wonderful pastries and puddings she concocted for you, I knew you had a mother-image of her fixed somewhere in your brain. Your mother made excellent pastries and puddings, didn't she?" I asked him.

His anger evaporated as I ferried his thoughts to the maternal bosom.

"She was the finest cook in Austria," he smiled vaguely, making a pretense of humor. "Her pastries and puddings were unique—positively marvelous!"

"And, in a feeling of gratitude, you stole your mother's garter and hid it in your subconscious all these years. Whenever a woman arouses the mother image in your mind, you—you indulge in your interesting hobby. Am I right?"

He flopped upon the couch in a gesture of baffled despair.

"It's no use, Herr Doktor," he cried out. "I can't hide anything from you."

"If you did," I reminded him, "you would be fooling no one but yourself."

He nodded automatically.

"Tell me," I shot out suddenly, "have you seen Fraulein Pola Negri lately?"

He showed surprise.

"Did I mention her to you?"

"Yes, in connection with the boycott of her pictures."

"I ordered Goebbels to lift the boycott, and she was grateful. I have her garter in my collection."

He grinned like a mischievous boy of ten, his hair trailing over his brow, which added to his boyish appearance.

"Does Pola arouse the maternal image in you?"

"She is over thirty," he said with finality, as if women in their thirties belonged to a curious race known as mothers.

"I don't understand," I said. "Do you mean that women in their thirties have no romantic interest for you?"

"Positively not," he snapped.

"How about Fraulein Braun?"

"So you believe the rumors about me and Evi, Herr Doktor?" he chided me.

"Not exactly," I said. "But the fact remains that Evi has

been with you in Berchtesgaden for as long as a week or ten days. People have a habit of putting two and two together. Besides, such a voluptuous girl as Evi—"

"She is over thirty," insisted Hitler, as if that settled the matter as far as he was concerned.

"Besides," he added as an afterthought, "she comes to Berchtesgaden on official business."

"Official business?" I asked skeptically.

"She photographs interiors, draperies, windows, vases, mantelpieces and me," grinned Hitler. "Then the whole business is carted to the official archives to gather dust for the antiquarians."

My patient was in fine fettle, as he always was when politics or women were discussed.

"Then you have no personal interest in Evi?" I quizzed him.

"We have but one thing in common," he smiled. "Odors."

I laughed.

"I mean *bottled* odors," he hastened to explain. "Evi is an expert in perfumes, and we have spent hours together matching each other's personalities with a scent."

"May I ask you what odor she has chosen for you?" I asked indulgently.

"A rare Oriental mixture," he gleamed, slipping into the strange role of the dandy. He sidled to the edge of the couch and asked expectantly: "Can you smell it?"

I was aware for the first time of the odor of decaying flowers, like a mass of funeral wreaths that had lain too long in the grave. Had Evi, I mused, been playing a practical joke on the Fuehrer, who could handle men with Machiavellian cunning but who was an easy dupe in the hands of a shrewd female?

"It smells like roses to me," I ribbed him.

"Never mind," he said, assuming a sudden stiffness, "the subject is too silly to discuss."

At another interview I asked my patient about Jenny Jago, with whom he was bracketed in popular gossip. Jenny, lifted to movie stardom by way of Herr Goebbels' bedroom, had been indiscreet enough to flourish a ten thousand dollar diamond bracelet in the Berlin night clubs, and she helped to spread the story that the expensive bauble was a gift from the Fuehrer himself.

"That little bitch," snarled Hitler, breaking into one of his rare moments of profanity. "That —— —— inveigled me into giving her the bracelet. It was blackmail!"

"Blackmail?" I asked dubiously. "Why didn't you take the matter to Himmler?"

"Jenny is under his protection," explained my patient. "She has been nice to the pot-bellied ape."

"Oh, I see."

"I couldn't imagine," I added, "how Jenny could have received a diamond bracelet in exchange for a garter. She is under thirty, I'm sure. In fact, she looks like twenty."

"She'll look like hell when I get through with her," growled the Fuehrer.

"What was the trouble?" I prodded him.

"It was all due to a little indiscretion of mine," said my patient cryptically.

"Indiscretion?"

"She egged me on," he murmured.

"To do what?"

"The usual thing," he said vaguely. "She put me completely in her power." His face assumed a weird, agonized expression. "How terrible," he thought aloud. "The master of the Reich becomes the slave of a half-witted harlot, a cringing slave!"

"The bracelet was a bribe for her silence, I suppose?"

"Yes."

There was a long awkward pause.

"It seems to me," I said to him, "that your only release from this slavery is Gita Alper."

He stared at me as if I had suggested something utterly incomprehensible.

"Don't you know that Gita is a Jewess?" he asked, incredulous.

"If Goebbels can turn Pola Negri into a non-Aryan," I said, "I don't see why you can't transform Gita Alper into an Aryan."

My patient scowled. He ground his teeth, as he often did

when his anger was about to break forth into oratorical imprecations.

"I don't like your sense of humor, Herr Doktor," he finally ventured, suppressing his wrath.

"I am serious, terribly serious," I insisted. "If the King of Roumania can love a Jewish red-head, I don't see why you can't live with a non-Aryan blonde, especially when she is more Aryan in spirit and temperament than Frau Goebbels herself."

The Fuehrer looked at me pathetically, as if he were sorry for me.

"It's a fact, is it not," I quizzed him, "that you forced Gustav Froelich to divorce her only so that you might have her for yourself?"

"Gita and I are very friendly," he dodged.

"She wouldn't turn you down, if you asked her."

"I don't suppose."

"You feel you could enjoy a normal married life with her?"

"I don't feel anything like that."

"Why?"

"Because it's too dangerous. When I am with her," he enthused, "I feel the tides of virility surging through me. I am like a dead soldier borne on the back of a Valkyrie who is shaken to life by the whirr of her mighty wings." He seemed shocked by his sudden flight of poetic imagination.

"I am like King Gunther," he rhapsodized, "who overcomes the cosmic strength of the naked Brunhilde. Instead of chaining me to the nuptial couch, I weld her, body and soul, to my iron will! I possess her utterly!"

His eyes looked crucified; they seemed to be dying with the thoughts behind them.

"Ah, Herr Doktor," he pleaded pathetically, "why have the gods doomed me to love a Jewess or remain forever—" His voice choked. His face assumed a certain tragic grandeur like one of his Wagnerian gods fated to clutch the body of his fair one in a mutual *Liebestod*. Was he reenacting in his mind the delirious death scene between Tristan and Isolde?

I remained silent in order to give him a chance to compose

himself, then I said tentatively: "There is always a way out, my friend."

He stared at me with puzzled eyes.

"You mean to exile myself with her?"

"Yes."

"That would be committing treason to the Reich. I couldn't do that, not even for Gita."

"Then you must cast your eye on some other woman."

"There is no other woman," he groaned. His face looked vacant and blurred.

"Nonsense," I chided him. "Gita has become your perfect love-image because she combines in your mind the virtues of the mother and the wife. Her sex-lure is smoothed over with a maternal tenderness that has an hypnotic effect on your psyche. You can love the mother and still feel that you are not committing incest."

"Dear God," he cried, like an animal in pain. "Can't you ever leave my mother alone?"

"My job is to cure you," I insisted. "As soon as I bring your thoughts about Gita to consciousness your mother's image will fade out of your mind like a phantom."

"She is flesh and blood—and life to me," he said. "I don't want her to be a ghost."

"She is no more real to you," I insisted, "than the goddess in your Wagnerian Valhalla. Gita is just another daughter of Wotan whom you must woo by plunging through fire. Since the task is impossible for you, you pursue it with heroic subtlety. Your passion for the mythical Brunhilde is your alibi for clinging to your impotence. The fact that the Aryan Brunhilde is really a non-Aryan makes it possible for you to shun a flesh-and-blood female like Jenny and hunger for some cloudy goddess who exists only in your Wagnerian dreams."

"I don't like the way you say that," flared my patient. "I look upon Wagner as the hope of the Aryan world."

The perfect Wagnerite glared at me in silence as if I had befouled the inner shrine of his fanatical faith.

"By the way," I said, trying to ease his temper, "I had a little chat with Wagner's grand-daughter."

"You spoke to Winifred's daughter?" he asked incredulously. "Winifred?"

"Frau Winifred Wagner, the widow of Wagner's son, Siegfried. She is English, you know." Hitler seemed too eager to impart information which I pretended not to know. "Did the girl come especially from Bayreuth?"

"Yes," I said. "She had something private to tell me."

"I know all about it," smiled my patient.

"You know all about it?"

"Last night while drowsing over Tristan and Isolde at the opera," explained my patient, "I caught the sound of the hunting horn at the very beginning of the second act. Instead of the horn, however, I seemed to hear Winifred's voice in the little bedroom which I occupy when I visit her at Bayreuth. It was a voice more seductive than that of Venus. Then the hunting horn sounded loud and clear and I knew that I had been dreaming."

"Dreaming about what?" I asked.

"Dreaming that Winifred wants to marry me," he said sheepishly.

"That's not a dream; it's the real thing," I replied. "Her daughter wanted me to act as Cupid. But I told her I prefer to practice medicine."

We both laughed.

"How did the minx know you?" asked my patient.

"Goebbels, I understand, mentioned me to her mother. He seems to be spending his week-ends with Frau Wagner."

"Yes," laughed Hitler, "the little pig occupies the biggest and the most lavishly furnished room in the house, while I'm shoved into a tiny bedroom with a single iron bed."

"But it is *you* that Frau Wagner wants," I remarked.

"I'm sorry, Herr Doktor, but I don't accept second-hand goods. I would rather woo my Brunhilde through a cloud of fire."

"You prefer Wagner the dream to Wagner the reality, my Siegfried," I chided him. "Of what did you suspect Frau Wagner? Do you really know her?"

"I know Goebbels," he grinned. "That's enough."

A few weeks later Frau Wagner herself came to my office on the pretense of apologizing for her daughter. Her staid English conservatism had evidently gotten the best of her, and she did not want anyone to believe that she had cast her net for the Fuehrer.

"My daughter went on her own initiative," she insisted, her fair, pale skin flushing. "The poor dear has the silly notion that I am in love with the Fuehrer and wants to see her mother married to the most eligible bachelor in the world."

"Come, come, Frau Wagner," I teased her, "you know that is exactly your desire."

The fair English lady, who wore her years gracefully, blushed to the roots of her shimmering hair.

"I am a devout Nazi and admire the Fuehrer," she cooed modestly, "but I can never hope to be his wife."

"Why not?"

"Because Tannhauser," she said obliquely, "has fled from the evil of Venusberg to do his penance in Rome."

"In other words," I translated her remark, "our friend Hitler has gone on a pilgrimage from Munich to Berlin."

"You doctors are so blunt," she laughed heartily. "Perhaps you can tell me what is wrong with our mutual friend?"

"Wrong?" I dodged her. "How do you mean?"

"As his physician," she spoke my thoughts, "I suppose you must keep a discreet silence."

"If you know anything, Frau Wagner," I said to her, "please feel free to enlighten me. I'm sure you would like to help the Fuehrer if it is in your power. I will keep everything you say in the strictest confidence."

"I sometimes think," she said, with a distant look in her eyes, "that the root of his trouble is in his nihilism."

"Nihilism?"

"Adolf is terrified by love," she said quite plainly, "and he tries to overcome his dread with a destructive hatred: hatred against life, against himself, against *me*." She fluttered to the couch like a wounded bird and sought vainly to hold back her tears.

"I thought you said you were a devout Nazi?" I said to her.

She nodded faintly.

"Are you not, then a nihilist?"

"Yes," she confessed, "like Siegfried. My husband was as impossible to live with as his father Richard. I've always wanted to dissolve my loneliness in love. But my husband gave me only hatred and the cruel taste of death. In Adolf, I saw the vision of consummating love in death, of burying that dream of celestial light in eternal darkness. But he does not believe in a *Liebestod,* because he doesn't know what it is!" Her face was clouded with a vague pathos as she begged me with her eyes to rescue her.

"What's the good of awakening your love in the image of Adolf," I asked her quizzically, "if you know it will only be destroyed in the end?"

"I see you are not a pagan, Herr Doktor," she smiled. "I look upon Eros as the genius of death with a reversed torch in his hand. Love lights us to hell and damnation, but how delirious it is to die with your lover in your arms, slipping from time into eternal bliss, into eternal nothingness."

"Ah, my lady," I scolded her, "that is what happens when you say *No* to life, with Schopenhauer, Wagner and our friend Adolf. It can only lead to destructive nihilism, to complete impotence."

"Now I have it," she cried exultantly, leaping to her feet. *"Adolf is impotent!"*

"I didn't, I didn't say that," I stuttered.

"You don't have to *say* it," she blurted. *"I knew it!"*

"What made you think you knew it?" I asked.

She circled the room like a dazed leopardess, thinking her most intimate thoughts aloud.

"Ah, what a fool I was not to realize it before," she told herself. "I offered myself to him shamelessly, like Potiphar's wife, and like another Joseph, he refused me. I thought it was his virtue, Joseph in a trench coat, but it was only his lack of manhood! No wonder he showed no interest in my nudity! And I thought I was too old for him! That he was after my daughter!"

"Are you aware of what you are saying, Frau Wagner?" I cautioned her.

She wheeled around, and I caught the fury in her face, slowly receding to a dead calm, and then breaking out in a forced smile.

"I don't mind if you heard it," she said hoarsely. "I have nothing left in the world but contempt for myself."

Three days later my patient appeared at my office in a state of deep depression. He stumbled into a chair as if his eyesight were impaired, brushing against my desk and knocking over the skull which I used as a paper-weight. I retrieved it and put it out of sight.

"You seem troubled," I remarked.

"I am going blind," he groaned, brushing his sleeve over his eyes in a gesture of despair.

"Calm yourself, old man," I soothed him. "Have you had trouble with your eyes before?"

"Never," he insisted, dropping his arm helplessly in his lap.

"Then you must be trying to frighten yourself out of the idea of eating your silly vegetables."

"That is no laughing matter, Herr Doktor," he barked, raking me with his bleary eyes.

"But I really mean it," I insisted. "There is such a thing as hysterical blindness, you know."

"Hysterical blindness?"

"If you are eating your starchless vegetables merely to keep your sylphlike figure," I explained to him, "it is possible that your stomach has revolted against its diet of spinach and has signaled your brain to blind your eyes until you feed it a juicy steak, or something especially delectable."

"How do you know I am confining myself to starchless vegetables?" my patient asked, amazed.

"You told me you had fired your pastry cook," I said, "the one whose garter you stole. I therefore assumed that you were not only eager to get rid of your mother-image in the Chancellory kitchen, but also that roll of fat around your stomach which might interfere with your chance of trapping a beautiful wife. Hence your elimination of your favorite vegetables, fried potatoes and baked beans."

"So you think my bad eyesight is due to spinach?" he asked skeptically.

"It might be."

"Might it be due to something else?"

"It all depends as to whether you have anything else on your mind but spinach," I ribbed him.

"I have Gita on my mind," he confessed. "Perhaps her beauty is striking me blind," he added with a grin.

"Perhaps," I said. "What was your last thought of her?"

"That she was divine."

"And the thought before that?"

"That she was human, only too human."

"Why?" I quizzed.

"Because she allowed herself to do a foolish thing," chafed Hitler. "She posed in the nude for a sculptor."

"As an actress," I reminded him, "Gita has exhibited herself to the public, in extreme decollete. She should be beyond the fear of showing herself to a man."

"But this was different," said Hitler, fidgeting with his hands.

"Why?"

"Because the sculptor was *blind.*" There was a long pause. I could see my patient eating his heart out with jealousy. Here was a sculptor whose blessing of blindness permitted him to curve his sensitive hands about the soft thighs and hips of the living Venus and transmute her palpitating form into the living clay. Perhaps Gita, pitying the dark world in which he lived, uttered the silent words of Venus to Tannhauser:

"Beloved, come, see yonder bower."

Perhaps she had reversed the blind Tannhauser's fate, and in her stark, glowing nudity had given him a vision of celestial light. Perhaps she had lifted him from the midnight of negation into the sun of affirmative faith, and made a mockery out of Wagner and the perfect Wagnerite. Perhaps Gita had given herself to a poor, blind sculptor and driven her fanatic worshipper into hysterical blindness, that he might touch her soft body vicariously and possess her in darkness whom he dared not enjoy by the light of the sun or the moon.

When I communicated my thoughts to my patient, he grunted, "Nonsense," but the following week he parked his Mercedes near my office and paid me a hurried visit.

"Your delirious poetry has proven to be sober fact, Herr Doktor," he exulted.

"You mean you can see again?"

"As far as that Jewess can travel," he said ominously.

"I don't understand."

"Gita is getting out of the country," he said with seeming relief.

Hitler's failure to find a mate is at the core of his failure as a human being, and is the source of his demonic, destructive spirit. Like the primitive savage, he has a horror of looking into a mirror, for fear that his face must reflect his soul and cause his spirit to revolt. At his suggestion I removed the wall-mirror from my office, but he cannot rid himself of the psychological mirror in which his mind crumbles into madness.

"Man is like the Basilisk," said Hebbel. "He dies if he sees his inner self."

The Fuehrer has not yet caught up with his tragic fate, but there are many women who have, and as a consequence they have found themselves ground beneath the wheels of his evil destiny. When I arrived in America I hunted up an intimate friend from whom I got the story of Renate Mueller, but this tragedy is worthy of a chapter all by itself.

CHAPTER TWENTY

THE TRAGEDY OF RENATE MUELLER

*A Gay-Hearted Titania—More About Frau Goebbels—
First Meeting—The Psychic Gesture—Karl Simon—
Goebbels Holds Court—The Police—The Whip.*

RENATE MUELLER, according to my informant, was one of the few movie stars in Germany who resisted Goebbels' advances and was still able to maintain her place in the theatrical limelight despite the resentment of the Evil One. The petite, gay-hearted Titania had revealed the asses' ears of many a high-ranking Nazi. But she continued to live a charmed life, free from nocturnal Gestapo visits. Hitler had become so fascinated by her baby-blue stare that he had put her under the personal protection of Frau Goebbels.

Unable to enjoy a love-relationship with Hitler personally, the beautiful Magda sought the favor of the Fuehrer by putting in his path lively young actresses placed in the Goebbles' apartment in the Reichstagplatz while Magda was serving Adolf with his favorite vegetables. Such a "blind date" was Renate Mueller, who was served to the Chancellor together with his spinach and green peas. On the night that the lovely woodnymph appeared at the Goebbels' apartment, "Putzi" Hanfstangl, a bosom friend of the midget clubfoot, was engaged in his usual mad antics, standing on his head, rolling the Goebbels carpet about him and yelling "whoopee" in the manner of a Wild-West Indian. The beautiful Renate was so entranced by his buffoonery that she uttered a gurgle of delight and threw herself in the arms of the entrancing Putzi.

This knocked Frau Goebbels' plans askew. Putzi did not suffer a dearth of sweethearts; in fact, he had more of them than her errant husband himself. Frau Goebbels took her club-foot to the kitchen and asked his advice.

"Suppose I take Renate for a walk in the garden," suggested the wily Minister of Propaganda.

"Oh no you don't," snapped Magda in her best *hausfrauish* manner. "Renate is *one* girl you're *not* going to rape."

By means of a ruse Frau Goebbels finally succeeded in getting both Putzi and her clubfoot out of the house. Then she took Renate aside and urged her to do her best to arouse the romantic interest of the Fuehrer.

"You are the only girl in the Reich who can give the Fuehrer confidence," she assured the blonde darling of the screen. "Why, you're such a delicious bon-bon, the Fuehrer would have no hesitation in devouring you. I'd devour you myself if I were a man."

"I don't want to be devoured," protested the German edition of Mary Pickford. "I draw the line at Cannibalism." Her laughter was so gay and loud that Frau Goebbels set up a clatter of plates to drown the noise of her merriment from the Fuehrer.

"You simply must do it," said Magda solemnly. "His remaining unattached is becoming a national and international scandal. Putzi tells me that in America he is being burlesqued as a she-man, especially in vaudeville, by Jewish comedians who are making him a common laughing stock. If Hitler cannot be taken seriously abroad, the whole movement will suffer immeasurably. The national honor must be saved."

"Mine, too," laughed Renate.

"Do it for the Reich's sake," coaxed Magda.

"I don't like to mix patriotism with love," Renate objected. "But in the case of the handsome Adolf, I suppose I'll have to make an exception."

Renate looked positively frightened. She tried to beg off with her eyes, but Magda's stern look made her feel foolish, and she yielded with a show of bravado.

"I'm not afraid of the wolf," she gurgled.

Magda slipped into the garden, and Hitler and Renate were alone. The Fuehrer rose from his chair, rubbed his mustache with his thumb, and put his two hands on her shoulders, looking wistfully at her.

She was making progress, she thought.

"You are very beautiful, fraulein," he said sweetly.

More progress. But real conversation was now in order.

"What do you think of Putzi?" he asked tentatively.

"I think he's amusing," she smiled. "I like his imitation of Joe (Goebbels)." She twisted her lovely face into an imitation of an ape, shot her arm bolt upright and let out a howl that made Frau Magda Goebbels appear post-haste at the door of the garden. Catching Renate's laughter she slipped back into the dark.

"Why do you think little Joe lifts his hand up when he speaks?" asked Hitler.

"To make him look taller," grinned the shrewd Renate.

The Fuehrer suddenly lifted his hand in a Nazi salute. He stretched his hand high and rigid and stared solemnly at the wall opposite. The actress eyed him curiously as he kept his arm up five minutes, ten minutes, twenty minutes, a half hour. Then her sense of humor got the best of her discretion and she burst into a gale of laughter.

"You're funnier than Putzi," she howled.

"Fraulein, this is no laughing matter," he assured her. "I wanted to prove to you that I never get tired like that jelly-footed Goering who collapses after a few minutes. Or that weakling Himmler, whose hand drops to his side in no time. I can salute for two hours. Fraulein, *do you know why?*"

The actress stared at him in amazement. He stabbed the air with his fist:

"Do you know why I can keep my arm rigid for two hours?" he insisted.

"Perhaps Freud can explain it," laughed Renate. "It must be some sort of compensation."

The Fuehrer dropped his arm to his side and dashed out, fuming. Alone with Magda, Renate told her of Hitler's passion for overtime saluting.

"Poor Adolf, what a strange way to show his virility," sighed Magda.

Renate's insult only served to arouse the Fuehrer's interest in her.

The next day he presented her with a horse, a party gift to

him. The entrancing movie actress rode the thoroughbred in the Tiergarden past intrigued Berliners, whose tongues began to wag as the horse trotted past them. One afternoon, as she was galloping along gayly, her eyes caught sight of one of those weird sadistic scenes which were being staged regularly by the Gestapo for the entertainment of the hungry Berlin mob. A young Jew, crawling on all fours, was forced to pull grass out of the earth with his teeth.

Renate dismounted and rushed to the scene of the circus.

"Beasts!" she cried, brandishing her horse-whip. "Have you no other way to amuse yourselves?"

"Jew-lover!" cried a young storm trooper, while the crowd yelled, "Shame!"

This was the beginning of Renate's conversion to tragedy. She never laughed, after seeing the young Jew crawling on all fours, not like the clown Putzi, but as a man who was being degraded into an animal for the amusement of the crowd.

The young Jew, Karl Simon, was the son of the Jewish millionaire, Dagobert Simon, who had been sent to Dachau for the crime of being non-Aryan. Karl objected strenuously to his father's undeserved fate, hence his public humiliation. Using her influence with Hitler, Renate succeeded in having Karl exiled to Paris, where she joined the handsome Israelite, leaving Hitler's horse behind her. It was love at first sight, without benefit of the Fuehrer's two-hour salute. She was so fascinated by her dark, sensitive-faced lover, that she forgot the crime of "racial shame" which was chalked against her by the all-seeing Gestapo. Thus Renate began her plunging cycles of hell which ended at the bottom of a suicide's grave.

Upon her arrival in Berlin, Renate was immediately haled before Goebbels.

"Your movie career is over," Goebbels warned her, "unless you give up that Jew-boy."

"I shall appeal to Hitler," smiled the actress. "The Fuehrer will understand."

"I am talking to you at the suggestion of the Fuehrer himself," said Goebbels. "Personally," he added cryptically, "I don't mind."

"*You* don't mind?"

"I know how women are," he smirked. "They are irresponsible creatures whose principles lie in their hearts. They are neither angels nor demons, but unconscionable animals who will betray God to adore a man who catches their fancy—even a dirty Jew like Karl Simon." He put his arm around her shoulder suggestively. "I will arrange things, if you're nice to me," his eyes told her.

She brushed aside his arm and gave him a look of unfathomable loathing. Her disgust stemmed from the very source that had eddied into passion when she had first glimpsed the young Jew debased to the role of the crawling beast. She did not wish to drag down but to lift up: she was like the Magdalen, who kissed the feet of Christ that they might ascend into the dawn of a new day.

But the fates had already set their trap for Renate, she was being pulled down surely into an inevitable doom. Goebbels was putting into motion the machinery of boycott, and Renate found herself less and less popular with the movie public. When her last picture was shown at a Berlin theatre, two SS. men appeared on the stage with a cringing, trembling girl between them. The hair of the girl had been completely shaved, save for a thick blonde tuft which made her look alarmingly grotesque, like a jungle maid in the Congo.

"This is one of the girls who has followed in the path of Renate Mueller," announced the storm trooper. "Let all Jew-lovers beware!"

Renate, fearing the worst, drowned her sorrows in drink, and soon found herself slipping into the state of a derelict. She made one heroic attempt to survive by renouncing her Jewish lover publicly in the presence of Hitler and Goebbels, and was immediately restored to public favor. Wild applause greeted her as she galloped through the Tiergarden, a slim Titania in a fantastic world of men with asses' heads. But even as she pursued her morning's trot, her mind's eye caught an open patch of green and a young, swart Levantine appeared, crawling on all fours, pulling at the grass with his teeth. Unable to drive the image from her mind, Renate flew to Monte Carlo.

But her lover, with whom she had been in communication through a mutual friend, was nowhere to be seen. Returning to Berlin, she found a police summons in her hotel room. The Gestapo arrived and she was led to one of the concentration camps in Berlin, established in the basements of abandoned buildings where cement cells has been erected no larger than telephone booths. In one of these upright cement coffins she found her Jewish lover, Karl Simon. He had evidently been kidnapped by the Gestapo to serve as an object lesson for her intractable spirit.

Stripped to the waist, the young man was led out of his cement cell and placed against the wall in a far-off corner. The cellar was suddenly flooded with light from a central high-powered bulb, and in the dazzling brightness of the basement, Renate saw the bodies of men and women piled in heaps in various parts of the shambles. Blood spattered the white cement walls, making grotesque patterns that moved like dancing maniacs in the rotating light. Renate fainted, but she was quickly revived by the guards, who placed a horsewhip in her hands.

"Beat that Jew!" bawled an S.S. man.

"No, no, I can't," shrieked Renate. "I love him!"

"Beat him!" demanded the human devil.

"Do as they bid you, Renate," begged her lover. "Your life depends on it."

"No, no," screamed the actress, stumbling over a corpse in her agitation. She fainted again and was awakened by the sound of firing. The guards were shooting at her lover, but deliberately missing fire. As he was being peppered with bullets, the young Jew kept sagging to his knees, his head drooping over, and his eyes partly shut as if to hide the inner anguish. She could stand it no longer.

"Give me the whip!" she screamed, throwing herself at one of the guards who was emptying his revolver over the Jew's head.

One of the fiends handed her the whip with mock gallantry, genuflecting before her like a Chinaman before a joss. Renate lifted the whip high and, gathering strength from some superhuman source, she rained blows upon her lover, panting to release him from that living hell of the abandoned warehouse. The blazing light in the cellar seemed to have entered her brain, driving her into a furious maniacal assault. As the lash of the whip echoed in her brain, she cried out her love to him, a love that would only be consummated in death. At last the twisted heap on the cement floor ceased to move. Renate, stung back to reason again, dropped her whip and with a hysterical cry threw herself upon the prostrate body of her beloved one. The S.S. guards looked upon the scene with sadistic delight, cracking jokes as she cradled the limp head of the Jew in her arms, sobbing into his dark scattered hair. . . .

Renate had only been in hell an hour or less, but it stuck in her mind like an eternity of torture. Dragged out of the cellar and bundled into a taxi, she opened the door of the speeding cab and flung herself out into the gutter, knocking her body against a passing limousine. By a quirk of fate, it was the Fuehrer's own car. He had seen her make the leap, stopped, and ordered her taken to the hospital.

When she returned to consciousess after almost a week of delirium, she was given a bouquet of flowers sent to her by Hitler. Her broken ribs began to mend and one day the Fuehrer appeared personally and offered his condolences.

"Those S.S. men overstepped their orders," he assured her. "Himmler only requested them to chastise the fellow in your presence. They forced you to do something which is too terrible a punishment, even for your crime. I ordered the brutes shot."

"Thanks. Heil Hitler," she whispered faintly. Even in her final extremity she could not suppress her sense of humor. Just as her recovery was considered complete, an internal hemorrhage drew the final black curtain over her life.

CHAPTER TWENTY-ONE

HITLER AND THE JEWS

*The Paradox of Affection—The Academy Complex—
"I hope you are well and unhappy"—The Humilia-
tion of Haman—Patronage of the Sturmer—Frau
Schneider.*

So MUCH of Hitler's personality revolves about his hatred for
the Jews that, naturally, a great many of my observations have
been made with regard to it.

On the basis of my own interviews with Hitler, I have come
to a seemingly paradoxical conclusion:

*Deep down inside of him, Hitler has a strong liking for the
Jews, a tenderness very close to love.*

Hitler's anti-Semitism is an obsessional neurosis which com-
pels him to think and act against his will. He is really fond of
Jews, especially Jewesses, because they possess what he so patently
lacks—virility and creativeness. His second-nature, nihilism,
which has led him into a career of destructive vengeance, has
smothered the better side of his nature, his first nature, his desire
to be an artist, and his hunger for normal sexual gratification.

All of his life Hitler has been pursued by the ghost of creation. He wants to create, but cannot. And wherever he goes, he
sees Jews honored for precisely that which he cannot achieve.
It takes no more than a doctorate after a Jewish name to remind
him of his rebuff by the University of Vienna. Since the Jew
symbolizes this shadowy executioner of his peace, he must of
necessity strike against him. But while he is compelled to persecute the sons and daughters of Jacob, he at the same time cannot
resist a secret love for their creative vitality.

Perhaps I should have argued the matter with my patient.
I didn't, however, and the river of hate that ran through his soul
constantly took on new force, and extended its boundaries. In the
old Vienna days when he was compelled to mix mortar for a
living, and was reduced to the state of a common laborer, Hitler
found himself equally repelled by his fellow-workers, especially
those who made efforts to convert him to Marxian socialism.

Hitler—who reads newspapers to the exclusion of all books except those which feed the fires of his pet hatred—never learned very much about socialism, Marxian or otherwise. But he has an artist's instincts about such things, and he knows what he likes and what he doesn't like. To him, Marx is just another Jewish artist who used politics for pigments, and tried to repaint the world in the image of the Jew-god Jehovah. Like Jesus, Marx to Hitler represents the universal element of Jewish creativeness, and so the Fuehrer has realized in an intuitive flash that Judaism, Christianity, socialism, Marxism and democracy were all expressions of the same creative impulse that came out of Jerusalem. It was this pregnant discovery that Hitler incorporated in *Mein Kampf,* which is a call to arms against the Jewish creative principle and preaches a nihilist revolt (the only kind of which Hitler was capable) against all forms of Jewish meddling in Western culture.

But though Hitler could no longer associate with Jews, he could not renounce his passion for Jewesses, whose Oriental lure and high-tensioned sexuality had a powerful hold on him. He sought them on the sidewalks, and when he found that even some of the sidewalk Jewesses were too proud to submit to him, he began to look for them in the lowest of brothels (the only ones he could afford). Shabby pickings, you are saying to yourself. But through them, Hitler retained his precarious relationship with the Jews in general. For the determination to forego sharing the cafe tables with Jews by day, he condemned himself to share the beds of their sisters by night. One might say, by way of balance, that Hitler was attracted to the Jews, and repelled by them in equal measure.

In a rare moment of hilarity, my patient told me of a letter he once sent to a beautiful Jewess whom he had picked up in a sidewalk cafe in Vienna. It consisted of one line:

"I hope you are well and unhappy."

Through this slip of the pen Hitler betrayed his growing obsession neurosis which compelled him to torment and persecute the object of his affection, a common phenomenon among the sadists.

Hitler has written: *"For our liberation we need pride, spite, hatred, and more hatred."* This racial antagonism which Hitler preaches was born in the womb of his own sexual and creative frustration, as is the case of Julius Streicher, who has also made anti-Semitism his life work.

Streicher first discovered his hatred of Israel, and the need for racial purity, when the girl with whom he was in love turned him down in favor of a Jew. I have had many conversations about the Jews with Streicher (who has always given me the impression of an animal badly in need of a bath). Oddly enough, I have never heard him say anything against the Jews except when he was ranting from a platform. What is in the make-up of such a man that makes Jews palatable to him on an ordinary level, and obnoxious when he has managed to climb several feet in the air? Is it a simple maladjustment of the affections, or a more complicated piece of fraud?

Those who have seen Hitler at close quarters have noticed that he has a habit of rubbing his fists against each other when they are clenched in anger or when he is distraught. Thinking of Lady Macbeth and her similar gesture, I wrung from him the confession that after his experience with the irate Jewish father who objected to his presence in his house, he became incapable of any sexual relationship with a Jewess without at the same time undergoing a sense of defilement. The Aryan concept of *blood and honor* promulgated by Alfred Rosenberg some years later had already become a fixation with my patient. Later his obsessional neurosis took full possession.

Julius Streicher boasts that *"the only newspaper the Fuehrer reads from the first page to the last is my Sturmer."* The reason for Hitler's strange appetite for Streicher's journalistic filth is obvious. Streicher excites the erotic impulses of his readers by picturing and describing acts of race shame between Aryan men and Jewish women, or *vice versa*. He dwells on such relations, because it makes it possible for Hitler to cloak his purely sensual feelings in a patriotic diatribe against racial pollution.

The Sturmer describes Jewish girls as large-bosomed, red-mouthed Salomes, whose alarming lust is salted with beastly cruelty that both repels and attracts neurotic minds like Hitler's who are in need of the sadistic stimulation to arouse the waning appetites of the flesh. While indulging in a vicarious orgy through the journalistic slobber of Julius Streicher, Hitler can worship a Jewish image, and at the same time bribe his conscience into a belief that a Jewess is a vile bestial creature, the Devil disguised as a woman.

Without the help of Streicher's *Sturmer* (and similar rubbish with which contemporary Germany compensates herself for the loss of the famous erotic picture-books of the Jew Fuchs), Hitler would have no way of easing the acute pain of his obsessional neurosis: his mind would be strangled by his overpowering Jew-hatred. He once walked into my office with the *Sturmer* showing out of a pocket of his.

"Do you like that sort of juvenilia?" I asked him.

He looked horrified.

"Are you trying to tell me that this stuff is actually read by children?" he asked.

"Certainly not," I reassured him. "Our youngsters have too much good sense."

Hitler looked relieved.

"I wish I could say as much for their elders," I added. But if Hitler saw my point he did not acknowledge it.

It is said by authorities that the dream is a microscopic world which reproduces in miniature the whole psychic universe. During one of my later interviews with Hitler he described to me a dream which graphically illustrated the fear origin of his Jew-hatred. He dreamed that he was standing on a Roman balcony, his toga blowing in the wind, addressing a large assemblage of Roman citizens. Suddenly he felt a dagger-thrust, and as he fell, he eyed the face of a Jew which floated toward him and then disappeared above the heads of the crowd.

One way of getting the most out of such revelations of the subconscious is to taunt your patient a little.

"I wouldn't tell that little dream of yours to your pal Benito," I suggested to him.

He looked surprised.

"Why not?"

"Can you remember any instance when the world held two Caesars and remained in peace?" I countered.

"Caesar was Caesar," he growled, "and as for Benito—" He left off with a contemptuous gesture.

My patient also had a recurrent dream where a Jew waved a knife over his body, and he (Hitler) found himself floating in two parts, one east and the other west. Plato's philosophical myth of the round men whom Zeus cut in two was thus given Jewish emphasis through Hitler's obsessional neurosis, with Jehovah substituting for Zeus. This prevented him from functioning as an organic unit, and he was caught between Eros and Death, the instinct for life and the instinct for destruction. Hitler's private war against Jehovah and his people symbolizes an hysterical effort on his part to break away from the creative principle by mobilizing all the fires of world-destruction in a final struggle against the Jew. In reality, he has been conducting a mortal battle with his better nature, the inner self which he denies.

The citizens of Munich tell of an incident which gives emphasis to the thesis of obsessional neurosis. The first day after the failure of the 1923 Putsch, Hitler found temporary refuge with Frau Schneider (a high-minded Jewess and patriotic German who did not condone any of the pettifogging anti-Semitism, and yet felt that the Nazis supplied the only honest German resentment against the unfair treaty of Versailles). The car which had picked up Hitler from the scene of failure got sudden warning of a searching police squad ahead, and the only one in the vicinity they felt they could trust was this woman. Risking her own personal safety by harboring a fugitive from justice, she took Hitler in, and for the twenty-four hours in which he stayed in her house, Frau Schneider treated the shabby fugitive as if he were a royal guest. Then, quite suddenly, Hitler decided to jeopardize his freedom by making a dash for the home of his friends, the Hanfstaengls.

Hitler explained this act to me in his own way. With all her gentle treatment of him, Frau Schneider would not send out to market for his favorite vegetables, and even insisted on his partaking of certain foods he had never seen before and which, he was quite certain, must have been Jewish ritual food—an imposition he resented as much as if the Schneiders had tried to poison him. It was a pretty story, but I do not pretend to have even made an effort to believe it.

Why did Hitler leave the home of the Jewess so precipitously, despite her solicitude?* Because, safe in his immediate physical

* I was amused to learn later that it was precisely the precautions of Frau Schneider in not sending to the market for Hitler's favorite vegetables that had

freedom, Hitler nevertheless found himself *unsafe psychologically*. He had dedicated his life to the hatred of the Jew, and here was a Jewess, meeting his hatred with love, and in Christlike fashion cleansing the atmosphere of the hatred on which he thrived, and in which he had his neurotic being.

Love is like oxygen—no one sees it, yet half of the solid crust of the earth is composed of this vital invisible element. Hitler felt himself strangled in Frau Schneider's atmosphere of love, *especially when her beautiful daughter, just budding into womanhood, sat at the table next to him.*

I obtained this bit of information from Frau Schneider herself on my last visit to Munich. This matronly woman was all kindness and sympathy when I visited her. She introduced me to her daughter, and I had to look only once at her to understand the strange guest's precipitous flight into darkness. She still radiated beauty like a sun, upon which invisible shadows played, endowing her loveliness with a subtle lure that must have caused Hitler to tremble with his phobiacal fear. The possibility that he might be "trapped" into an act of "racial shame" and then be forced to wash his hands like a murderer, must have shaken him to the roots of his being.

"Whenever Rachel appeared in the room," said Frau Schneider, smiling at the queerness of the recollection, "Herr Hitler would suddenly stop pacing the room and stare at her as if she were a ghost. Then he would mutter to himself, hurry into the kitchen, and there pretend to be busy with something, till it was quite certain that Rachel had settled in another part of the house. Rachel and I would laugh together—he acted so much like a student who was too shy to look at a beautiful girl."

"Perhaps he thought you might consider using your daughter as a bait for his favor," I suggested to her.

"I didn't," she replied. "But I can tell you this. I have been spared most of the humiliations that have been heaped on the rest of the Jews in Munich during the past few years. I suppose I can thank the Fuehrer for that."

kept the police from finding him that day. When the Hanfstaengls began to pamper their fugitive, sending out for his favorite foods (already well-known to the police), catching up with him was only a matter of routine.

CHAPTER TWENTY-TWO

Caress or Annihilate

The True Story of the Hess Escapade—My Friend
Dr. B-------Roehm as a Bad Example—Fraulein Hess
—The Hess Dream—The Accusation—"Men Must Be
Caressed or Annihilated."

THE BUSINESS of a refugee in America is to adjust himself to the life of his new world. I have done this, and profited immensely thereby. But there is a natural inclination which the refugee cannot resist to be on a constant lookout for former comrades-in-arms who might also have been lucky enough to reach America. I have yielded to this inclination, too, and it netted me heavy dividends, with the discovery of Dr. H----- B----, who apparently enjoyed the Fuehrer's confidence for quite a while after my flight. The pleasure of running into a fellow refugee from the old country is only half in the search. The other half is in the comparing of notes which inevitably follows. This Dr. B---- had more than ordinary curiosity for me, since our common interest had grown into the common interest (and loathing) of mankind.

There are questions of diagnosis and treatment in connection with our celebrated patient's malady and its cause and cure on which Dr. B---- differs with me, and others on which we do not agree at all. In most instances, however, our disagreement is only partial. As to the Fuehrer's impotence, for example. Dr. B---- agrees with me that it may have been due to his dread of the recurrence of syphilis. But he thinks that it has been sustained in him more than a little by his fear of contamination with Semitic blood.

I had consulted Dr. B---- as well as Dr. Sauerbruch on four or five occasions during my tenure of favor. When I left Ger-

many, Hitler called in Dr. B---- and, such is the infinite variety
of human nature, even said some very nice things about me to
him. Dr. B---- had continued advising the Fuehrer until the back-
firing of an unfortunate effort he made in behalf of Rudolf Hess
before the latter made his world-famous flight to England. Having no relations of his own to worry about, Dr. B---- had himself
called to Rome, went from Rome to Portugal, to England, back
to Portugal and from Lisbon by Clipper to the United States,
where, naturally, I was among the first people he sought.

I obtained from Dr. B---- a great deal of interesting inside
data on German events since my involuntary exile, especially as
it illuminates that most melodramatic escapade of the last decade,
the flight of Rudolph Hess to Scotland.

The theories have been, mostly, political, and therefore of the
wildest possible nature. From those who concluded that Hitler
had sent his deputy to stir up revolt in Scotland, to those who
felt certain that Hess bore a personal offer of peace from *Der
Fuehrer* to Churchill, speculation ran amuck. One such speculation picked up by Dr. B---- in England seems never to have
reached this country. According to this, Hitler was prepared to
march into Russia, and ask England for an armistice, if Churchill
promised through Hess to accept it immediately for the British
Empire.

But those who had some inside knowledge of the mind of the
Fuehrer, especially with regard to this most extraordinary of
his associates, took it for granted that Hess fled the wrath of his
erstwhile bosom friend because he had fallen out with him politically.

Dr. B----, who had the privilege of seeing these gentlemen
together several times before the actual event, assures me that
the tension between the Fuehrer and Hess (who worshipped the
former with a slavish, almost dog-like adoration) was wholly
psychosexual, and involved a Jewish girl who, in the opinion of
Dr. B----, existed wholly in Hitler's own lurid imagination.

Let me give the reader the whole amazing story in my colleague's own words as he related it to me while we drank beer
at a sidewalk cafe near Central Park, a place frequently visited
by German refugees.

"You know the nature of the Hitler-Hess friendship. Hitler, complete boss; Hess always willing, obedient to the point of committing himself to brutalities not entirely within the natural outlines of his own nature.

"More slavish subservience to one man by another has not yet been recorded. Yet Hitler has always been ready to sacrifice Hess, as he sacrificed Roehm, the man who lifted him bodily out of the gutters of Munich. In trying to understand Hitler, it is natural that the names of Hess and Roehm should present themselves at the same time, almost in the same breath, though these two ex-bosom friends of the Fuehrer represent opposite poles of his ambivalent psyche. Hitler suffers from a strong Oedipus complex, and this emotional ambivalence is a common fixation with those who suffer a pathological hatred of the Father."

I here interrupted my colleague to inform him that Hitler's Oedipus complex was no stranger to me, but that I was most anxious (as is, I believe, the rest of the world) to get a better insight into the Hess affair.

"Please forgive me," he said apologetically, "if I insist on keeping in mind the Roehm parallel. Roehm was doomed naturally, by reason of what transpired between him and Hitler in the Munich barracks in 1919. But this was by no means the whole story of the Fuehrer's secret hate for Roehm. Hitler also resented the father-dominance of the man who alone ruled him intellectually as well as physically. As long as Roehm lived, Hitler was compelled to lean on him, as a rebellious child is forced to depend on its father who supplies the proper discipline necessary for survival."

"When you talk of Roehm alone dominating Hitler physically as well as intellectually, Doctor," I interposed, "you are not forgetting the youth Schiller who later tried to blackmail him?"

"I know. He took the precaution of running away to Switzerland," he replied. "But if it's all the same to you, I would rather not place too much credence in the affidavits of a blackmailer. I do not shock you, Doctor?"

"No, but you amuse me a little."

"Very well, then; though if I had my way there would be a law forbidding a scientist to as much as blush. In the days of the Roehm predominance, Hitler must have been an underling to him in every sense of the word. He did nothing when his superior's behavior threatened to turn the S.S. elite corps into a haven for homosexuals. Aspiring as he did, both consciously and subconsciously, to the role of Caesar, he felt, however, the need of a veneer of social approval of a movement the whole appeal of which was rooted in the purity and virtue of his *Herrnvolk.*"

"It didn't always seem so to me," I put in, remembering my own argument with Hitler on the subject.

"That was probably because of the indifference of your attitude," Dr. B—— replied. "Outside your office, Hitler had Roehm to contend with, and even an ordinary conversation with Roehm was no small trial of patience.

"Far from being of the same mind as Hitler on this important party issue, Roehm, if you remember, had an idea he discussed quite openly, which set up sexual degeneracy as a new national code of ethics. It is a species of reasoning that sounds strange in America, with the sunlight of Central Park pouring over us. Luckily we do not have to try to get the Americans to understand it.

"If we take drunkenness as a norm, for example, soberness becomes, by comparison, a sorry freak of nature. Roehm dreamt of a new order where the sexual degenerate would be looked upon as a human behavior pattern of a very high sort, and so redeem him from the sense of being a pariah, a social outcast. That was why he flaunted his degeneracy in public and talked his cronies into doing likewise.

"Eventually, Hitler found it necessary to liquidate Roehm and his homosexual friends, chiefly because, by their public conduct, they became a threat to his will to dominate the world. The bloody purge of 1934 (from which you were quite lucky to escape) succeeded in solving many problems for Hitler, problems both political and psychosexual. In the first place it eliminated the fear of assassination on the part of Roehm and his friends. It cut him loose from the intellectual and erotic domination of Roehm and the hateful father-image which Roehm represented. Lastly, with that butchery accomplished, Hitler could pose before the German people as the guardian of social purity, the protector of the home and the saviour of Aryan manhood and woman-hood!

"Rudolph Hess stepped into a dominating position in the party when, with Hitler's authority, he took the place vacated by Gregor Strasser. But he stepped into Hitler's mental life soon after the June, 1934 purge, a very important psychological moment. The Fuehrer needed a companion whom he could hurt and dominate as he himself had been hurt and dominated. He needed somone who would submit to his own sadistic need of mastery, as he himself had submitted to the Reichswehr captain. It was so ordered and done.

"Hess submitted to his master's will with a slavish canine obedience. Hitler snapped the whip and Hess jumped through the hoop like a circus dog. Hess was smart, well-groomed, and had plenty of space in the Reich in which to exercise his own evil inclinations. But he never failed to tender his deep loyalty to his master. Every whim of the Fuehrer's was a divine command to Hess, brought down to him from the holy mount of his ego.

"Hess, I should explain to you, since you had very little contact with him, is a sort of dual personality. On the surface he appears strong and masculine, and at first sight, the popular reference to him as *Fraulein Hess* seems like an unfounded slander. But he is, in reality, a little like Daudet's *Tartarin,* who was two persons in one. Tartarin, the bold, if you remember, hunted lions, while Tartarin, the meek, shrieked with dread at the sight of a mouse. Of this dual nature Hitler must have been consciously aware from the very start. He knew by evidence of his own nature that a man could have equal capacity for courage and cowardice. Was he not himself capable of killing a dozen men single-handed on the battlefield, and creep away on his hands and knees from the sight of an arresting officer? His great dread, from the beginning, must have been that his slave might try to turn master, like Roehm, or rebel against his slavishness by seeking normal relationships with a woman."

"What about Hess's marriage?" I interrupted. "Are you forgetting that he contracted a wife with whom he begot two children?"

"I am not forgetting that. Hess married at the time when the Fuehrer himself was considering doing the same thing. It was a marriage of convenience, not consent."

"Who would expect the Nazis to be so delicate on the subject of sentiment?" I interposed.

"You should know that the most brutal people are always the most sentimental underneath," he chided me. "Anyway, Hitler is sentimental, as was illustrated to me in the last phase of my association with him.

"The Fuehrer called me in when, as in the biblical case of the Pharaoh, his psychic terror dramatized itself in his mind in the shape of a dream. He had dreamed that he saw Hess in bed with someone, a voluptuous brunette who was unmistakably Jewish. In his dreams, he felt the urge to step out of the room, but found himself rooted to the floor in holy terror. He remained there until the whole action was completed and then the scene faded from both layers of his consciousness.

"I had a pretty good idea of what was happening. But before going on with the analysis, I thought something might be accomplished with the good weapon of levity. I asked him how he could be certain that the woman he saw with Hess was a Jewess. 'Did you see the star of Judah against her bosom?' I asked him, 'or maybe some other such token by which a woman who is a Jewess might be recognized from a world of voluptuous women who are not?'

"His reply astonished me. 'I know the woman must be a Jewess because he would not be in there with her if she were not,' he said.

" 'You mean you think Hess is incapable of congress except with a Jewess?' I asked him.

" 'I know it,' he replied firmly.

"I tried to reason with the man.

" 'But Hess is not *married* to a Jewess.'

" 'Marriage has nothing whatever to do with this sort of thing,' he declared irritably.

"The analysis of the dream was immediately simplified for me. Through the medium of the dream-image, Hitler was looking for an excuse to break with Hess, and at the same time give vent to his manhood by craving a normal relationship with a woman. It was of no importance that Hess already had a wife, and a very fine and charming woman, too. Congress to Hitler meant a Jewess, and without a Jewess no such thing can possibly take place.

"The Jewish girl symbolizes Hitler's ambivalence, his desire for gratification, and his fear of the contamination that had overtaken his trusted friend Hess. His inability to leave the scene where the love-act took place evidenced his desire to witness an intimate relationship between a man and a woman who ultimately brought him back to the hateful, obscene act of his father, who had once embraced his mother in his presence. That resulted in his Oedipus complex and his urge to wipe out every vestige of the father image, whether it took the shape of Roehm or Hess.

"Hitler did not confront Hess immediately with the accusation. But when Hess one day asked for leave to go to Spain, his request was peremptorily denied. On inquiry he found that Hitler had already spoken his accusation against him to others. There was no telling where he really stood with the Fuehrer. He had a curious idea that I had some influence with Hitler and came to me with his predicament.

" 'Why don't you wait till he springs it on you?' I suggested.

" 'That might be too late,' Hess replied. 'The day he springs it, it will probably be too late to argue with him. Why don't you get to him, lead the matter into the proper channels? Chances are he will listen to you!' Luckily, the Fuehrer himself came to me with his dream. I assured him that its significance affected him only. 'After all,' I insisted, 'it was you dreamed the dream.'

"A man dreams all of his dreams entirely about himself, never about the people who appear in it. The scenes in a dream reveal the dreamer, never the person dreamed about.

"But I could not move Hitler in this matter, as, I understand, you failed to move him in others. This dream of Hitler's was Hess's complete undoing. The Fuehrer was certain that Hess had defiled himself by associating himself intimately with a Jewess, and when he finally confronted Hess with the accusation, it was as if he had seen it in reality, and not as the result of an exposure of his own subconscious mind.

"When Hess denied the allegation, Hitler went into one of his uncontrollable furies and threatened him with the vengeance of the Gestapo. As Hess and Himmler had never gotten on very well, it did the trick. To avoid the humiliation and grief of having to be tortured into a confession, Hess revealed the name of a Jewess in Berlin whom he had met casually at an out-of-the-way cafe. The Jewess (who was on the merest nodding terms with this exalted *lumpf*) had to undergo the most monstrous indignities and ended by committing suicide. But before putting the bullet through her brain, she got her revenge on Hess by leaving a note for him where the Gestapo was sure to find it. Once this note reached the Fuehrer, it meant the end of Hess, whose only piece of luck in this whole business was his being apprised of what had happened in time to make his extraordinary getaway.

"Hitler's political dominance must be due, at least partly, to a piece of advice of Machiavelli, whom he is very fond of quoting. 'Men must be caressed or annihilated,' said the cunning Florentine. 'They will revenge themselves for small injuries, but cannot do so for great ones; the injury, therefore, that we do to a man must be such that we need not fear his vengeance.'

"Hess flew to Scotland because he knew that Hitler would not hesitate to remove him in true Machiavellian fashion, while I took the first opening for Italy, in fear that Hitler might promote my interference in behalf of Hess into a major act of treachery. The idea of having to reason the matter with the Fuehrer was so obnoxious to me that I turned down every other possible avenue of escape."

CHAPTER TWENTY-THREE

Dream Blitz and Nightmare

Wanted: A Clear Conscience—Machiavelli—The World of Sleep—Rationale of Insomnia—Mystery of the Two O'Clock Bath—Nightmare, the Achilles Heel.

DURING the last few of my interviews with Hitler, I found my patient growing more and more irritable, cantankerous and bleary-eyed, like an insomniac who has been battling with the fiends of restlessness and cannot crush them into slumber. He had achieved the great position he had striven for, but he was not yet fully master of the Reich. And I knew that he could not rest until his powers as well as his tenure of office were beyond dispute.

There are only two ways of accomplishing this objective, by merit or by force. Hitler, I realized, would have to go about his work by violence, and his whole psyche was in a state of horrifying anticipation.

"I can't sleep, Herr Doktor!" he suddenly exclaimed in the midst of one of these interviews, interrupting a line of questioning I was only too willing to abandon.

"I've tried sleeping powder, sleeping tablets of all kinds," he continued, wringing his hands. "But it seems to me of no use. I'm a wreck. Perhaps you can prescribe something."

I looked at him meaningfully.

"I certainly can—and will if you ask me to."

Instantly he was suspicious.

"What?"

"Just a clear conscience," I said gravely.

"Rubbish!" he barked. "I need only a drug strong enough to put me to sleep without also killing me."

"That's where you're mistaken," I cautioned him. "Drugs

can only penetrate one layer of consciousness, the outer one. Your unrest lies much deeper than that. There *is* a drug that can help you, the courage to honestly consider the place you occupy in the world of men."

He looked at me as if he could not believe his ears.

"Can you really mean courage?" he asked.

"Why not?" I demanded.

"Do you dare to preach courage to me, who have thrown down the gauntlet to a whole world?"

There are distinctions in spirit which are very difficult to explain, especially to those untrained in perceiving the more delicate dividing lines of human speech.

"I don't want to appear to underestimate the courage involved in your offer to measure swords with some of the oldest faiths in the world. It is a species of courage which I hold in high esteem. But the kind I recommend to you is a very different one, and much more difficult to practice because it requires a man to face himself, and admit that he has perhaps placed the emphasis of his life on the wrong things. I am speaking to you of a more obvious courage—the courage a man needs to be able to fall asleep. Do you know why you really don't drowse off easily at night? I will risk telling you. You don't *dare* to. You're afraid of what will happen to you in your sleep. Rather than risk having to grapple with nightmares you stay awake nights, and read Machiavelli."

He gripped the side of his chair with sudden fierceness.

"You talk as if you'd been looking through my window," he said tensely.

"Through the window of your mind," I retorted. "Machiavelli has always been the Bible of those who love power. Kings and queens have been known to sleep with copies of Machiavelli under their pillows."

"But they slept!" he groaned, gnashing his teeth in rage, as if he were jealous of royalty that could ride roughshod over humanity and sleep in peace. The desperate tone in his voice and the dark glimmer in his eyes gave him the look of a hunted animal.

"I'll try to help you if you will let me," I said to him. "But I won't be able to do anything, I warn you, unless you surrender yourself fully to my cross-questioning. Don't tell me what you like; tell me in every case what I ask for."

He nodded gloomily, but his willingness to cooperate with me was a very negative gesture.

"Sleep is a world all by itself," I explained to him by way of beginning. "Just as your waking hours form the world of the upper layer of your consciousness, sleep forms the retreat world to which the upper layer descends regularly for refuelling, revitalization. There is, naturally, a constant flow of communication between those two worlds, most of which consists of stray words and actions which each accepts as symbols in a whole code of vital interrelationship.

"So that you may know the blessedness of complete rest you must let me explore your world of sleep, as if I were its Columbus. Let me single out the howling demons in its jungle depths and put them to silence. Once we have plowed through your field of sleep together, you will be able to steer your way through the rest of the terrors, the milder ones. In fact, if we manage the matter well enough, the terrors will disappear, because you will recognize them as no more than substanceless shadows, cast up into the upper layer of your consciousness by the lower one."

"Just another way, I suppose, of asking me to tell you my dreams," he growled.

He was right and I admitted the truth of his guess with a nod.

From time to time I had asked him about his dreams, it was true. Occasionally he had yielded. Usually, however, he had put me off with a very interesting variety of excuses. He did not dream. Or if he dreamed he could not remember the dream in sufficient detail to be able to report it properly. He could not recollect even what the dream had been about. But now I knew I had him. A dream that continues to hurt long after you have dreamed it is a dream that has left definite recognizable traces behind it. He would tell.

"Yes, I would like to hear your dreams," I admitted, "and go through them with you. You must have had some nifties during the past few months."

He nodded heavily.

"If only Hindenburg had some of my dreams! But I want you

to know in advance, so we won't have any misunderstandings, that most of them are absolutely idiotic, and make no sense."

"All dreams make some sense," I assured him. "Only the reality behind the dream can be nonsensical."

"They are confused and disordered," he continued with a despairing gesture of the hand which was one of his most frequent ones.

"And neither are dreams ever confused or disordered," I corrected. "Only a man's conscious mind can be disordered."

"You are insulting!" he suddenly raged, jumping to his feet. "Good day, Herr Doktor."

Like all schizophrenics suffering from infantile regressions, Hitler was given to periodic blow-ups which disappeared as fast as they came.

Five days later he expressed a wish to see me, and once more I was back in his office, he sitting before me as meek as the proverbial lamb. One sleepless night after another, following in powerful procession, had knocked out all his cocksureness, and he again placed himself in my hands.

"Do you think it counts too much against a man if he yields to his doctor?" he asked in one of his isolated attempts at whimsy.

"I don't know," I replied. "But he is one step ahead of the man who has yielded to the undertaker."

"Before I begin telling you my dreams," he began, "I'd like you to explain a mystery to me, something that has caused me no end of embarrassment."

"I'm listening," I said.

"Every afternoon at exactly two o'clock, no matter what occupies me, I have to stop and take a bath. I can almost set my watch by it."

"How long has it been going on?"

"Practically all my life."

"Tell me about it," I suggested.

"There is not much more to tell," he grumbled. "Comes every day of the week at two o'clock. I am forced to leave everything, even important meetings of the party, and rush to the privacy of a bath. Two weeks ago I turned home when I was already halfway over to see Fritz Thyssen, and you know how important

I WAS HITLER'S DOCTOR

these appointments with Thyssen are. As my luck would have it, he almost never reaches his office before two o'clock when I am in my bath."

"How did you go about it when you were at the front?"

"I underwent all the motions as if I were at home. If I was near water, I'd dip my hands in it and touch them to every part of my body. If not, I would rub my body with my dry hands."

"Why don't you find a substitute here?"

"I try," he said, "but it makes me look a bit funny, and if I did it as a matter of habit it might be interpreted as a symptom of developing epilepsy. It would be scant encouragement to my followers."

My patient could not refrain from chuckling at his own dilemma. When I joined him in his merriment, he assumed a tragic mask once more, as a signal that we must return to the business at hand. He demanded that I produce my explanation, if I had one, which he doubted.

Knowing well his infantile regressive tendencies, I began my inquisition by inquiring about his mother's bath-time habits. He assured me that his mother had never made it her business to bathe at two o'clock in the afternoon.

"Think back," I urged him. "Can't you remember once when your mother took a bath at about that time?"

"How should I know?" he jibed. "I didn't have an alarm clock."

I liked the introduction of the alarm clock. It was a definite symbol.

"Perhaps there was an alarm clock," I suggested, just to see what would happen at the repetition of the word.

His face suddenly grew vivid; he stared at me open-mouthed.

"You are amazing, Herr Doktor!" he cried. "Every time I step into a tub, it seems to me as if I hear the ringing of a bell in my mind."

"Of an alarm clock?"

He looked a little doubtful, but I could see that he was trying desperately to remember.

"The truth is, I have never associated it with a clock," he mused slowly. "But now that you have associated my mother, bath-time habits, and an alarm clock, I feel sure I perceive a connection, it becomes clearer and clearer by the second."

"What is the connection?" I pressed.

"A very simple one. When I was seven or eight years old, or perhaps even a little older, my mother, who was bathing, asked me to bring in the clock. She had an important appointment, she said, and wanted to avoid being late. Because she asked me to, I put the clock on the table where she could see the face from her place in the tub. 'It's two o'clock! I'll be late if I don't hurry!'

" 'Where are you going?' I asked dejectedly.

" 'You're going with me,' she answered quickly, as if covering up something. 'We're going to meet your father.'

"My anger knew no bounds as she told me this during the process of dressing me. My fury broke loose. I tore away from her, rushed to the table, seized the alarm clock and flung it to the floor. Instantly it began ringing, and nothing I could do would get it to stop ringing. After some forty years it is still ringing in my ears."

I was laughing quietly at him.

"It won't ring any more," I assured him, "and you can take your bath in the morning from now on—if you prefer it."

His face lit up with amazed wonder.

"You mean that?" he asked. "You mean that this twin plague is over, that I'm through with the ringing in my ears and the two o'clock bathing forever?"

"Certainly," I assured him. "A compulsion neurosis is like a dream. Once you know what's behind it and understand all its workings, it disappears like the ghost of Patroclus after Achilles awoke from his nightmare."

"So Archilles had nightmares too?" he mused.

"All strong men have bad dreams," I assured him. "That is their common Achilles' heel, their fatal weakness, the price they must pay for the exercise of more strength than is allotted to common humanity."

I had good reason for making this point. By associating his nightmares with physical power and greatness, I would find less difficulty in dragging the more intimate and significant of his dreams from my patient's memory.

CHAPTER TWENTY-FOUR

Dream Blitz and Nightmare
(Continued)

*The Tall Building—Primary Effect of Hunger—His
Mother and the Jew Sachs—The Rendezvous—The
Garden—The Dreadful Suspicion.*

Most of Hitler's dreams had some direct or indirect relation to
his mother-fixation and his Oedipus complex, his infantile desire
to "liquidate" his father and take the latter's place in his mother's
affections. Others dealt with homosexual tendencies resulting
from his inability to escape from the mother-image. Still others
were nightmares caused by his fear of assassination. But the most
dreadful of his dreams were those which resulted from his
pathological Judaeophobia.

One night, after receiving a present of a high-power car
from one of the great industrialists he had won to his movement,
he dreamed that he drove it up the front of a tall building, and
that as he reached the roof he saw a garage which had a poster
on it announcing a picture starring Gita Alper. (Hitler was
inordinately fond of this resplendent Jewess, the idol of all German movie fans, and on one occasion he almost forced me into his
waiting limousine to see her in a new picture just delivered to
him.) Finding the garage locked, he shot down the back of the
massive building, drove it against a vast expanse of field, and
found himself at the side of a cave on a hill that had an over-
arching slab of granite, which seemed to him like a protruding
Hapsburg lip.

It was obvious that in this dream Hitler was making a
desperate effort to normalize his sexual life. The building was, of
course, his mother, something he even guessed in his subcon-

scious, for he quickly tried to overcome the horror of mounting it by substituting the high-tensioned sex-image of Gita Alper for the mother-image, at the moment when he reached the roof, at the split second of congress. Finding the garage, Gita Alper barred, he dashed away from the body of his mother, only to find himself back in the maternal womb (the cave with the Hapsburg lip).

This mother-dream, which is both farcial and tragical in its implications, makes use of the common symbols of civilization— a house, a car, a garage. But Hitler has had Oedipus dreams as primitive as those dreamed by the Crow Indians. As when he dreamed that a wild beast tore into his house and dragged his father away into the woods. When his father staggered back to his mother's room, one of his fingers was cut to the joint. This symbolic castration of his father gave him intense delight. Celebrating the event in his dreams, he gorged himself with food, as if to increase his potency to the measure and dimensions of his father.

Following a present-day cultural pattern was Hitler's dream of his father on stilts: trying futilely to bend over and kiss his wife, he was prevented from accomplishing this for fear of taking his hands from the stilts. His father's legs finally gave way, and he fell. The humpty-dumpty flop was so ludicrous that his mother broke into wild laughter.

I discovered one day, in a remark made by my patient, that one of the reasons he feared the adventure of falling asleep was the dread of sleep-walking out of his house and finding himself without a bodyguard amongst hostile communists and Jews. He was afraid that after such a walk he would return to his bedroom a corpse, which would mean the end of his great crusade to deliver Germany from her enemies.

I traced Hitler's sleep-walking to his "primary effect hunger."

"What is 'primary effect hunger'?" he asked eagerly.

"It means maternal love, affection, care," I explained. "The phrase was first used by the psychologist Levy."

"A Jew?"

I nodded.

"The theory is either cock-eyed," he snarled, "or just another Jewish trap to snare Aryans."

But the facts I subsequently coaxed out of Hitler proved that both Levy and I were right.

"Do you remember telling me in the early part of our conversations," I reminded him, "of your habit, when you were eight or nine years old, of sneaking into your parent's bed in the dead of night on the pretense that you were afraid?"

He nodded.

"Can you remember finding yourself surprised to wake up in their bed, wondering how you got there, because you could not remember having consciously made the trip there?"

His eyes took on a strange look.

"Of course. I do remember. Is it your point that I actually walked in my sleep those nights?"

I smiled.

"Perhaps a more accurate way of putting it is that those were the days when you got into your sleep-walking habit. Think back, man."

His head began to droop.

"I am thinking," he mused, "and remembering."

"What?"

He shook his head.

"That is one thing I can't tell you," he averred.

"Why not?"

"It's just a little too private," he whispered.

"The things we deal in," I reminded him, "are of the very stuff of privacy. There can be nothing especially private in any phase of the interviews with an analyst. . . ."

"I understand," he said, grinding his teeth slowly. "But this is a secret I intend to take with me to the grave."

"The grave is not very far off," I taunted him, "if you won't assist me to help you to get rid of this dangerous somnambulism of yours. You talk of being afraid of walking into a nest of communists. Suppose you just walked out of a three-story window?"

He remained silent for fully three minutes, staring blankly at a mirror in front of him. His own reflection must have horrified him, for he squirmed in his seat as if he had just discovered something in the outlines of his face which boded disagreeable sensations.

This is the sort of a situation in which the analyst must guide his patient rather than drive him. A few leading questions, I thought, and perhaps I would pry it out of his mind with his own consent as a dentist removes a sensitive tooth.

"Suppose you tell me," I asked, "whether this remarkable thing—which you feel that you must hide from the rest of the living world—is something you experienced inside or outside of your own home?"

"Outside," he replied automatically.

"It was the first time you had sleep-walked outside of your own house?"

"Yes."

"Did you find yourself walking to the front or to the rear of the house?"

No answer.

I repeated my question.

"To the front or to the rear?"

Still no answer.

I thought I would risk the question a third time, and repeated it slowly, gently:

"To the front or to the rear?"

My patient leaped from his chair in a fuming rage, shook his fist in my face and bellowed:

"You have no right to do that. You should not impose on me that way!"

I had to pacify him.

"I thought you realized by this time," I reminded him, "that a secret is still a secret, when the man who shares it is a doctor. Besides, it is no longer a secret as far as I am concerned."

"You really know?" he said with open mouth.

I nodded.

"You entered the Garden of Eden," I said to him, "and found Mother Eve with the Snake. He was not your father, was he?"

His face went ashen-white. I could see him shudder even as I framed the question.

"I hope not," he replied.

I met his eyes with an intentness I rarely attempted to exercise.

"Who was he?" I asked.

He spoke unflinchingly, and the words snapped out of his mouth with a hatred which must have resembled the aboriginal passion itself.

"A Jew."

This was one of the few occasions on which I found myself pitying a patient. A convulsive terror shook his body; his face changed from white to crimson. I seized his shoulder to keep him from falling. But he shook himself from my grip and fell back into his chair with a groan. I let a few minutes pass to give him time to regain some of the harmony of his senses; for unless the man examined enjoys a certain amount of relaxation, his revelations are not of much use to his physician.

When I felt I could safely renew the questioning, I asked him: "How did you know the man was a Jew? If you were asleep, how did you recognize him? Sleep-walkers make the very worst witnesses."

"It was part of a situation that had begun earlier in the same day," Hitler explained. "My father was away on some official errand. He did not often go away, but when he did he stayed away for at least one night. I remember those nights for the best of all reasons. They were the nights I occupied the bed alone with my mother. I object to your seeing anything improper in them, either. There is a certain kind of warmth in which the race is cradled and, cradle or not, it is the right of the mother to continue to give such warmth to her progeny as long as she likes.

"That was one of the days preceding such a blissful night. It was early afternoon, to be exact, and I still remember my astonishment when the local grocer, a Jew by the name of Sachs, entered our house and remained alone with my mother for almost an hour. I knew that we bought our groceries from Herr Sachs, and that he sometimes delivered them. The order for the stuff was, however, always given in the Jew's own store, and when he personally delivered the order, he never went byond the door. Seeing him enter the house was bad enough. But the hour he spent in it was the most tormenting I had ever known. It was more painful than those long nights spent watching my father's back, knowing that his face was toward the face of my mother. Naturally I had no definite idea of what I suspected. But the feeling, the most penetrating I have ever encountered, came over me, and made me both suspicious and miserable."

"We are still in the house the afternoon of the day of your father's absence," I reminded him.

"I saw nothing. But his presence in the same room with my lovely mother was enough. The lecher's intentions were written all over his fat, greasy face."

I pried into him with my eyes.

"You are quite sure those were the feelings you had then?" He nodded vigorously.

"Go on. What followed?" I pressed.

"That night, Doctor, I tossed in my sleep like a prisoner in a dungeon. It was mid-August, and several times as I turned about on my pillow I felt as if I were choking for air. I can't tell you definitely what happened, because it's one of those things which belong half to our conscious and the other half to our unconscious lives. I must have sleep-walked into the garden. But at the sound of my mother's laughter I woke suddenly.

"My awakening in such an awful situation was of course the essence of the tragedy. And it was due to nothing so much as my mother's laughter. Almost anything else she might have done would have left me in a comatose condition. But the laughter of my mother was a peculiar kind of music, and it had the most astounding effect on me, no matter when I heard it.

"I awoke suddenly into an enchantment of night and stars such as I can't remember having gone through before or after. I looked away from everything to follow the strains of that laughter, and neither my eyes nor my heart rested till I tracked it down. She was lying down on the grass under a tree, and the golden moon shining through the branches illumined her marvelous face and hair. None of the angels in the prayer books we read on Sunday mornings in church could have compared with her as she lay there in that enchantment of warm darkness.

"Beside her lay the fat Jew fondling her shimmering hair, and desecrating her naked breasts with his ugly paws. If only I could have done something about it. But what was there to do? My hatred of the Jew was not greater than my fear of displeasing my mother. I rushed back into my room and vomited all over the floor.

"The next morning when my mother asked me how it happened I told her I did not know, that it must have occurred in my sleep. I never told. She never found out."

There is such a thing as a dream fitting so snugly into the principles of analysis that the analyst becomes suspicious of his patient, and even the primary principles involved. This was certainly a case where I had to be doubly suspicious to make sure of being approximately correct.

"Are you sure that what you saw in your garden was not some hallucination?" I inquired cautiously.

"If you had any idea how hard I have tried to believe that!" Hitler said with a heavy sigh. "For the sake of my mother, the integrity of my home, I have more than once tried to talk myself into the idea that the whole incident was but a stark delusion born of my bitter dislike for my father. But it was no use. There were too many dreadful possibilities to consider."

"How old were you then?"

"About ten."

"How long had this Jew known your parents?"

"A year or two before I was born."

"Then you might be a non-Aryan yourself," I murmured. "That's the dreadful possibility that haunts you, my friend."

He pounded a fist into the palm of his hand.

"I know what I am, Herr Doktor!" he cried. "You needn't worry about that. And as for that damned Jew, I promise you I'll make every German and Austrian Jew pay for that piece of infamy. Heads will roll—and if that garden still exists when I get to it, it will know a red dew."

CHAPTER TWENTY-FIVE

DREAM BLITZ AND NIGHTMARE
(Continued)

The Vital Suspicion—The Bite of the Snake—The Conditions of Dreaming—The Historic Role Hitler Does Not Relish.

ONE THING I realized at the end of my previous interview with my patient. The suspicion of his mother's relationship with the Jew Sachs, and its dreadful implications involving the nature of his own origin, was undermining his reason. If he was ever to return to a state even resembling normalcy, that suspicion would first have to be ousted from his mind.

I have since learned from Fritz Thyssen that the Jew Sachs was not the only source of Hitler's uneasiness with regard to his origin, that Chancellor Dolfuss actually had proof of the Fuehrer's Semitic origin—proof that led to his murder, and has since disappeared. But even if I had known of the existence of this additional matter, it would have made no difference in my attitude. It is the business of a doctor to heal his patient, and it does not matter whether he does so with the truth or with lies, though the healing itself is based fundamentally on the truth.

The next time we met I hastened to reopen the subject.

"I'm glad we had it out," I said to him, "because it involves everything we are trying to achieve with these interviews. I refer to the very texture of suspicion, your suspicion in particular. A thing suspected is a thing non-existent, or its presence would be based on a much solider foundation. You must, I tell you, you absolutely *must* forget the suspicion you entertain of your mother and the Jew Sachs, or you'll never get rid of your sleep-walking habit as long as you live. Suspicion and hatred are great social luxuries, and he who dares indulge in them must pay heavily and bitterly. Your punishment for continuing to entertain that suspicion will be that you will not only persist in the habit of sleep-walking out of your house—you will eternally go about through the world as through a garden searching for your non-existent snake."

He scowled fiercely.

"But I don't have to search for the snake," he snarled, "I have already found him."

"You have?"

"Of course I have. It's the Jew, the whole damned race of him."

"The snake is a sexual, not a racial symbol," I reminded him.

"The Jew is a sex-mad snake," stormed my patient.

"While we're on the subject of snakes," I said by way of detouring him, "have you had any snake dreams?"

"Any number," Hitler replied quickly. "One last night, for instance, couldn't be classified as anything less than a nightmare, and drove me to call you today. It was awful."

"Tell me about it."

He leaned forward intently.

"I dreamed that I was trying again to reach that cave on the side of the hill, but on the way, I was waylaid by a thunderstorm. Yes, it was the same cave and the same hill. They recur in my dreams like the lines of a ballad. As I now remember I seem to have plowed my way through rivers of mud, and swum across endless miles of water, with the cave in my mind, but nowhere in sight. Then suddenly I tumbled into a mud-hole alive with snakes. You can imagine how realistic and terrible this dream was, because it awakened some people in the next room, among whom was my friend Captain Roehm. He came rushing in to wake me, but it was not at all necessary. I was already wide awake."

"Perhaps not as wide awake as you think," I smiled.

He frowned; heavy suspicion darkened his brow again.

"How do you mean?" he asked.

I decided to dodge.

"Were you out with Roehm last night?" I asked.

"Of course. We had a tremendous dinner and I might have guessed I would have a sad time trying to sleep. When I got to my bed, my whole stomach felt sour with indigestion. No doubt this nightmare was due to that, and nothing else."

"In part you are right," I granted. "If a man could eat only the things agreeable to his stomach, perhaps he would be able to keep himself from the clutches of nightmares. You know that it is not good for you to overeat, don't you?"

He nodded.

"Then what makes you eat so much—when you already have plenty of trouble trying to fall asleep?"

He shrugged.

"Gluttony, I suppose."

I shook my head.

"You are practicing a species of self-deception as old as the race of mankind," I declared to him. "When you have eaten overmuch you have bad dreams, and when you have bad dreams you declare to yourself that you have simply overeaten. As a matter of fact, is it not possible that if something in you demanded the introduction of a nightmare into your life, it would suggest to you the sort of body conditions (indigestion, say) favorable toward that kind of dreaming? Isn't it more plausible that you overeat by an inner direction beyond your control than that you are so stupid as to do so merely because food has been placed before you?"

"What you say does sound plausible, Doctor," he admitted slowly. "I ought to watch my food!"

"And Roehm as well," I smiled.

Hitler laughed loudly. He understood the warning.

"It's been a long time," he confided in me, "since he's tried to seduce me."

"It's too bad you can't rid yourself of such scum," I said, as a matter of course, not dreaming that in the end he would not only follow my suggestion in its most violent possible implication, but almost include me in the general sweep of its malignity.

"Some day I may manage that little thing," was his quiet rejoinder. "Right now he's one of the most useful of our leaders. A good organizer. Orderly. And the best living trainer of militia. We need militia to keep down subversive forces within the Reich, and we need men at the head of such forces who have instinctive ruthlessness without any compensatory moral qualms. Roehm and his gang of homosexuals fit perfectly into this picture of the needs of Germany. Never have men lived who had less pity in their hearts. But when our goal is reached, and we can surrender once more to the milder things in life, there will be changes, I assure you, very important, vital, terrible changes."

I shook my head warningly.

"When you give a man a horse to ride, it is important to beware of frightening the steed. A frightened horse is liable to stampede your own horses and cause you irreparable damage."

He gave a contemptuous snort.

"No need to worry about frightening my steed, I assure you," he declared. "I have learned well Mussolini's technique of purging undesirables. Machiavelli is not the only Italian whose methods are worth following, my dear Doctor."

"But the method of murder works both ways," I continued to caution him. "If you keep your hand on the trigger, your enemies are likely as not to beat you to the draw."

He smiled with a consciousness of superiority.

"Yes, I know," he said. "But believe me, Doctor, it is all a matter of timing. There is a drawing and still another drawing of a weapon. When it comes to political murder, there is only one thing to know—one must strike fast and furiously, and without any sort of compunction. The blitz attack can never fail. And once the wild naked terror has been loosened—"

"Like one of your nightmares," I broke in.

He smiled grimly.

"Yes, Herr Doktor. The galloping nightmare may be loosened even while one enjoys Wagner at the opera.* I shall not hesitate to do my duty when the time comes."

"You have a genius for making trouble, my friend," I jibed. "Because your own life has been made psychologically unbearable, you would like to make the life of the rest of the world as intolerable as yours. Don't you think you're assuming too much of a load, my friend?"

My patient looked at me hotly. I could see that he had suddenly become speechless. He was in fact so angry that when he spoke again his voice was almost soft, as soft as a dark cloud holding back a thunderbolt.

---

* The truth is that on the night Hitler's henchmen murdered Austria's diminutive Chancellor Dolfuss, Hitler passed a pleasant evening at the Opera, entertaining celebrities in his box, while the music of Wagner continued to pound in his ears. Is it possible, I ask myself, that the man really could have planned this treacherous murder so long in advance; or, when he made that remark to me during the analysis, was it only the accidental illumination of one detail in a pattern of conduct that had already been determined at his birth? These answerless questions, and others, continue to plague my self-exile.

"Aren't you afraid that you may presume a little too much on my patience one of these days?" he asked.

I saw that I had gone a little too far, and decided to retrench as gently as I could.

"I did not mean to criticize your actions," I assured him. "As a doctor I see no difference between the practice of condemning a man and that of the silly practice of judging and punishing animals which prevailed in the Middle Ages. You think along a definite mental pattern, and you can no more help following it than I can help following the one which represents to me my place in the world. You are not the first man with a messianic complex, nor are you likely to be the last. Socrates had his demon, Isaiah and Joan their divine voices, Goethe his image of the rose, Napoleon his star, Bismarck his blood and iron, and you—you have your Jew!"

He made a sour face.

"I don't think I like the idea of being associated in history with the name Jew," he complained.

"No one would think so from your behavior," I laughed. "If you don't stop harping on it, you'll be fixed forever, like Haman, on the gallows of Jewish derision."

"What a historic sense you have," he scoffed. "To compare me with Haman. You forget that Haman was outlived by the Jews. When I am dead there won't be a Jew left to write a lie about me."

Which took me right back to the business at hand.

"By the way," I said to him, "you should have a few Jewish dreams to dispose of, too."

"Plenty," he rasped. "Talk of being plagued by them in history books! They're doing much worse to me. They're following me into bed. The latest Jew-dream I had, last week, was so fantastic it would serve you right if I told you about it."

"Why don't you?"

"Don't worry," he laughed. "I'm handing this one over to you cold."

The dream my patient proceeded to relate me was so magnificent and of such significance that I must frame it in a separate chapter.

CHAPTER TWENTY-SIX

DREAM BLITZ AND NIGHTMARE
(Concluded)

The Sky-Dream—Magda Berg—The Peace of the Waters—The Jew and the Aryan Woman—The Desert —The Interpretation.

"I DREAMED," began my patient, "that everything in Munich had stopped. Cars, trains, buses, lifts, people and animals. Only the cave in the hill, usually quiet, revolved, and I with it. Suddenly, gathering momentum, I was flung on the back of one of four galloping horses. The other three were mounted by bearded Jews in Polish kaftans and long curly earlocks. As I landed on my steed, the Jews and their horses disappeared, and I galloped on alone through space.

"In the next phase of my dream I was riding this miraculous horse along the skies when, suddenly, the three horses that had vanished reappeared.

"But instead of the Jews whom they had borne when I last saw them, they were mounted by naked Amazons. I was so sure that these Amazons were those self-same Polish Jews that I tried to pierce one of them with my spear. But the spear broke against the side of the woman, and I myself sank to the earth, the wings of my horse collapsing under the shattering blows of my lance.

"My horse and I landed on the ground lightly. But as I lay sprawled, dazed from the impact, a beautiful Jewess grew out of the horizon, came toward me, and offered to help me up and take me to her home. I insulted her in the vilest language I could think of, but instead of leaving me, she began to cry.

" 'What are you bawling about?' I demanded.

" 'I thought you were Christ descended from heaven,' she said to me. Can you imagine that?

" 'What's your name?' I asked her.

" 'Magda—Magda Berg,' she said. 'I have come straight from the fourteenth century to greet you. I thought you were my lover.'

"With that, she fell to the ground in a swoon. I stooped down to kiss her, but I had no more than bowed my head toward her than she disappeared into the earth. Shaken with grief, I sought my horse, but the horse, too, was gone. I began to walk on foot, but found myself flying again on my own unassisted power over the hills and valleys, over cities and villages. I landed finally in a valley where a giant sprang out of the earth and engaged me in mortal combat. I overcame him by looking at him and just resting my arms on his shoulders. He sank into the earth as if I had dealt him a mortal blow. As he began his descent, I snatched up his sword, castrated him, picked up the bleeding member and hurled it deep into the earth after him. A red rose sprouted on the spot, but as I touched it, it faded slowly to white.

"I flew on and on until I reached a garden full of red and white roses, and I decided to rest from all my adventures. It was in my mind to look at the flowers, and no longer risk the peril of touching them, but rest was not for me. I had no sooner lain down on the soft twilit earth, when I heard the screams of Valkyrie over my head. Following it brought me to a grotto, then a castle over a wide blue, wonderful lake. Dressed as Lohengrin, I rowed about the lake, while a concealed orchestra played the music spattering the lake with its beautiful golden notes. Out of the boat I arose, and found myself floating back to the grotto again, and then once more to the lake with its inclosing tall airy castles.

"Then I knew the peace of the waters, and I rested with my head toward the liquid blue about me. It was then that my own image rose out of the water to plague me. For on my head I discovered a crown and a scepter in my hand. It was a sign that I belonged to the royal house before me on the shore of the lake. I crossed the moat and ascended the stairway of the castle to the throne-room. There, on the throne, sat Ludendorff, who proceeded to crown me with a crown of red rubies. The red rubies no more than touched my hair than they turned to blood which trickled down my face and chest. Before I could see how it happened, the trickle became a stream which swelled to a torrent; this torrent rose above my ears and buried me in a tide of crimson.

"Choking and gasping for air, I opened my mouth, only to feel my lungs filled to the bursting point with blood. I tried to swim away from it, but the more I swam the wilder and more furious were those great heavy threatening red waves, with not a glimpse of merciful shore in sight.

"Then, as suddenly as they had come, the waves died, and I was plunging through a field of tall grass. I was hungry, devoured the grass like a famished ox, and kept crawling on all fours till I reached the edge of an arid desert. I stumbled through the dry blistering heat, and when I finally achieved a cool oasis beside a pool under a palm tree, I beheld there the spectacle of a Jew in the act of congress with an Aryan woman. The ill-assorted couple continued to enjoy each other while I watched, and my only thought in the state of my stupefaction was: 'We slip out of the maternal womb, all of us; but only a part of us, a tiny fraction of us, returns to the womb in adult sexual intimacy.'

"As this peculiar notion ran through my mind, the Jew suddenly vanished out of sight, and I was again being pressed down to the soft grass by the nude woman, who proceeded, without any encouragement, to have her will with me.

"I tossed her aside angrily, and rushed beyond the oasis. Once more I struck desert, and I seemed hell-bent toward the heart of it. To add to my confusion a sandstorm arose behind me and swept me on even more fiercely, until I was caught up in the blinding roar of the storm. I was flung so high that I mounted a cloud, from which I was able to look down on the devastation below. By this time I had achieved a state of mind that, by comparison, could be described as peaceful.

"But in the security of my cloud-mount I found myself surrounded, suddenly, by the intemperate elements of Wagner's flaming fire-magic. So completely did I become immersed in it that after a while I felt as if I were myself a raging fire, shooting flames from every pore of me and shouting in Latin, a language I had never studied: *'Qui iuxta me est, iuxta ignem est, qui longa est ami, longa est, a regno!'*

"A vast multitude appeared in the midst of the desert, every member of it seeking to catch the spark of my fire, all except the Jew whom I had discovered lying with the Aryan woman in the oasis. As my sparks shot down to the multitude below, the laughter of this Jew, from a distance unknown and unmeasurable to me, became louder and louder, drowning out the noise of the sandstorm and reaching a maniacal fury, like the laughter of a man who has gone violently mad, so that his voice sweeps all other sounds before it. The multitude ceased catching the sparks of my fire, and dissolved together with the Jew in the storm.

"I was left alone in the sandstorm, bobbing up and down like a piece of wreckage on a storm-tossed sea. My anguish had become so acute that I screamed, and so awoke."

At the end of this recital, the most remarkable in my whole career as an analyst, I maintained a long and painful silence. I was really waiting for my patient to say something more to seal my intuitive feeling about the whole thing, and when I had waited long enough he broke out into a loud guffaw.

"Here you've been begging me all these years for a real dream of mine, and when I fairly scrape out the inside of my skull for you, you sit there and keep quiet. Is there nothing at all you have to say about all this?"

I gave him a slow smile.

"Don't worry on my account," I said to him. "There is plenty to say. I am wondering how patiently you are going to take it."

"A man who has had the patience to live through such a nightmare," he said mockingly, "should be able to stand a bit of good doctor's acid."

"Very well, then," I said. "You can't say I haven't warned you." As I got into my interpretation of his dream, I could see Hitler steeling himself for the sort of assault on his pride of privacy which he most dreaded.

"We will dispose first of the adventure in the castle," I began. "As a diversion from your tremendous effort to escape from your mother's womb and from the homosexual tendencies which usually surround one in the predicament of one suffering a mother-fixation, your psyche has sought release in the fantasy-world of King Ludwig of Bavaria whose castle you entered, to be crowned king by your own famous partner in the beerhaus *Putsch*. It is natural that this fantasy-world should dissolve into blood; the nightmare of every would-be conqueror becomes the nightmare of all humanity.

"I want you to notice that at every step of your progress through this nightmarish world of yours you knock against the hard fact of the Jew. That is your fault, not that of the Jews. Because it was you who threw the gauntlet down before them, not they who chose to make war with you.

"Your encounter with the Jewess Magda Berg was a little puzzling to me until I remembered something in a pamphlet by your friend Alfred Rosenberg, which you apparently noticed as well as I did. It concerned the case of Sister Mechthulde of Magdeburg, a thirteenth century nun who dreamed of Christ as a handsome youth inviting her to his couch of love where she might 'cool herself with him.' It was simple to connect Magda Berg with Magdeburg, just as the Greek was able to tell Alexander that he was going to besiege Tyre when he dreamed of a satyr. Magda Berg symbolizes your ambivalent drive, your desire to gain the mastery of some voluptuous Jewess against the opposition of your consciousness, which you have taught to believe that such an intimacy would be shameful.

"Your attempt to kiss her results in the same tragedy that attended the effort on the part of Orpheus to kiss Eurydice—she disappeared into the earth.

"As for the Jew who was having congress with the Aryan woman in the oasis—he was, of course, the grocer Sachs whom you found in the garden with your mother and whom you deeply suspect of being your true father. Your thoughts as you observed them prove that you are still bound by the maternal womb, and the erotic dream-picture of the woman having her will of you was a symptom of your inverted effort to arrive at normalcy, just as your attempt to pierce the galloping Amazon with the spear which you finally broke with a direct and symbolic effort on your part to accomplish the same end.

"Driven on by psychological frustration, you sought in the desert to substitute yourself for your own father, and the Father of all mankind. Having castrated your father (the giant whose mythical counterpart is Kronos, a variation of the Oedipus theme), you proceeded to endow yourself with the cosmic virility of Jehovah, the great Jew who rules the earth and the heavens, so putting all your apparent ambitions in the shade.

"As a fire-god, you would naturally strike a Jew as trying to enact the incident of the Burning Bush, which is something to convulse any Jew with laughter. Those boys invented the story, and no one has ever been able to make out with any certainty what they really meant by it. Do you know the meaning of the Latin sentences you recited to me?"

Hitler shook his head.

"They are from Origen," I told him, "and their meaning roughly, is about as follows: *'Whoever is near to me is near to fire. Whoever is far from me is far from the Kingdom.'* Beautiful words, eh?"

He nodded and looked at his watch.

"What do you say if we call it a night?" he asked.

"Do you think you will sleep?" I asked him.

He smiled sourly.

"Tonight I shall sleep the sleep of the humiliated."

CHAPTER TWENTY-SEVEN

The Attempt at Assassination

*A Good Press—An Unusual Strength Through Joyite
—The Wooing of Goebbels—The Seizure—In the
Library—Utter Destruction.*

I WAS TALKING the other day to a fellow German exile who once did Hitler's publicity in Washington, and mentioned vaguely the possibility of putting into cold type some of my intimate knowledge of the life of the Fuehrer. His comment was surprising.

"The old devil sure enjoys a good press," he said.

"A good press?" I asked skeptically. "I wonder what you call a good press."

"A good press is a steady press," he replied. "A press that never stops talking about you, and, always, with a lavish sprinkling of capitals and italics. The attention newspapers and magazines are giving Hitler all over the world is nothing less than devotion. I notice that when they run out of legitimate news they take to speculating why no one kills him. Greater love hath no correspondent than that he is willing to lay down his subject's life in the interest of good copy."

"Now you have a pretty good idea of the nature of the things I have to tell," I reasoned with him. "Do you think Hitler enjoys reading that sort of stuff?"

"I don't know as a certainty," was the reply. "But I'd lay odds that he laps it up like a hungry kitten. Don't you see that beyond every other consideration it's a kind of guarantee of immunity? As long as people discuss publicly the merits of extinguishing him, no one is likely to try it."

"Sounds a little too far-fetched."

"The proof of a theory is in its working out. Fact is, no real attempt to assassinate Hitler has yet been made."

"But hasn't there?" I asked.

The general impression throughout the world is that, but for the several attempts staged by the Nazis for propaganda value in connection with some international dispute, no honest attempt to kill Hitler has yet been made. This is not true. At least one attempt was made, of which I myself know. There were two reasons why it was not given publicity. In the first place, it revealed the only way Hitler can be reached, something neither Hitler nor his henchmen want known. The second reason is that there are inner horrors which even the Nazis shrink from divulging.

About six months after his accession to power, Hitler began hearing strange rumors of a young girl, a member of a female unit of the *Strength Through Joy* movement, whose devotion to him was an exceptionally personal one. Not that it was anything unusual for such a girl to bestow her favors freely on members of the inner circle. . . . They give themselves so completely to the work of the party that they have surrendered any hope of a future as wives and mothers. The more attractive gravitate naturally into a sort of sex service de luxe for party members too busy with their jobs to lean on the comforts of home. The *most* attractive of them were taken up by the Nazi chieftains.

This particular "service" girl was so beautiful that she came instantly to the attention of the upper bracket of Nazi males. She never failed (whoever the recipient of her favors for the night happened to be) to thank her lover for the privilege, and to express the pious hope that she might some day be allowed to enjoy the opportunity to offer the same sweet homage to their beloved Fuehrer.

She drifted about for several weeks among the small fry, till she reached, first, von Sirach, who could be tempted only rarely out of his masculine associations, then Ley, then Goering, and lastly Goebbels, where even she was expected to turn sour. But no, she yielded herself willingly to the little club-foot, and even pretended the next morning to have enjoyed herself.

"And now," she sighed, "there is only the Fuehrer left to complete the circle of my service."

But Goebbels was too much of a swine to let such a morsel slip by, especially to Hitler, whom he held in such utter detestation. Lisa was much too sweet to let go of so quickly.

"Would you really like to meet the Fuehrer?" he asked her.

"It is the one wish of my life," she replied.

"Well, you know that if anyone can get you to him I can?" She nodded.

"I'll make a bargain with you," he suggested. "If you'll stay with me, and me alone, for a whole week, I'll personally introduce you to the Fuehrer."

"It's a bargain," she agreed.

But at the end of the week he begged off.

"You know it isn't because I can't keep my promise," he pleaded with her. "I just haven't the heart to let you go, my dear Lisa. You know how easy it is for me to commandeer women, not only in number, but in quality. Much as I love the Fuehrer, it would be almost an act of suicide to turn you over to him when I have barely learned how wonderful it is to love you. Please let me have another week."

Lisa gave Goebbels another week, and another week after that. When, at the end of the third week, he tried to beg off again, she looked at him sternly and said:

"We deal in love, Herr Goebbels, but not exclusively in that branch of it by which men and women deceive each other. If you do not keep your promise tomorrow morning I will go to Herr Goering, who I am sure will not only accommodate me, but offer to explain to the Fuehrer how you have detained me all this time on my way to him."

There was nothing left for Goebbels to do but surrender, bitter though it was. When he got to Hitler, the Fuehrer surprised his Minister of Propaganda by showing that he knew all about Lisa.

"Send her to me about nine o'clock tonight," he ordered. "She'll be taken to my library. I'll find her there and introduce myself."

The next evening, as Lisa approached the Chancellory, two

men stepped out of the doorway and seized her. She was taken by force into a chamber on the ground floor, where every article of clothing was torn from her body. At first, she was too frightened to cry out, but when a long steel knife was discovered inside her brassiere, there was little left for her to say or cry about. The weapon having been taken away from her, fresh clothes were brought. She was dressed as forcibly as she had been undressed, and taken several flights to a large, luxuriously furnished library. The taller of her captors, apparently the one in charge, said to her:

"We do not know why the Fuehrer should want to bother with such scum. But since it is his wish we have brought you here. In a few minutes he will come to speak to you. If you value your own hide you will be very careful how you behave in his presence."

With that she was left alone. In seizing her, the men had been careful not to manhandle her too much. She felt sore in two or three places where very powerful fingers had pinioned her for a few minutes. But in general, fright had been her only experience thus far. And now, suddenly knowing that the man she wanted to kill was about to enter and remain alone with her, she grew calm, sank into a cozy chair near the fire and waited.

It did not take long. The door opened and closed softly. As she turned about, she advanced toward that most familiar of dreaded faces. He did not offer to greet her, but drew a chair near where she was sitting, crossed his legs in a gesture of weariness, and spoke to her in a low, tired voice in which there was barely visible a trace of emotion.

"It took you a very long time to get here, didn't it, fraulein?"

"It was the shortest way I could think of."

"It may turn out to be the longest. Why did you want to kill me?"

"Why do *you* want to kill so many people?"

"I never tried to kill you."

"Yes, you did. On the night following your triumph a group of your followers attacked me. It was not their fault, or yours, that I was not killed."

"You were one of those communist girls in the hotel?"

She nodded.

"I know all about it. I heard of it the next day, and I was sorry. What could I do about it? The men were drunk, and where men get drunk there is always violence. That is why I myself do not drink."

"Whatever they did, it was in your name they acted, and with the assurance of your protection. Two of my comrades did *not* survive."

"And so you decided to assassinate me by pretending to be anxious to love me?"

"To assassinate you I had to get to you, and there are few other ways open to a woman."

"I don't know why you shouldn't have thought so, since you fooled everyone but me. Even people as astute as Goering and Goebbels. You might have fooled me, too, if my destiny had not warned me. The men who seized you, were they in any way unnecessarily violent?"

"No, they did their job as well as they could, under the circumstances."

"That was in accordance with my orders. If I had not specified that you were to be treated with consideration, they would have torn you to pieces."

"I suppose you expect me to thank you?"

"No, you and I are beyond all ordinary civilities. I had two reasons for wanting my men to spare you. The natural curiosity of wanting to see you exactly as you were, and as you might have been, if you had really wanted me and loved me. And that you would reward my patience by telling me the names of the communists in this conspiracy with you against my life."

"I have nothing to tell you. The idea of taking your life was a piece of vengeance I planned for myself."

"But surely you discussed it with someone?"

"I would have stopped myself from uttering a word of it even if I had caught myself talking in a dream."

"There is no one among the communists who knows about that hidden dagger of yours?"

"I left the communist movement the day after the assault.

I have not seen a communist or spoken to one since. The whole blame (if it's to be called blame) is mine."

"You're quite sure of that?"

"Quite sure."

"That's a very serious decision to make. Remember, if you don't turn in a co-conspirator, I will simply have to return you to the men who captured you. They are waiting outside my door. Do you know what they'll do with you if I turn you over to them?"

"You said something about their tearing me limb from limb."

"But that's not the worst of it. There won't be as much as a trace of you left when they get through with you. In the most literal sense of the word you will be annihilated."

"I don't care!" she cried, "since I have had this opportunity at least of venting my wrath on you."

The heaviest object near her was a marble clock. She sprang to her feet, seized it and, turning toward him, hurled it ferociously at his head.

"If I hadn't dodged quickly enough," Hitler told me the next day, at one of our regular interviews, "she would have achieved her purpose. Instead, a mirror before which I had been standing was shattered to bits."

"And what did you do with her?" I asked.

He shrugged.

"The crash of the glass brought the men in and they took her away."

"You didn't try to stop them?"

"Can you tell me why I should have bothered?"

"I don't know. Do you know where she is now?"

He shrugged again.

"I doubt if God could find her if he wanted to," he replied.

CHAPTER TWENTY-EIGHT

AN ODYSSEY OF TORTURE

*The Jew of Mystery Turns Up Again—Invitation to
Brandenburg—The Note—Routine Latrine—Religious
Prisoners—The Hanging Beam Torture—To Branden-
burg—Barsch Again—Return from Hell.*

DURING the course of one of the last of our interviews, Hitler
rose suddenly from his couch, brushed the Nazi eagle in his
buttonhole with his sleeve (a nervous gesture that always came
with his sense of haste) and apologized for interrupting the
session so abruptly.

"Sorry," he said, "but I'm going on a trip."

"A trip?" I asked out of curiosity.

"I am driving up to Brandenburg," he explained.

"The concentration camp?"

"Yes."

My eyes must have betrayed surprise, for my patient blurted:
"I suppose you must think I'm a sort of sadist who enjoys a
spectacle of torture for its own sake."

"What makes you think so?" I asked.

"Well, you just brought out the fact that my father wept
over his dead canary and gave it an elaborate funeral because
his balked love sought an outlet in animals and birds. He hated
his neighbors, beat his wife and lavished his true love on his pet
canary. He was a sadist and I suppose that leaves me a chip off
the old block."

Hitler grinned with smug satisfaction, as if he were showing
off my utter stupidity by drawing a conclusion from my line of
inquiry.

"I said merely that your father made me think of Junius

Brutus Booth, whose love for birds and animals did not prevent him from engaging in homicidal attacks upon his fellow actors," I reminded him.

"But you also said, Herr Doktor," Hitler insisted, "that Junius Brutus was the father of John Wilkes Booth, the actor-maniac who killed Lincoln. Like father, like son." He grimaced and again brushed the Nazi eagle with his nervous gesture as he continued: "I am an actor on the world stage, who uses real bullets to shoot down villains. That makes me a sadist, I suppose."

Turning at the door, he wheeled about suddenly and asked: "How would you like to come with me to Brandenburg, Herr Doktor?"

"As an observer or as a prisoner?" I grinned.

"Some people consider it an honor to be the Fuehrer's prisoner," he chaffed.

"I most respectfully decline the honor," I said. My patient emitted a good-natured laugh. He was in the canary-stage of his father's mentality; at that moment he looked sweet-tempered enough to weep over the fate of a dead sparrow.

He left the office in high spirits.

In the afternoon a note arrived by messenger which made me regret that I had rejected the Brandenburg trip. The note had been smuggled out of that camp by a Seventh Day Adventist, one of the many members of that cult in Germany who take the Bible seriously. The man who handed me the note was an ex-patient of mine, an ex-resident of the Brandenburg camp.

I glanced over the letter without reading it, and noticed the letter X at the bottom instead of the signature.

"Who is this Mr. X——?" I asked the messenger.

"He told my friend that he had once come to your office to make a special request," said the stranger enigmatically. "He thought you would remember him best as the Nordic Jew."

"Of course!" I cried, as that marvelous figure swam back into my recollections. And so the horror had finally caught up with this Zionist who wasn't interested in Aryan culture and wanted only to be left alone. He had left a painful wound in my mind which never healed despite all my efforts to forget his existence.

When the messenger was gone I sat down to read the letter.

"Dear Doctor," it began, "the man who will be instrumental in bringing this note to you is a God-fearing Christian. When his time was up, he refused to swear allegiance to Hitler, and so was shoved among the Jewish *'Schweinerei'* as a punishment. It is the duty of the *Juden company* to clean the latrines, empty the chamber pots, and get down on their knees while their own urine is being poured down their throats. My Christian friend was able to stomach this dose of Aryan culture until an S.S. guard forced him to undress and exhibit his uncircumcised state before his Jewish comrades once every hour, while he was beaten on the bare back by a steel-corded whip. On the seventh day he succumbed and swore undying loyalty to the Fuehrer.

"Just before he left the 'Judenschweine' to their private hell in their own block of cells, he begged me to write a letter exposing conditions at camp, and promised to take it with him at the risk of his life.

"It is impossible for me to describe conditions in Brandenburg in all their stark horror. Those who are crippled or mutilated by the sadistic practices of the guards go to Lichtenberg or Orienburg, where I understand there are doctors or nurses to take care of the sick. But this arrangement is only for Aryans; non-Aryans must continue their round of slow torture, urine swallowing, latrine cleaning, and compulsory surrender to the lusts of the S.S. men until their hearts or their minds burst and they either go to their graves or go mad. Yesterday, the Jews in our bunker were forced to put latrine pots on their heads and stand at attention for five hours to the amusement of the S.S. men. When my knees began to sag, I was kicked in the groin.

"I fainted, and was revived again only to be forced into the weekly 'cock-fight' or gladiatorial exhibition between Aryan and non-Aryan prisoners. The Christian prisoners, mostly against their own will, are forced to knock the Jews unconscious. Any Jew who, by accident or design, fells an Aryan prisoner, is marched off to the square of the camp where, in the presence of the Oberfuehrer, a hard, bull-faced sadist, he is given the water treatment, which is invariably fatal.

"This morning the most religious of the prisoners broke out into an oblique rebellion by yelling slogans from the Bible and Nazi literature which they are allowed to read in their bunks.

" 'Be not deceived, God is not mocked; whatsoever a man sows, that also shall he reap!'

" 'Verily, I say unto you,' howled another, 'inasmuch as thou hast done it unto one of the least of these, my brethren, thou hast done it unto me!'

"Another, a social democrat and an ex-Reichstag deputy, yelled an ironic statement from Rosenberg's Myths: 'There is nothing higher than the German people and its honor!'

"Another shouted a reputed statement by Goering: 'If anything should go wrong, we can always get Adolf to weep.'

"An hysterical prisoner struck a guard and was shot dead.

"Then as the corpses were spirited away, all of us in the square showed our solidarity as human beings by raising our fists high and shouting, 'Durchhalten!' (Hold fast!), which as you no doubt know was the slogan of that old hero, Frederick the Great, and has become the rallying cry of all the victims tormented in Brandenburg.

"Our punishment was swift and sure. Those who had yelled their individual slogans were suspended from the 'hanging beams' for three hours, their joints breaking in the process after several three-hour periods. Thirty Jews were picked at random to undergo the same torture, since the Oberfuehrer naturally assumed that the Jewish prisoners were behind the demonstration.

"While the Jews were hanging from the beams, they were ordered to display their circumcised state to the 'idiots' (those who had lost their minds through torture and who grinned harmlessly all day). The idiots were highly amused by the grotesque exhibition, some pointing to the signs on their backs which read: 'I am an idiot,' as if to excuse themselves for their delight in a fellow-human's torture, on the grounds of insanity.

"When I was released from the hanging beam (yes, I was called and chosen), I was dragged to my bunk more dead than alive, and to prevent myself from slipping into unconsciousness,

I read aloud in Hebrew from the psalms of David. This action irritated one of the guards, and he flogged me in the groin, and in the kidneys, until I spat blood. Then I was forced to stand outside my cell at attention with the other prisoners. We were given two hours of the silent treatment, and then locked up in our cells for the night.

"In the morning, at dawn, when we were routed out of our beds, five prisoners, three Jewish and two Gentiles, failed to awaken. This was a concession, since normally we were roused from our sleep while it was still dark. A young Gentile confided to me swiftly in passing that six prisoners, three Jews and three Gentiles, were marked for execution to terrorize the rest, and that I was one of those chosen.

"Back in my bunk, I thanked the Lord that he was ready to release me from my anguish. I read from the psalms again, but silently this time. An hour later I heard the first shooting in the courtyard, and a burly brute opened my cell, grinned at me idiotically and asked: 'How would you like to be shot next, Jew?'

" 'God willing, I am ready,' was my reply. But I was not called.

"I cannot go into further details, Herr Doktor. They are too terrible and obscene. In the three months I have been in here, I have grown at least forty years older and lost sixty pounds. I am a broken old man, ready for the grave, although in years I have scarcely passed my thirtieth birthday.

"I plead not only for myself, but for all the prisoners of Brandenburg whose hearts have not yet been broken and whose minds have not yet been deranged. If you are still seeing the Fuehrer, intercede in our behalf. There is a limit to human anguish. Even 'hold fast' may sound hollow after a while. To what shall we cling, if the last ray of hope is gone? Yours in true, brotherly love."

I called my nurse, who also acted as my secretary.

"Listen, Berta," I said, "do you remember that tall Aryan-looking Jew who came in to see me?"

"Yes, Herr Doktor," she smiled. "He was very handsome."

"He isn't handsome any more," I said grimly. "He has been at Brandenburg for the last three months. Now please call up the Chancellory, first thing in the morning, and tell the Fuehrer I am ready to go to Brandenburg with him whenever he is ready. He has only to pick me up at his pleasure."

"Yes, Herr Doktor."

Two days later my nurse, looking at the falling snow from the window, turned about suddenly and exclaimed: "It's the Fuehrer! His black car is approaching."

"I'm glad it's not the 'Green Minna' coming to take me to the 'Alex'," I laughed. (The "Green Minna" is equivalent to the "Black Maria" and the "Alex" is Berlin slang for the police station in the Alexanderplatz.) So many of my acquaintances were being dragged off by Goering's Feldpolitzei, Himmler's hatchet men, or the regular police, that I had the impulse to dash to the Zoolischer Garten station and start on my way to the border.

An hour later I was in Hitler's private car, speeding toward the hell which he had conjured out of his tormented imagination and thrown into the heart and soil of Germany. The car was full of S.S. men, as were the cars that flanked us, and I had the unpleasant sensation that I was being whisked to an unknown destination where I might be done away with, like so many other Germans who, as the Americans put it so vividly, "were being taken for a ride."

As we reached the camp, two Black Guards, flanking the iron gates, stood at attention. Their uniforms flaked with snow, they looked like a couple of marble giants that had suddenly come to life. Someone behind the picket fence bawled: "Achtung! Attention!" The prisoners were evidently being prepared for the arrival of the Fuehrer.

Inside, we were whisked past a line-up of prisoners evidently being discharged from the prison camp. They looked like lepers, broken, mutilated men. The skin on their faces and hands, like their winter clothes, was shreds and patches.

As they stood forlorn in the huge empty square, surrounded by ancient wooden guard-houses and shacks, unmindful of the flurries of snow that whipped into their faces, one man held out his hand in a Nazi salute as the Fuehrer passed him. It was a gruesome bit of burlesque that was more eloquent than words, since the hand had only one finger, a finger of accusation pointing to the heavens.

There were other prisoners with ears chopped off, legs and arms severed at the elbow or thigh. There were those who found themselves disintegrating through the psychic disease of sadism that had swept through the camp. Judging from their meager clothing, I realized that some had suffered frost-bite, necessitating minor and perhaps major amputations.

I looked furtively for the face of the Jew, but he was not in that line-up.

In the Oberfuehrer's quarters we were served a regulation German meal of frankfurters with ham and sauerkraut. Hitler had his egg and spinach and seemed ecstatically content. He appeared to be listening to an invisible Wagnerian orchestra, pounding into the sky-rhythms of the marching gods of Valhalla. His fork was a conductor's baton; he was stabbing the air with its prongs and conjuring up in his weird mind a vast symphony of madness, madness so wide and intense that it needed the world for *Lebensraum*.

Heil Hitler!

An idiot had burst into the room, Heil Hitlering with massive fantastic gestures, his huge ears wiggling automatically, the saliva dripping from his mouth. I was amazed to find him in the funereal uniform of a Black Guard. Was this a bit of luncheon entertainment that the Kommandant had planned for the Fuehrer?

"Barsch!" cried Hitler gleefully, embracing the thin, emaciated man who looked like a grinning skeleton in a black uniform. Then, turning to me, he said: "Don't you remember Barsch, Herr Doktor?"

"You mean—" It seemed too fantastic to be true.

"Yes, the village idiot," gloated my patient. "I had him taken here from Orienburg, where he was a holy terror with the Judenschweine! I made an S.S. guard out of him and he's doing fine."

Barsch grinned, his mouth wide open and his ears flapping grotesquely as he laughed. But Hitler snapped back into his morose trance and ordered the idiot from the room. We finished the meal in silence.

The Kommandant led Hitler, with myself following, out of the dining room into the square.

In the dead center a heavy wooden contraption resembling the goal-posts of a football game had been erected. A center horizontal bar was fixed firmly to the tops of the two posts, and from it, silhouetted against an angry and threatening sky, swaying in the wind and the occasional snow flurries, hung ten human beings. Chains held their wrists together, and it seemed to me for the first minute of my shocked gaze that they were lifting their arms in supplication to the heavens. But no. They were living men, the toys of the elements and men, whipped about by an occasional gust of wind that turned their faces to the horizon. As we drew nearer, I observed that they could not even give real expression to their pain, because their mouths had been taped with court-plaster. Suppressed sounds escaped from them from time to time.

But the sight that froze my blood was Barsch.

He was the happiest human being I had ever seen. He was parading back and forth in front of the "hanging beams," and as he walked, he did not look to see which way his feet took him. He had worn a path in front of the beams, a deep path, but he never turned his head from the hanging victims. His face and eyes were always riveted to them, no matter where he turned or which way he walked. On his face was the blissful look of a man whose heavenmost dreams have come true, for whom life has no more to give.

Occasionally one of the victims, gathering strength from heaven knows where, would give a slow upward jerk, flex his arm muscles and ease the strain on his back muscles. Then Barsch would fix his gaze raptly on this man, and notice the slow, downward inching of the body as the arm muscles gradually began to give way. When the body sagged again, and it seemed to be held only by joints and ligaments because the muscles had no more resiliency, then Barsch's face twisted into a beatific smile and he looked back at us to notice if we were enjoying the spectacle as much as he.

No one spoke. From time to time the Kommandant half turned to Hitler as if to ask for a silent approval. But Hitler's mind was on Barsch, as he watched this jubilant spectacle of his own early agonies. He turned to the Kommandant:

"Isn't he a jewel, Kommandant?"

"Ja, ja!" the Kommandant replied, with wide satisfaction beaming all over him. "We don't have a better man than Barsch in all Germany."

We passed the hanging figures in the wind, and their eyes seemed to bore into my back. I felt a wave of frozen hatred strike me.

When we reached the Jewish quarters, the Kommandant ordered the inmates to stand at attention outside their cells. There was no prisoner in front of one of the cells. It was unoccupied.

"The Jew in there hung himself last night," the Kommandant explained with not a little gusto. "He was a strange one, with strange notions about discipline. But we have another one to take his place tomorrow from the bunkers. Not exactly a Jew. An Aryan with Jewish ideas. We'll have him circumcised and then he'll be all Jew!"

CHAPTER TWENTY-NINE

INSANITY FAIR

A Dark Traffic — Susceptibility to Fraud — Aryan Platonist and Adviser—Nazi Reincarnation.

THROUGHOUT human history, a social crisis has always been accompanied by a mental crisis. The coming breakdown of society casts on all its members the sinister shadow of neurosis, sexual pathology and madness. While Hitler was soapboxing in Munich, casting his spell on the hungry mob, homosexuals duly licensed by the police were mixing in the crowd and openly hawking their bodies. The more normal elements in the crowd preferred to drug thir economic misery with Hitler's Jew-hatred and a promise of a Nazi paradise.

These homosexuals later found their normal place in the world by joining Roehm's storm troopers battalion; Roehm, a sexual psychopath himself, had made pederasty and perversion a social norm, a consummation devoutly to be wished, and the sex-inverted storm trooper parading in his brown shirt and leather boots felt himself superior to the male onlookers who persisted in the degenerate habit of making love to women as Adam made love to Eve, with the dangerous possibility of begetting offspring as abnormal as themselves.

In a society where the rational has become the irrational and the psychotic is king, it is inevitable that a wave of superstition, fraud and charlatanry should sweep all classes of the population, as happened in the days of the dying Roman Empire when Christianity had to compete with the numerous miracle-mongers of the East and the native witch-doctors who had, every one of them, his own religious and philosophical nostrum guaranteed to cure the disease known as living. As Hitler and the Nazis sat

297

at the deathbed of the Weimar Republic and sped its departure by feeding it subtle poisons of propaganda mixed with violence, the rest of neurotic Germany was rushing to the astrologer to discover its fate in the stars, in the palms of its hands, in its handwriting, in the bones of the skull, in occult cabalistic numbers, in the ghost of its dead grandmother and in all places except the right one—in a rational, just society breeding rational, just men and women.

Nazi politics, cooked up in the witch's cauldron of Hitler's *Mein Kampf* and Rosenberg's *Myth of the Twentieth Century,* was a powerful potion for the disillusioned and degenerate who swallowed doses of anti-Semitism, autocracy, anti-humanitarianism and anti-everything, and were ever ready for endless orgies of violence, hatred, spying and counter-spying, treachery and murder.

It is an error to believe that Hitler, Goebbels, Goering, Himmler et al, consciously misled the German mentality. They were themselves to a greater extent than is credible the dupes of their own fantastic lies and grotesque propaganda. A morphine addict like Goering, a club-foot like Goebbels, a sadist like Himmler and a homosexual like Roehm would not have been attracted to the Nazi movement in the first place, if it had not been a contagious mental disease whose germs were already lodged in their own twisted mentalities. Even comparatively sane people like myself were sucked into the whirlpool of national pathology with its currents and counter-currents of hatred, terror, blood and violence. No person who is a part of a pathological community can escape that "contagious magic," as Frazer puts it, which seizes hold of his mind and drags it down to the primitive level of the Dyak head-hunter in the Malay jungles.

Least of all Hitler himself. The Fuehrer's great strength lies in the fact that he believes fanatically in his own lies, deadly disease germs which he has spread throughout the dying mind of our age. Through the process of sympathetic magic, however, Hitler has been victimized by the sensation-mongering, witch-brewings and hocus-pocus of other neurotics like himself, many of whom have had an equal faith in their remedies and nostrums for a dying German folk.

It is hard to differentiate between the self-deluded Messiah like Hitler and the out-and-out charlatan like Cagliostro, who, in the process of peddling his lies to the public, becomes so fascinated by his psychological wares that he accepts them as genuine works of truth, together with his duped customers. That Hitler could be fooled by lesser magicians than himself is not generally known, but it is a fact that on numerous occasions he has been victimized by charlatans and fakers, as well as by clowns and practical jokers who thrive in a country gone hilariously mad.

I became aware of the Fuehrer's susceptibilty to fraud early in my relationship with him when his Messiah-complex was no more than a secret between himself and his handful of friends. One morning, after a cursory interview, he handed me a card, neatly engraved in letters of gold. It read:

THE OPHRASTUS BOMBAST VON HOHENHEIM
ARYAN PLATONIST AND ADVISER
BY APPOINTMENT ONLY

"Have you heard of him, Herr Doktor?" my patient asked curiously.

"Yes," I said, "his name sounds familiar."

"He's staying over at the Kaiserhof," said my patient a bit sheepishly. "His ideas about love are a bit strange, but there's a lot of truth in what he says."

"What does he say?" I asked.

"He says that love is nothing but a shadow in a cave. There is nothing lovely or beautiful except that which does not exist. He believes with Schopenhauer that woman's beauty exists merely in man's imagination; woman is merely a clumsy, two-legged animal who appears attractive to man through a trick of Mother Nature, who demands that we love women to bring children into the world."

"Thank God he blames man's sex instincts on Mother Nature and not on the Jews," was my amused comment.

"On the contrary," said Hitler seriously, "he does blame the Jews for fostering virility in the male, and so helping to keep men in bondage to women and the race. Satan, the Jew and the sex organ are one, all one and the same thing, he says, 'the evil worm that the world doth pierce.' That's a favorite quotation of his—he says it's from Nietzsche."

"It's from Dante," I corrected him. "Herr Bombast's ideas are as unique as the knowledge of his sources. Do you really take stock in him?"

"His teaching about the Jew being the seducer is true," snapped Hitler, his eyes lighting up with a strange fire as they always did when the Jew-devil stuck his prong into his consciousness. I remembered his bizarre statement in *Mein Kampf*: "The black-haired Jewish youth lies in wait for hours on end, satanically glaring and spying at the unsuspicious (Nordic) girl he plans to seduce, adulterating her blood and removing her from the bosom of her people." Judging from Hitler's emotions when he indorsed Herr Bombast's ideas about Satan, I must say that the above quotation is one of the Fuehrer's lies which he ardently believes in. The Jew is not only the Devil, but the Devil's grandmother with nine hundred heads, each of which contains a separate nefarious plan to appropriate everything in the world, from the stock market to the sex instinct.

"I don't think you should see Herr Bombast any more," I cautioned my patient.

"Why not?" he demanded.

"Because he is making it difficult for you to normalize yourself."

He looked befuddled.

"He is associating sex and the sex organ with the Jew," I explained. "I once pointed out to you that your psychic impotence may be due to that. It certainly cannot help you to have this more strongly emphasized in your mind."

My patient thought.

"You have an excellent sense of humor, Herr Doktor," he finally managed to say.

A week later I asked my patient to take me to the Kaiserhof to see Herr Bombast, the Platonist. I found a blonde young fellow, no more than thirty, surrounded by a group of admiring cultists, some of whom were obvious homosexuals, and others staid looking burghers on the lookout for a thrill. "The land of chimera is the only paradise for the living," he was telling his open-mouthed dupes. "Death is at the roots of life. To make life tolerable, we must dream our way out of reality into the super-reality of comradeship. The love of man for man is the only true affection between humans."

I was introduced to Herr Bombast by Hitler. He shook my hand warmly, expecting a new initiate. He handed me a card with a gracious gesture.

"The Ophrastus Bombast von Hohenheim," I read aloud. "Are you also known as Paracelsus?" I asked quizzically.

"Yes," he said cordially.

"I admire your boyish appearance," I said admiringly.

"My philosophy keeps me young," he bubbled.

"Quite remarkable," I said, "considering the fact that you were born in 1490."

Hitler eyed me with a puzzled expression, a cross between amazement, amusement and chagrin.

"Oh, you misunderstand," said the young charlatan with complete poise. "I am not the original Paracelsus; I am his Nazi reincarnation."

His devotees seemed to be satisfied with his explanation, but Hitler was not. Later on I discovered he had been sentenced to a long term in prison. It seems that the Nazi Paracelsus had advocated castration as a way out of the dilemma of breeding men and women only to shoot them down on the battlefield or from the bomb-laden skies. Hitler needed cannon fodder for his imperial dreams, and a race of German eunuchs could not supply him with the necessary corpses to pave his road to glory. When the People's Court sentenced Paracelsus and he was examined by the prison doctor, an exciting discovery was made. Paracelsus was a Lesbian, a woman disguised as a man! Suffering from a castration complex, no doubt, she had hoped to castrate the German male in the name of Plato, Hitler and the Third Reich!

CHAPTER THIRTY

Insanity Fair (Continued)

Fan Dancer—Countess—The Hitler Cult—Grasping for Venus— One May Show Too Great an Interest in Architecture—Psychic Revenge.

When the Fuehrer rose to power, Goebbels, the master magician, merged all the fantastic nonsense circulating in the Third Reich into the single grotesque myth of the Fuehrer himself. Just as the numerous gods in Rome, collected from all parts of the world, finally faded into the single god of St. Paul, Hitler became the divine depository of all the insanities, vanities and inanities that plagued the minds of the German people since the day when they arose one morning to discover that they had lost a war which they had already won. The German nature substituted *Heil Hitler* for *Gruess Gott,* and so deified their own neurosis by placing a great psychopath on the throne of Jehovah. The wily Goebbels *Heil-Hitlered* the German people into an acceptance of madness as the normal way of life.

Heil Hitler! Even the charlatans and the fakers had to accommodate their star-gazings and table-wrappings to the demands of the Nazi salute invented by the Cagliostro with the club-foot, the cunning minister of lies. Here is an amusing example.

Just before Hindenburg surrendered to the Bohemian corporal with the Caesar complex, I attended a party at the home of Dr. Goebbels at the special invitation of my patient.

Frau Goebbels, to whom the Nazi movement was merely another exotic and erotic cult, like Shinto and Voodoo, had invited a Buddhist to talk on the Hindu-Aryan origins of Hitlerism. "Buddhism entered China," said the speaker ecstatically, rolling his eyes toward the ceiling, "Buddhism entered China during the

Han period; it will enter Germany during the Hanfstaengl period. Heil Hitler!"

This was the signal for an outburst of laughter on the part of the distinguished guests, which included some foreign ambassadors and celebrities. Hitler seized me by the arm and we both barged out together. As his chauffeur Schreck opened the door of his Mercedes, my patient spat three times on the curb, cursed Putzi, whom he suspected of the blasphemous association of his name with a Chinese emperor and a Nazi clown, and then let out a vile cuss-word which I had never heard him use before. The Fuehrer, I suspected, was becoming impatient with his role of playing God to Germany, and its people: he was rational enough to realize, at times, that he was less than God, less than the angels, and even less than a man!

This feeling that he was not the meeting of earth and sky, the mirage of the German Ulysses seeking an impossible harbor, overcame the Fuehrer during those moods of despondency when his sexual helplessness in the face of a beautiful woman brought his maimed psyche to focus. Instead of rising to the moon with his dupes, he sank into the ocean of despair, right into the bottomless void of melancholia. It was then that the tears would come to his eyes and he would cry like a child. The hero of life was caught up in the throes of death.

The Christians have their cross, the Moslems their crescent, and the Germans their swastika, but I know from personal observation that the Fuehrer carries the burden of the swastika on his soul as painfully as the lowliest man in the Reich. He sometimes goes completely wild, announces that his ancestor was the god Saturn, and threatens that some day he will travel back to his home in the clouds. It is his troubled mind trying to overcome its perpetual nightmare by a leap into Olympus, where the dead gods of Greece once danced out their lives in bawdy merriment while the slaves below labored and died in the salt mines of Hellas.

To overcome his sexual frustration, Hitler would now and then seek the company of women with a vengeance. But only at a safe distance, at a ball or party, where he could receive the adulation of beauty without being obliged to reciprocate with

anything but a smile or a handshake. But the word had spread
in the female world that the Fuehrer could not tread the seven-
fold path of Buddhist bliss that led to an orgiastic Nirvana.
Consequently he became the whipping-horse for the disappointment of women who yearned to bask in his affections.

"My dear," said a lovely blonde at a party within earshot of
Hitler, "the Fuehrer, like Frederick, is a coquette: to keep his
sweethearts, he never satisfies them."

This made my patient wince. At another affair, a friend of
Frau Himmler exclaimed: "Methuselah waited nine hundred
years for the perfect love; why can't Hitler wait ninety?"

The Fuehrer, who had overheard the jibe, was patently disturbed. He felt himself in low company, and despite the high
jinks that was taking place under his nose (Goebbels was making
violent love to a Russian countess while Himmler was spiriting
an actress to his sleeping quarters), he chose to engage in a
technical conversation with a suave English architect who appeared equally oblivious of the goings-on about him.

An English fan dancer (a sad imitation of Sally Rand)
pounced upon the center of the floor and began her nude erotic
gyrations, to the delight of the high Nazis and their low ladies,
who felt equally high at the sight of the fan weaving about the
hard, emotionless dancer in such a way as to make her nudity
mysterious and inviting. They knew art when they saw it, but
Hitler did not deign to look. The dancer tried hard to attract the
Fuehrer's attention, almost brushing her nude body against him,
but Hitler was too preoccupied with his architectural discussion.

The dancer broke into a sweet smile, tickled his face playfully
with her fan, but all she elicited from Hitler was this remark
addressed to the architect: "Can you explain, Mr. Dorchester,
the fan-vaulting of Henry VIII's chapel at Westminster?"

The Fuehrer's academic knowledge of architecture is phe-
nomenal (all his biographers have commented on this), and
Hitler took the Englishman completely by surprise. He also
shocked the fan dancer. His reference to the fan-vaulting of
Henry VIII's chapel seemed to her an oblique belittlement of her
art, and her nude body became taut with suppressed fury. The

fan moved and hissed about her thighs like a coiling snake that
was about to dart at the Fuehrer's throat.

"You've insulted my art," screamed the dancer in bad German
and worse taste. "You're a homo building a crazy house for
homies and degenerates! How dare you ask questions about a
chapel, about a house of God?"

In twenty minutes the irate dancer, fully clothed, was on her
way to London, while the guests were listening to an opera star
singing *Horst Wessel* to placate the Fuehrer.

But the Fuehrer could not be soft-soaped or soothed into a
state of mental peace. He couldn't leave, either, for fear (as he
confessed to me later) that the tongues left behind him would
wag so fast and furiously that his sense of female persecution
would reach an acute stage. Instead, he continued his abstract
discussion on architecture with the English gentleman.

Goebbels, disturbed by the rumpus, stomped out of a bedroom
with his exotic Russian. Or perhaps her delirium was due to too
much champagne. In any event, Goebbels and his exotic, as well
as erotic and alcoholic, countess, goose-stepped over to the
Fuehrer and demanded to know in a loud voice the cause of the
disturbance.

Hitler remained silent. His face was pale.

"You look at me as if I were a mass of corruption," fumed
Goebbels. "I won't stand it."

"Corruption can always stand on its own club-foot," smiled
the Fuehrer, while the women tittered.

It was the first time in my experience that Hitler had made
a retort that completely demolished his adversary. But Goebbels,
like Roehm, was an easy target; the two were "fate-doomed"
people, as my patient put it, and therefore, when it came to a test
of strength, were as harmless as Putzi, the clown, whose insults
no one took seriously because he was the Nazi court jester,
planted to amuse the beggars who had become the princes and
kings of the Third Reich.

Goebbels slunk out of the room like a beaten dog with his tail
between his legs, while the Russian countess remained to pick up
the pieces of the broken spear of her Nazi knight of arms who
had been so terribly humiliated by the Fuehrer. Hitler could now

leave the party with grace. He knew that any unfavorable gossip that the English fan dancer had whipped up against him was cancelled by the brilliancy of his verbal sword-play, at which he was a master in the Reichstag, but a flat failure in the drawing-room. He had slain the dragon and it lay bleeding at his feet.

But the sense of triumphant masculinity did not last with the Fuehrer for long. It was easy to make a woman hate a man but it was harder to make her love him, and even harder in Hitler's case to reciprocate her love. The jibe of the English fan dancer stuck in the Fuehrer's mind like an internal wasp stinging him to furious outbursts of temper and pathological behavior.

I saw indications of my patient's dangerous mood one night when we were guests of Putzi's. Putzi had developed a fondness for me because I could converse with him in broken English on Shakespeare and the Elizabethan classics, which had at first interested me as masterpieces of literary homicide and sadism. Putzi's official job, as head of the foreign press services, was to entertain the foreign correspondents with jokes and make them feel that the good old German *gemuetlichkeit* was still in existence despite the "brown Hitler horror" which was attributed to Jewish-inspired propaganda abroad.

While Putzi was "kidding" the correspondents in true American fashion, Hitler was making a faint effort at flirting with an Italian lady, aristocratic to her painted fingertips, who was evidently the wife or the mistress of an Italian press man. Hitler kept patting her as she sat beside him and playfully asked for her garter.

The lady was shocked. She lifted her tweezed eyebrows in obvious amazement.

"Mio caro," she said ominously, *"non si deve desiderare l'impossibile."*

The Fuehrer rose from his seat in a huff. He evidently considered his request a modest one, as proper as a man's request for a woman's telephone number. But he was unaware that the possession of an Italian lady's garter by a man and its subsequent flaunting would be an out and out indication of something much more intimate. Ignorant of this subtle cleavage in the mentalities of the German and the Italian, this proud lady appeared to him as a Borgia, who had poisoned his dark soul with some insidious Italian words more terrible perhaps than the public insults flung at him by the nude fan dancer whose art he had outraged by indifference. The Fuehrer, unlike his mentor, Mussolini, has made no effort to learn any other language, and the words of the Italian lady, which were a flat statement of the impossibility of desiring the impossible, made no impression of recognition in his closed mind. She continued to sit in somewhat injured silence, and he stalked over to the ornate mantelpiece which graced the room. His eye caught sight of two bronze book ends between which Putzi had clamped three books, to wit: *Mein Kampf, Psychopathia Sexualis,* by Kraft-Ebbing, and a German version of *Alice in Wonderland.*

Ordinarily, the Fuehrer would have laughed at the significant juxtaposition of the three volumes, which hinted without words that Hitler's magnum opus was a product of childish fantasy and pathological gropings.

At this moment, an English journalist sauntered over and seemed engrossed in the arrangement of the three books. He looked at Hitler, Hitler looked at him; neither said a word for a few moments.

Then the Englishman spoke:

"Funny, the arrangement of the three books, eh what? First, Kraft-Ebbing's, a compendium of all of man's knowledge of the 'wolves' of the dark side of sex. Then gentle *Alice in Wonderland,* of which nothing is left to be said, and then your work. Symbolic of something, no?"

Hitler faced him and drew himself up straight. He seemed to be looking at the Englishman as if he were a god on a throne from which he was to utter an ill-embracing pronunciamento.

"*That* is the way it should be," he said in a hard, brutal voice. "*Alice in Wonderland* is the world, and it is flanked on the one side *by a magnificent work of a magnificent German mind,* and on the other by my book, which is more than a book, because it is a man who will place the world in precisely the position that you see *Alice in Wonderland:* by the *German mind* on one side and by *myself and the righteous power invested in me to set the ills of the world aright, and remold it in my image!*"

He almost screamed the last few words. When he stopped, everyone was at attention, including the Englishman, who, puffing on a pipe to taunt the Fuehrer's pathological dislike of tobacco, looked him over, up and down, as if he were examining a new specimen of insect at close range. Finally, he gave him a last look, shrugged his shoulders as if he had just observed a nonentity, and casually, sauntered off nonchalantly. A few subdued titters broke out among the assemblage. Hitler continued to glare. Then the titters burst out a bit louder, and he seemed to wilt a trifle.

He turned and glared at Putzi in a corner of the room.

Putzi was a trifle ill at ease and nervous:

"Not a bad criticism, eh?" he laughed in his best clown-fashion.

Hitler suddenly picked up one of the bronze book-ends and flung it at Putzi's head. The head of the foreign news service was in the hospital for a month. The assemblage broke up at once, while Hitler walked up and down the floor, raving like a maniac, hurling imprecations, promising all and sundry that some day the world would bow down to him.

Hitler sent Putzi flowers daily while he convalesced in the hospital. After he had calmed down, he realized that he had been wrong. Putzi was a clown, and a clown's immunity was something sacred from time immemorial.

But the flinging of the book-end at his jester's head in a sudden surrender to a homicidal rage, was not, in my opinion, an expression of wrath directed against Putzi, but against the fan dancer who had inserted the wasp of doubt in his mind and stung him with the terror of homosexuality.

CHAPTER THIRTY-ONE

INSANITY FAIR (Concluded)

The Grand Celestial Couch of Aryan Blessedness—
Liebestod—"We Are All Going to Hell."

THE PSYCHOPATH, with a paranoid mentality like that of my patient, needs the crutch of a devastating and continual hatred upon which to lean, and to use as a bludgeon against a world of imaginary enemies. In the symphony of horror crashing through his brain runs the sadistic *leitmotif,* the recurrent theme of hatred which expresses itself socially in Hitler's case in homicidal attacks upon Jews, Marxists, liberals, radicals, Catholics and Protestants, until the whole gamut of human possibilities is plumbed.

During the period of my association with him, Hitler strove desperately to capture the love of a woman, which, as Goethe and Huxley have pointed out, opens the heart to those human emotions which often overflow into the love of all mankind and into a passion for God himself, the religious goal of the mystic and the saint. By clinging to the body of Venus he made a pathetic attempt to fly from his own sadistic-masochistic impulses, the dark destructive tendencies that were causing havoc in his soul.

Sex, like opium, creates its own climate of heat and cold, summer, winter, spring and autumn, seasons of the mind that guard against the outer weather and give the soul an illusion of eternal bliss. Hitler sought to bring May to his troubled mind by gratifying himself sexually with a girl of twenty or younger, and his successive failures at consummation finally resulted in an act of sadistic-masochistic madness which I hesitate to reveal, save for the fact that I have already analyzed my patient's state of mind at the moment, and I am sure that the reader will consider his fantastic action with the objectivity of the psychiatrist, and not with the moral indignation of the puritan or the laughter of the clown.

Losing faith in my slow, scientific treatment of his case, and preferring the blitz-technique of the magician and the witch doctor, who can create health by an act of will accompanied by hocus-pocus, herbs, prayers and ritual, Hitler secretly visited the temple of Aryan Motherhood, a patriotic brothel run by some conniving Nazis in company with some Hindu whom I had always suspected of being an American Negro from Harlem and whom, in fact, I met later on Amsterdam Avenue in the heart of the Harlem black belt. He was a quadroon, or perhaps an octoroon, and easily passed as an Indian to Hitler, who had rarely seen a Negro in the flesh.

The attractive and attracting feature of this temple was a huge bed, called the Grand Celestial Couch of Aryan Blessedness. The couch, a vast, gilded affair draped in lush, exotic-tinted covers, was in the center of a large room filled with suffocating Eastern perfumes intended to arouse the amorous desires of those who wished to propagate a Walkyre or a Siegfried for the sake of Hitler-Wotan and the future of the Third Reich.

To add an air of occult mystery to the Temple, the charlatans who ran the patriotic brothel contrived a bit of fiendish sadism for the customers in the name of a secret rite that would forever bind the woman to the fraternity of "blood and honor," the Nazified Aryan community. An S.S. man's dagger of honor was handed to the male as he consummated his act with the eager victim of his lust, and he carved a swastika between the breasts of the girl or woman as she lay panting with the climax of the patriotic ritual. When Hitler arrived at the Temple he ordered the Hindu to remove four middle-aged aspirants from the bed, and centred his attention on a girl of the League of German Youth, who felt herself so highly honored by Hitler's presence on the couch that she almost fainted from the shock.

Like all other innocents, the young blonde girl soon realized that the task of conceiving an heir to the Nazi throne was not so easy as she thought. The Hindu was called in to ease the difficulty, and he suggested a remedy according to the sacred books of Hindu sex lore. My patient, reduced to a primitive level of thought and emotion, readily consented. The wasp, an actual physical insect and no creation of his own tortured mind, was applied to those parts which he was told would assure his virility, but he only succeeded in turning the knife of masochism outward and attacking the helpless girl with the "dagger of honor" in such a way as to nearly mutilate her for life.

Hitler subconsciously was taking revenge for the insult of the fan dancer by maiming and almost killing a member of her sex whose love he craved but could not conquer because he could not establish erotic contact with the divine Walkyre of his dreams, and like Wagner, the occasional pederast, had to turn the love of man for woman into a terrible *Liebestod* without the soothing fire-music. When my patient brought the girl into my office, I had an immediate image of the fan dancer as soon as I unwrapped the blanket from her nude body. In her unconscious state, she looked as stiff and immobile as the danseuse who had reviled him because he had ignored her and stung him with the wasp-like suspicion of homosexualism that had driven him into an act of homicidal madness.

As my patient confessed his crime to me he broke into a fit of hysterical weeping. At the hospital where I rushed the poor deluded girl, I found that her wounds were only superficial and that the only dangerous cuts were between her breasts where my patient had begun his act of sadism in the mad belief that he was performing a patriotic role.

CHAPTER THIRTY-TWO

Conclusion

I Am Ready to Pull Out—The Murder of Hitler's Brother—Hitler as a World-Conqueror—The New Physics—The Kaiser Passes Judgment—Apologia.

HITLER often chided me for my failure to marry and raise a family. "Perhaps you're afraid of the shadows of your own psychic images?" he once suggested.

I laughed. When it pleased me, I told him the truth. Life in Nazi Germany was too pagan to complicate with Christian responsibilities.

In June, 1934, with the whole German horizon blackened with the smoke of the purge guns, I was glad I had made no new vital ties. "Maybe in the new world, if I ever get there," I thought, and made secret arrangements to leave Germany for Switzerland. The railway tickets came to me by messenger the very next morning. At two o'clock that same day a train would pull me out of Berlin.

I had not expected this first important part of my plan to be consummated so easily and so quickly. Most of my affairs were in order, but there was still plenty of planning to be done, whereby I would be pulling up all of my stakes without appearing to do so. I got word to my uncle to get to my office as soon as possible. I was expecting him when my front bell rang at about noon.

The man at the door turned out to be an old doctor I had been chummy with in Munich; a party man, but one of the more decent fellows.

"What are you doing so far away from a good glass of beer?" I said by way of greeting. He was one of those Munichers for whom Munich is first in everything good, especially beer. "What the deuce are you doing in Berlin."

"Plugging up a lot of holes for our Fuehrer," he snorted,

"like a good German burgher. Do you happen to have a stiff drink on you?"

I brought forth brandy and soda. He drank and made a sour grimace. "I can't stay long," he gasped, putting down his glass. "I'm here, really, to entrust you with a confidence."

"What!" I exclaimed. "Is the age of trust in Germany about to begin?"

He laughed.

"Not this very moment. But look here, I have to tell this to someone or bust." He paused and resumed in a much graver voice. "I've been looking at some corpses, Herr Doktor, corpses more or less fresh. Do you, by any chance, like corpses?"

"I would like them better," I replied, "if they were selected with more care."

"Not much love goes into the selection of corpses," the old fellow rumbled. "But I just saw a corpse that would have taken your breath away."

"Come, come," I protested. "I hope it would take more than a corpse to do that to me."

He met my eyes at an even level and asked:

"How would you feel about a corpse with the name Adolf Hitler?"

I almost fell out of my seat with surprise.

"No, not the Adolf you're thinking of," he hastened to assure me. "Remember the fellow who's been going around telling the world that he's Hitler's brother?"

I remembered easily enough. "Wasn't his name Robert?" I asked.

"That was the name he had been known by in the lower cafe elements of Berlin. But there's something very few people know, which I am about to impart to you. Keep it quiet, if you want to go on living. In 1923, while the Fuehrer was imprisoned at Landsberg, this very same fellow told the prison authorities that he himself was Adolf Hitler, and that the prisoner, Robert Hitler, had assumed his name as well as identification papers in order to escape military service in Austria."

"I've heard that story, too," I told the old doctor, "and I must say that I was not too impressed with it."

The old doctor eyed me significantly.

"If the poor fellow's story needed any corroboration," he said, "Hitler has certainly attended to it. He was among those killed yesterday."

I could not help whistling.

"Is it possible that you have made a mistake?" I asked.

"Even with that pierced left ear of his?"

I remembered only too well the malformed bit of ear.

"I don't expect there's anything to be done about it except keep the peace," I said to him as he rose to go.

"I suppose not," he agreed dryly. "Look me up when you get to Munich again," he called back to me from the door, "and see what we can do down there by way of a real drink."

Those last words of his rang in my ears for a long while. *Look me up when you get to Munich again.* Would I ever again get to Munich?

*   *   *

From an apartment on New York's West Side, I have been observing my ex-patient hammering his way at the head of startling mechanized armies through Austria, Czechoslovakia, Poland, Denmark, Norway, the Netherlands, Belgium, France, Yugoslavia, Greece and Russia. Wherever he comes, his troops are overwhelmingly superior in numbers and equipment; his planes are faster, his tanks are bigger, and his guns shoot the farthest. Except over England and Russia, his air force finds no flying formations strong enough to oppose it. The military experts avow with bated breath that no man before Hitler has ever conquered and held in subjection so much of the civilized world. Undoubtedly it is so. Yet I am not impressed. I do not begin to see him in the role of the invincible world-conqueror.

Perhaps I am simply viewing my ex-patient's triumphs in the light of Spinoza's *sub specie aeternitatis*. But it appears to me that brute conquests such as Hitler's must eventually bow before the power of reason, the rational universe itself. When the present-day democracies (which give true expression to the ultimate rationality of man) make full use of the scientific techniques of warfare exploited at present by the dictatorships, it seems inevitable that those great imponderables—anger, tenacity and courage—the qualities Wellington's soldiers picked up on the playing fields of Eton—will once more shoot to the fore, and become decisive factors in the struggle for world-control.

Perhaps my judgment of Hitler is not entirely objective because of the geographical distance from which I survey him. Where I live today, the arts of peace still predominate, in spite of occasional fugitive alarums. Nor do I look at Hitler through the telescopic lenses of the military experts, or could, even though I wanted to. I think it was Guy de Maupassant who originated the saying that no man can be a hero to his valet. How much less are his chances of shining in the eyes of his doctor. While the aforementioned experts see Hitler at the head of his all-pervading legions, directing penetrations of whole peoples, dismissing in short order difficulties of terrain and economy, mastering at the same time problems of construction and devastation, I see only a terribly lonely, frustrated man, followed wherever he goes by his fear and distrust of women, his loathing of a people he has good reason to believe are his own flesh and blood, and the vital, unfulfilled, organic desires that bark at him like dogs from the chilly uncompanioned compartments of his life; a sick man looking furtively at a medicine bottle.

I am given to understand that Hitler has not only invested Europe. He is already in the process of adjusting its economic and spiritual forces to his own prejudices and the needs of German economy. It is incredible to me that this could be anything but a temporary state of affairs. Under any imaginable circumstances men are capable of either one of two relationships: they must either co-operate or fight. Co-operation means peace, and in the arts of peace Hitler is bound to be beaten. Peace requires a machinery as specialized as the machinery of war: only those competent to arrange the world's peace will know how to keep it. Should the world miss out on peace, however, and the war continue, Hitler (or his successor in power) will be beaten with the weapons of the new physics more decisively than he was able to subdue the world with the weapons of the old.

The Germany Hitler took over and turned into the war machine with which he has conducted his feverish transcontinental *tours de force* was a country whose laboratories enjoyed all the advantages of learning and research developed by democratic institutions in the spirit of modern progress. When Hitler turned these laboratories (conceived for the nurturing of the spirit of man) into conspiratorial chambers for the aggrandizement of the weapons of war, and harnessed them into the production of demoniac powers great enough to overwhelm all the known forces of civilization outside the Reich, he committed his grand act of usurpation, and achieved victory. But this triumph can remain in his hands only as long as the weapons he holds are charged with the maximum of destructive power.

But it is not a secret that the new physics is preparing a complete revolution in all present scientific concepts of power. Instead of the power of steam and electricity the laboratories are nurturing what may be described as atomic energy. Within the range of this new research, man will be able to extract more force from a glass of water than he is now able to get out of a month's pumping of the oil fields of Baku. The instruments of destruction forged from this new power will render all of the present known weapons of war as obsolete as the battering ram with which an all-conquering Rome pried open the gates of Alexandria and Jerusalem.

Possibly fifteen or twenty years still separate us from the triumph of the new physics already visible in experiments conducted in Europe and America. But while it is true that Hitler keeps the laboratories of Germany frantically busy on these very researches, the German scientists are considerably behind the scientists of democracy, and slipping further back each day. The obvious truth is that scientific investigation cannot be conducted by powers either besieging or undergoing a state of siege. If America gets ahead of Germany in these developments of the new physics by no more than a year, the comparative and overwhelming superiority of the new forces over the old will be such that Hitler's armed strength, mechanical and human, will melt under them as snow melts under a strong sun.

No, I cannot see Hitler as anything but a sick man and Germany as a very sick country. It seems quite certain now that Hitler will never recover. And it seems questionable whether Germany herself can survive the Hitler era. The novelist Joseph Conrad was fond of showing how, once a man had been committed by accident or destiny to a certain attitude, it hounded him to the bitter end of his life. By reason of the fatalities of the last quarter of a century (as if the heart of Germany had succumbed to the picture of herself painted by the enemy propaganda during the war of 1914-1918), Germany has committed herself to the support of as vicious a set of lies and liars as has ever dominated a community of men. Can Germany of her own free will ever shake off this evil commitment? I hope so. But is it possible?

*   *   *

If Germany is ever rescued from the psychic evils of Hitlerism, it will be only through the instrumentality of her strong, courageous race of exiles scattered over the whole face of the earth. From gentle Thomas Mann to thundering Otto Strasser, the solidified will of the exiled forces of Germany is for a return of Germany to her ancient ways and virtues. They do not merely condemn the vile practices of the seducers of their country; they presage the day of reckoning when it will be cogent to remember German qualities now almost forgotten.

Of all the pronouncements on the Hitler regime by Germans in exile, I have been moved most by the statement of the late Kaiser Wilhelm II, Hitler's direct predecessor in absolute power. In the course of an interview at Doorn with W. Burckhardt, the Kaiser said:

"There's a man alone, without family, without children, without God. Why should he be human? Oh, without doubt, he's sincere. But this very excessive sincerity keeps him apart, out of touch with men and realities. . . . He builds legions, but he does not build a nation. A nation is created by families, a religion, traditions. It is made up out of the hearts of mothers, the wisdom of fathers, the joy and exuberance of children. Over there an all-swallowing state, disdainful of human dignities and the ancient structure of our race, set itself up in place of everything else. And the man who, alone, incorporates in himself this whole state, has neither a God to honor, nor a dynasty to conserve, nor a past to consult.

"For a few months I was inclined to believe in national socialism. I thought of it as a necessary fever. And I was gratified to see that there were associated with it for a time some of the wisest and most outstanding Germans. But these, one by one, he has got rid of, even killed. Schleicher, Neurath, and even Blomberg. He has nothing left but a bunch of shirted gangsters.

"This man could bring home victory to our people each year, without bringing them glory. Of our Germany, which was a nation of poets and musicians, of artists and soldiers, he has made a nation of hysterics and hermits, engulfed in a mob and led by a thousand liars and fanatics."

Upon rereading the galleys of this book, I find myself in the peculiar frame of mind of the irate husband whose wife gave birth to twins, and who refuses to admit that the second child is his own. The second infant as presented by the translator seems a stranger, although it bears a marked resemblance to my first child, the original manuscript which I finished and completely revised while taking up permanent residence in America.

Professor Boaz has discovered that the children of immigrant parents in America are affected by the Yankee climate and environment to such an extent that the very shapes of their heads are molded and changed to fit into the new *milieu* they find themselves in. Similarly, a literary work which migrates from one language to another often takes on the peculiar contours and coloring of its second tongue. Language is, in its very nature, a social expression, the product of a unique people, and the translation of this book is as different from my original manuscript as English is from German.

Upon second thought, however, it is possible the moving of my own psyche into a new world of ethical and spiritual values may have caused this obvious change in style and content apparent in the new draft of my book. In New York I naturally drifted into the company of German refugees, the majority of whom were Jews. As a pure Aryan, I harbored a latent anti-Semitism which rushed to the surface of my mind and possessed me utterly during my last few years in Germany, when Hitler sprayed the psychic atmosphere with the deadly microbes of Jew-hatred. Daily contacts with German-Jewish refugees in New York completely cleansed me of my anti-Jewish bias and, in fact, has given my mind a definite Hebraic tinge. It is not only the shape of one's skull but the shape of one's thoughts that is altered by the environmental pressure of a cosmopolitan city like

New York where racial and religious frictions have been reduced to a minimum.

Therefore, when I began revising my manuscript, I found myself eliminating every trace of anti-Jewish and anti-humanitarian bias, cutting out entire chapters that made me blush with their obviously Nazi-inspired prejudices. But it was not till I had actually seen most of these pages in galley proofs that I began to understand to what depths I had been influenced way back in Munich by the visit of that Aryan-looking Jew. I now realize that, whatever be the nature of their value to themselves, the value of the Jews to us Gentiles, to the rest of the living world, is the example they set us of fortitude and honor in the face of ever-imminent eclipse.

Together with the new democratic bias which crept into my final draft, almost against my will, came a light-hearted, almost frivolous turn of phraseology which is, I suppose, the product of my new democratic optimism. Laughter in Germany is a lost art, despite Herr Goebbels' effort to resurrect it by decree. But in America, and especially in New York, the comic spirit is the natural by-product of the sense of freedom and comradeship which one American shares with another. However, I must confess that the translator, who is a professional humorist, has given my satire an irreverent coloring which no German, however Americanized he may be, can possibly imitate.

* * *

To every man at different times, fate assigns some dark unreasonable trial of the spirit. Building shelters under the noses of destroying guns. Going hungry amidst plenty; living loveless in the midst of a spawning people. Working without thanks or compensation. But being a refugee pounds away mercilessly at the heart of all hope.

I drew the dank air of exile, first in Switzerland where it has matured into a tonic. Later in England, I lived in a state of waiting, and a brief spell in America raised only hopes. After that came France, Italy, Spain and Portugal where the air was more and more chilly to the hapless emigre. Wait till you settled down in America, whispered my heart. . . . I found America rich and tolerant; but I am no less a refugee here than I was in Switzerland.

There is a group of public benches in lower Central Park (not to be described too closely) where refugees from Hitlerism the world over congregate irregularly. A refugee will stroll over here for the sunlight, or because his pockets happen to be full of good things he can spare, or, conversely, because his pockets are utterly empty. The gaiety of the conversation of these hopeless people is a subject for scandal.

Yesterday afternoon I found four of them, all better known to me than I am to them, for I do not any longer tell people that I am a doctor. The Belgian with the heavy knotted stick was there. The hatless little gray-headed Pole, older than God, but gyrating like a windmill. The Czech, tall, skinny, with inky blue eyes; he must have been a printer. And the gay little middle-aged Jew who is selling carbon paper and threatens to make a business of it.

The sun was spilling all over the green and brown about them in a wild effervescence, and they were talking about Hitler. Can you think of a subject more legitimately their game than the man who smashed their countries, stole their homes, ruined their families, and consigned each of them to the exquisite timeless torture of exile? Strange, I thought, as I sat down among them. I have heard hundreds of refugees on a hundred occasions in a dozen cities. This is the first time I hear them talk of Hitler. . . .

"A queer fellow," the Czech was saying. "First he asks us to hate the Poles. Then he demands that we join him in destroying the Jews. Before we can realize it, he has us tearing away at one another's throats so enthusiastically, it is a wonder we are still intact. And all the time he keeps crying that it is all for our own good. As God is his witness, he is our protector, and sends us the ugliest and most avaricious of his ministers to administrate our affairs. And what is the upshot of it all? We laugh at him. In the cellars of bomb-shelters in Prague little Czechs play a game called Leap Swine, in which one little boy bends over while the other little boy jumps over him. The little boy leaning over is called Hitler. All in good fun, mind you. . . ."

"We didn't need Hitler to teach us hatred," the dapper little Pole exploded, as if he'd been listening to his own thoughts rather than to the Czech's words. "By a sort of divination of nature, we've been pretty good haters from the start. Maybe because so much of our land is always barren. Perhaps because the poor among us are always so many more than the rich. At any rate, Poles have always more gallantry than good manners, more pride than courage, more courage than patience. I sometimes think we hunger more for the substance of hatred than for the things which keep us alive. In our crazy craving after things to hate we go on hating the worn-out overhated Jews. Would you believe it, there are Poles who even take time off to hate Hitler?"

"The trouble with the Poles, as with the rest of the nationalities of Europe," chuckled the Belgian, twirling his stick, "is that you let Hitler break you by failing to return a blow in some vulnerable part of his armor. We Belgians realized right away that Hitler's tanks would crash through our fortresses; nevertheless we fooled him. I'm not joking, gentlemen; we fooled Hitler so badly I often wonder where he got courage to go on into France. What do you think Hitler had in mind when he flounced into Belgium? Our little piece of country? He wanted our diamonds. He broke in with his apron all ready for a shower of the glittering stuff he had always envied us. But Belgians know what a poor fellow has in mind when he crashes a jewelry store, so they sent their diamonds to England. When Hitler spread his silly apron, the Belgians just dumbly turned out their empty pockets. . . ."

"In that case what happened to Antwerp should stand unique among the jokes of the world," scoffed the Jew. "The truth is, Hitler never needed your diamonds. When he got to Belgium his apron was already filled with the diamonds and rubies the German Jews had generously poured into it. Why? Just the squaring of an old historic account, that's all. Jews have never felt right about those valuables of the Egyptians which they borrowed and had no time to return, before crossing the Red Sea into the desert of Sinai. It was taken from Pharaoh and returned to Hitler, that's all. He doesn't use us gently, I grant you. But how gently is he using the English, the French, the Greeks, the Russians, his own people? . . ."

After that all turned expectantly toward me, the only true Aryan German present. But I dare say something has happened to my German sense of humor in the last few years. I was not up to it. The words I had in mind to say melted into a lava of emotion which swiftly rose to my throat and almost choked me. I mumbled an apology, got up, and left them.

The sunlight of that marvelous Manhattan day crowded me every step of the way. My brain became like a nest of sparrows in October. "You, a doctor, a scientist, had the care, the vital disposition of that monster for fifteen years. And what did you accomplish? You have only to consult a map, or the face of the first refugee you come across.

"Yet what could *you* do? What *can* you say?

"Who knows how much more God secretes in a man than in a race? Or is it the other way? Is there more of a man in his hope than in his dread? What is the virility of a man in his body as compared with what flows through the more tenuous fabric of his shadow?

"I am a man as well as a doctor. I am only what I have learned of life as I lived it with other men. I was not given a god to direct, but a fellow human being to succor.

"And if I had believed his pretensions, his posturings, would that have rendered him more formidable in my eyes, more dangerous? Would I have had a better scent of the approaching doom that is now gradually overtaking the civilized world, and, perhaps, acted on it?

"No, my historic sense would have kept me, as it still keeps me, within bounds. I would still have brought him medicine instead of poison. Xerxes was a conqueror, too. And didn't he follow bad advice once too often? Is there not somewhere a Themistocles for every would-be world-conqueror?

"Caesar founded an empire because he met Cleopatra when he was too sated to care. Antony almost ruined Caesar's legacy because he met the same foul baggage when he was too hungry to smell. Somewhere there is a bag of bones for every conqueror to choke on.

"No, even if I had known the worst about my patient in Munich my historic sense would have insisted that my duty was simply that of a doctor, that everything would continue to go well with the world if everyone just attended to the proper business before him. If my historic sense is a true measure of the security of one individual, perhaps there is still something for the body of mankind to hope for. . . ."